HYDROFOILS DESIGN BUILD FLY

FIRST EDITION

Ray Vellinga

Peacock Hill Publishing

Gig Harbor, Washington

Library of Congress Cataloging-in-Publication Data
Ray Vellinga
Hydrofoils: Design, Build, Fly
Originally published: 1st ed. Gig Harbor, Wa USA 2009

Printed in the United States of America
ISBN: 9780982236116
Library of Congress Control Number: 2009909202

Copy Editor: Scott Smith

Peacock Hill Publishing
5114 Pt. Fosdick Drive, NW # E210
Gig Harbor, Wa 98335-1733
patvell@peacockhillpublishing.com
http://peacockhillpublishing.com

PART D – Actual Designs

PART E – Bibliography and Index

The *Wall Street Journal* is written, in part, for people who want to profit from stocks. As one of those people, I sometimes search for information on industries and individual companies. To my frustration, a positive story on the front page is typically balanced by a negative story within. Why don't they just say, "Buy General Electric", or "Sell Airlines"? It might be concluded that the *WSJ*'s goal is to inform, not to sell. So it is with this book. The goal is to inform the reader about hydrofoils. Hopefully, in the reading one can learn to design, build and fly one, but the book avoids advocating a specific path to creating a specific hydrofoil.

The reader might wonder, why so many details. With hydrofoils, just like financial information, there is good news and there is bad. Why not, like in the old Johnny Mercer song, "accentuate the positive, eliminate the negative"? That would work, if this were a plan book. Follow the plan and you will succeed. However, if the reader chooses to deviate from the plan, and it is hoped he does, he needs to be aware of the unintended consequences. When the correction of one problem creates another, the designer needs to know the fundamentals in order to regain a balance.

For example, using a surface piercing main foil that has dihedral might make a hydrofoil boat roll stable. This is because as a boat rolls, the hydrofoil on the descending side will increase its wetted area creating a righting force. However, by designing the foil to penetrate the surface, the possibility of air being introduced to the topside, low-pressure side, of the foil is increased. This air will break the relative vacuum, disturb the flow, and destroy lift. If these adverse characteristics are not corrected, the boat will be unstable. Thus, a designer needs to be aware of the negative as well as the positive.

In explaining how things work there is usually a choice to either verbalize or use mathematics. Generally, numbers provide a more precise explanation, but words are understood by more readers. Also mathematics slows the pace of reading. To keep the ideas in this book accessible and to keep up the reading speed, math has been used only where deemed necessary, and wherever possible the math has been simplified.

Some readers will welcome this, others not. Personally I like the mathematics, as long as a computer is sitting in front of me to do the grunt work. For those who don't, there is a way out: skip the math part and simply use the dimensions provided for the various boats. These numbers should work for the reader; they worked for the original builder. Any original design efforts will be greatly aided by doing the calculations. To keep the monologue flowing, in the chapters I've limited the presentation to the basic formulas along with explanations. Elaborations and variations of the formulas may be found in the index.

Keeping it simple may be a problem for the technically oriented. Some of my colleagues trained in math, science, and engineering have hinted that the explanations should be more precise, more in depth, more mathematical. My answer is, if you are the head of a design team of a publicly funded aerospace conglomerate charged with the task of building the next generation of passenger carrying ocean-going mega-hydrofoils, this book is not for you. Given enough time and funding, everything in this book can be requisitioned from the technical libraries of MIT, Boeing, and Grumman; all in excruciating detail. This book is for the individual who just wants to understand and build a hydrofoil—using one source, if possible.

Throughout the book, terms will be introduced that may be unfamiliar to the reader. If the flow of the text can be maintained, the term will be briefly defined at the point of introduction. If an unrecognizable word is found, it may be defined elsewhere. In that case, the definition can be retrieved by referring to the index and going to the page cited. Hopefully, all unfamiliar terms will be defined.

For those who wish to verify or to explore in depth the information presented, a bibliography is provided.

Although toward the end of the book specific examples of hydrofoil boat designs will be given, the major part of this book is dedicated to explaining how hydrofoils work. The book is divided into four parts.

> ➢ Part A touches on history, introduces the theory of hydrofoil flight, and explains the coined word, *aquadynamics*.
> ➢ Part B covers the flight characteristic of hydrofoils. This is the short treatment of aerodynamics as applied to hydrofoils.
> ➢ Part C applies the principles of flight to the design process. The reader will find information on configurations, stability, maneuver management, component selection, and flying technique.
> ➢ Part D gives specific examples of hydrofoils that have been built or ideas that show promise.
> ➢ Part E holds the Bibliography and Index.

This book is dedicated to my Patricia, my wife and best friend. She makes life an adventure. I was lucky to find someone who shares a love for boats, cruising, and traveling.

I know she loves these things, because she wrote a book about them. *Sailing There: Cruising Across Europe and the Mediterranean,* recounts the adventures of our 19 years sailing the Mediterranean and through the canals of Europe. It is published by our company, Peacock Hill Publishing, 5114 Pt. Fosdick Drive, NW #E210 Gig Harbor, Wa 98335-1733. www.peacockhillpublishing.com.

To the following consultants and contributors go my heartfelt thanks. My friends and I have in common, more than anything, a love for hydrofoils and other things that fly. This book is the result of many hours of dreaming, designing, building, testing and, best of all, talking about hydrofoils.

Throughout this book you will be reading the names of boats, friends and historical figures. Whenever possible, examples of real people and actual boats are used in an effort to aid the reader in fleshing out the hydrofoil experience.

California: The *La Jolla Design, Build, Fly Group:* Dwight Filley and Steve Ball are human powered hydrofoil designers and builders. Terry Hendricks, PhD., is a hydrofoil knee-board designer and builder. Ray Johnsen, retired aerospace engineer, serves as a skilled technical advisor. Bob Martin, PhD., is our marketing consultant.

Also in La Jolla: Gene Cook, civil engineer, generously contributed his professional support. Gene was especially helpful with the stress calculations in chapter 11. The book's first reader is the talented writer, Steve Farnow, PhD., author of *Photoshop, Just the Skinny*. When I thought the book was grammatically flawless, Jim Bixby, electrical engineer, offered to take a look, and he proved that in the hands of a skilled wordsmith, there is always room for improvement.

California, Orange County: Sid Shutt is generous in sharing the secrets of Hydro-ped, his record setting human powered hydrofoil. Sausalito: David Keiper who inspired me in the early 1970s about wind powered hydrofoils by rowing me out to show me his famous sailing trimaran, Williwaw, moored in Richardson Bay. He later sailed Williwaw 20,000 miles across the Pacific to as far south as New Zealand. David was lost to a heart attack in 1998.

Washington state: Harry Larsen, former Boeing executive, designer, and builder of Talaria IV, the 24' flying Bayliner cabin cruiser. Harry is a master at adapting hydrofoils to conventional motor driven boats and creating complex electronic control systems. Harry permitted Pat and me to take videos of Talaria IV for YouTube.com publication. Tom Speer is a Boeing Aerospace Engineer and expert on aerodynamics and electronic control systems, and he has been generous in providing me with many technical explanations. Arthur Hager has adapted hydrofoils to his family cruiser. Arthur holds the record for drilling the most holes into the hull of an otherwise seaworthy Bayliner.

Indiana, Elkhart: Jake Free of Free Enterprises fabricated the CRP front foil and strut assembly for Hifybe. Jake is a regular visitor to Southern California and a leader in the art of making human powered hydrofoil boats.

Florida: This is the state where Scott Smith, the book's Copy Editor, restores and flies vintage hydrofoil boats. He is a manufacturing engineer who is very knowledgeable about hydrofoils and has over a decade of professional experience editing technical reports. From early on, he believed in the book and worked months refining the final print. His keen eye for detail and a fine technical sense made a significant impact on this book. He also provided the popular Dynafoil video shots that were edited and posted on YouTube.com.

Also in Florida: Doug Lord builds and sells scale model hydrofoil sailboats. Doug shared detailed information used in creating the chapter on designing the Moth sailboat.

United Kingdom: This is the home of the engineers of Anglican Development, Limited, Isle of Wight, who designed and built the Hi-Foil. They were an inspiration in 1969 when they allowed this stranger from the USA to fly their prototype. This fine little machine confirmed my early belief that there is a place in the water world for personal hydrofoil craft. Adam May contributed information on the design of the Moth class hydrofoil boat.

Thanks to the International Hydrofoil Society (IHS) for their encouragement, and for providing a forum for hydrofoil information. In particular, thanks to Martin Grimm, Australia, a great resource for information. He is a contributing member of the IHS and is an authority on building radio controlled scale model hydrofoils. John Meyer has written several books and compact disks available through the IHS. Special thanks go to Malin Dixon, U.K., Mark Bebar, Barney Black, George Jenkins, and Robert Stevenson, USA.

Australia: Thanks go to John Ilett of Fastacraft, Ltd. for fabricating the CRP rear foil used on some of our human powered boats as well as on Hifybe. John and his brother Garth are credited with creating the first inline hydrofoil Moth class sailing boat. Bruce McLeod was very helpful in providing data on various Moth variations. Ian Ward, PhD., has been helpful in sharing information about the Moth class sailing hydrofoils.

Brazil: A note of appreciation goes to Henrique José Caribé Ribeiro, an accomplished Brazilian naval architect, who helped me appreciate the serious international interest in designing hydrofoils.

Holland: This is where Joris Robijn built his Draagvleugelboot at the same time I was creating Hifybe. Also, Willem Hekman is a student attempting to convert his dad's kayak into a hydrofoil (no word from Dad). His intelligent questions provide clues about what needs to be answered in a book about hydrofoils.

France: This is the home of Gerard Tisserand who designed his Tetrafoiler with a unique height sensing device. He and his brother fly the Tetrafoiler off the coast of Corsica.

Japan: Thanks go to Kotaro Horiuchi for allowing me to review his fine book, *Locus of a Boat Designer 2*. The text is interesting, and informative, and the illustrations are works of art. Also appreciated is the video footage of the OU32 provided by Horiuchi-san that is presently viewable on YouTube.com. Of all the videos posted by me, the one of his OU32 is the most popular.

YouTube.com earns credit for providing a forum for the more than 16 hydrofoil videos created by the author from personal footage as well as material provided by others credited herein. At time of publication the number of views is approaching 1,100,000. To see them, go to YouTube.com and search for *Flying Hydrofoil Ray* or *Ray Vellinga*. Contributing camera persons are Patricia Vellinga, Dave McKinney, Bob Wilcox, Dwight Filley, and Steve Wright.

Nothing would have been possible without Dorothy and John Vellinga, my parents. Mom always encouraged me to follow the path less travelled. Dad led the way by always inventing. His support during testing in the frigid winter waters of Illinois was important to early successes. And thanks to Pat's Dad, Stanley Altenbernd, who in 1969 demonstrated bravery by being the first co-pilot, Figure 1-9b.

Throughout this book are more than 270 drawings, charts, and tables. These are all original figures created by the author representing existing and historical hydrofoil boats, devices, and facts. To create them, the needed information came from self-generated, published, or private photographs; and/or written factual descriptions. In the case of images, seldom does a single photograph or description provide enough information to complete a drawing, and therefore they are always a composite of information and visual clues from various sources gathered in small samples. While creating original work is a high priority, care is taken in creating images that are honest and accurate. The purpose is to educate, and to stimulate further interest about hydrofoils.

Chapter 1

A Brief History of Hydrofoils

- o Definition of a hydrofoil
- o Why hydrofoils?
- o Thomas Moy
- o Meacham brothers
- o Early development
- o Post war progress
- o US Navy hydrofoils
- o Personal hydrofoils
- o The future?
- o Book's purpose and method

Definition: A *hydrofoil* is a wing that flies in water. The cross section of the wing, called a *profile,* may have the shape of an aircraft wing or a modification thereof. Typically the main lifting wing is combined with another, and struts are used to attach them to a buoyant body such as a boat hull. Given sufficient speed, the hydrofoils provide lift to support the hull, and the hull rises above the surface of the water. As with aircraft, about 2/3 of the lift is generated by the upper surface of the wing. *Hydrofoil* can also refer to the boat itself as a shorter way of saying *hydrofoil boat*, and *foil* can be a shortcut to saying *hydrofoil wing*. Hydrofoils, like airplanes, are elegant and sophisticated flying machines.

Hydro*foils* are not to be confused with hydro*planes*. Hydroplanes are beasts without wings that accelerate beyond their maximum hull speed, force themselves to mount the water and skip (plane) along the surface. Miss Budweiser is a well know example of a large, fast, and powerful hydroplane.

Why Hydrofoils? The purpose of this book is to create a place where sailors, manufacturers, hobbyists, and inventors can meet and discover the secrets of hydrofoils. Over the past century the popularity of hydrofoils has risen and fallen like the tides. Until now, the most that an interested sailor could hope for was to see a hydrofoil in a museum or possibly be a passenger on one between some foreign islands. Hopefully with this book, that will change. Until now there has not been a single source where one could learn all that is necessary to design, build and fly a hydrofoil boat. Hydrofoil popularity could surge and history will be written. To understand the future, let's take a look at the past.

Thomas Moy tested airplane wings in water in 1861 because, he claimed, there was more accuracy than when testing in air. As a bi-product of aerodynamic studies, Moy inadvertently discovered hydrofoils.

Meacham brothers. Between 1895 and 1916 the Meacham brothers of Chicago were the first to design and test a true hydrofoil. Others in Europe and the USA came close and even received some patents, but the Meacham brothers created a flying machine that would today be recognized as a hydrofoil boat. My warm feelings toward the brothers may be influenced by the fact that they tested their craft in a tributary of the Illinois River, the same river where I tested my first flying prototype 70 years later.

The most amazing thing about the Meacham brothers little heralded achievement is that their 100-year-old sketches resemble the most sophisticated submerged hydrofoils and mechanical systems being used today, see Figures 8-5a and b. Looking closely, it appears that they were handicapped by their lack of knowledge of airfoils. Today, airfoil information is easily available to anyone.

Early development of hydrofoils somewhat coincides with the development of aircraft. Even the Wright brothers were attracted to the idea. They attached hydrofoils to a catamaran about the same period they were experimenting with other flying machines.

In 1906 an Italian engineer named Enrico Forlanini bolted some ladder foils onto a 2,650 pound hull and flew over Lake Maggiore at a blistering 42.5 mph. A 60 hp engine with counter-rotating airscrews propelled the boat. See Figure 8-1b for a drawing of this remarkable boat.

Around the same time, Alexander Graham Bell hung up the phone long enough to read a *Scientific American* article written by one of the Meacham brothers. He was so inspired that he and his associate, Casey Baldwin, began designing and testing model hydrofoils. During a world tour in1910-1911 the two inventors met with Forlanini at Lake Maggiore and were lucky enough to get a ride.

So impressed were Bell and Baldwin that by September 1919 they had designed and built a hydrofoil that set a world water speed record of 70.86 mph. The HD-4, seen in Figure 1-1, was propelled by two airscrews each turned by a 350 hp U.S. Navy Liberty aircraft engine. The configuration had two ladder foils set wide abeam amidships, one ladder foil at the bow and one ladder foil trailing at the stern.

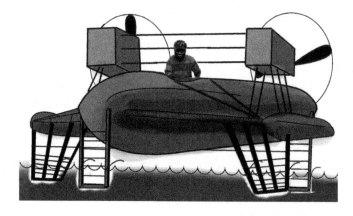

Figure 1-1. Sketch of the Bell HD-4 Hydrofoil.

Professor Oscar Tietjens created another exemplary hydrofoil. He patented a surface-piercing hoop-shaped foil that was simple, efficient and stable. In 1932 on a river running through Philadelphia his 500 lb craft obtained a speed of about 25 mph.

About 1938, using some of Bell and Baldwin's innovations, Phillip L. Rhodes created a 6500 lb., 35-foot boat, with a 650 hp engine. The craft was called Miss USA. It set a new record for hydrofoils at 80 knots.

Post war progress. An important name in the history of hydrofoils is Christopher Hook. Beginning in 1945 at Cowles, England, he worked on a system of variable lift front foils. These foils are connected to surface "feelers". The feelers are on long arms extending forward of the craft. They sense the surface in advance of the boat. The feelers continuously adjust the angle of incidence of the front foils to control the bow flying height.

Not every idea worked. In the 1950s Dr. Vannevar Bush, scientific advisor to the US President began design work on a 3,500 ton hydrofoil ship. He believed that a huge hydrofoil ship, due to its small underwater profile and high speed, would be safe from torpedo attacks. Unfortunately, his design did not scale up. The large engine needed to make this behemoth fly would leave little room for cargo.

Judging by the number of boats created, more than 150, the most popular large hydrofoil was the type designed by the late Baron Hanns von Schertel. Baron von Schertel immigrated to Switzerland following WWII, and employed his knowledge gained earlier designing surface-piercing hydrofoils for the German Navy. In May, 1953, on Lake Maggiore, Italy, a boat of his design was employed in the first commercial hydrofoil passenger service. One year later, the Leopoldo Rodriquez Shipyard in Messina, Italy, under license from the Baron's company, Supramar, began building passenger carrying hydrofoils. These boats are popular throughout the world, and many are in commercial service today. Other boats of the same style have been built under license by Hatachi Zosen, Japan, and Voster Thoryncraft, England. The largest of the series is the Super Jumbo RHS-200 with a capacity of 254 passengers. It looks similar to the RHS-160 in Figure 1-2.

Figure 1-2. RHS-160 Rodriquez surface piercing hydrofoil.

In 1958 the Canadian Government funded the design and construction of a 17-ton aluminum hull boat named Baddeck in honor of Bell's Canadian home. Two 12-cylinder 1,500 hp Rolls Royce engines powered her two airscrews. This expensive prototype was considered a flying failure; however, valuable conclusions were drawn from her testing.

Like the last Bell-Baldwin boat, the Baddeck had its main wings, consisting of twin ladder foils, positioned slightly ahead of the center of gravity. A smaller ladder foil was located at the stern. This is called the *conventional* or *airplane configuration*. Up to that time it was believed to be the best performer; however, during trials it was determined that it functioned only over a narrow range of angles of attack and performed badly in rough waters.

The designers concluded that surface-piercing configurations should have a big wing aft of the center of gravity supporting most of weight. A much smaller foil placed forward should support a small fraction of total weight, perhaps 10 or 15%. The forward foil should act as a surface "feeler" and be, in effect, a trimming device for the larger rear foil. The forward foil should have a higher wing loading and therefore be less sensitive to changes in angle of attack. This allowed better performance in turbulent waters. *Wing loading* is weight divided by area and it will be explained further in chapters 13 and 15. Following the lead of aircraft designers, many of whom were French, they named this a "canard" configuration. Canard means *duck,* and it is so named because when the big wing is aft of the bulk of the flying machine it rather looks like a duck in flight.

It should be noted that hydrofoil *sailing* boats usually favor the conventional wing configuration. A good example is David Keiper's Williwaw. Williwaw is a 32 ft. hydrofoil trimaran that in the late 1960s and early 1970s sailed almost 20,000 miles including a voyage from California, to Hawaii, to New Zealand, and back. Then Keiper wrote *Hydrofoil Voyager*, a book about the adventure and the boat. In the 1970s I met with the now deceased Mr. Keiper on Williwaw, in Sausalito, California. Visiting with him boosted my interest in hydrofoiling.

Figures 1-3a & b. Two very different hydrofoils. (a) The artist's impression of David Keiper's single-handed sailing boat. (b) Depiction of Boeing's 400 passenger high speed Jetfoil.

The Hobie TriFoiler, designed by Greg Ketterman; the Windrider Rave, by Dr. Sam Bradfield; and the Monitor, by Gordon Baker, are other examples of successful hydrofoil sailboats designed with the larger wing forward of the center of gravity.

Despite these civilian sailing successes, the Canadian Navy had long ago given up on sailing ships and committed to the motor powered, surface piercing, canard idea. This gave birth to their 151 ft Bras d'Or in 1967, Figure 1-4. Weighing in at 200 tons and capable of flying at 63 knots in 4 ft seas, she is big and beautiful. Her mission was anti-submarine warfare. However, in 1971 Canadian defense priorities changed. According to the International Hydrofoil Society, the importance of anti-submarine warfare was eclipsed by a need for "the protection of sovereignty and the surveillance of Canadian territory and coastlines". She retired in 1972 and today can be seen on dry land at the Museé Maritime Bernier in Nova Scotia.

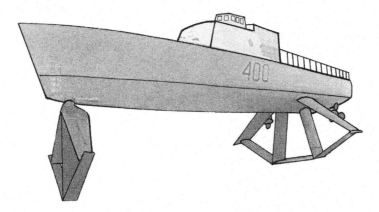

Figure 1-4. Canadian Navy's Bras d'Or.

Back in the USA, in 1954, the morale of the US Navy sponsors was raised when a new speed record of 74.4 mph was set by William P. Carl's XCH-4, Figure 1-5. William Carl was a very successful aeronautical engineer credited with the design of the speedy twin-boomed P-38 Lighting.

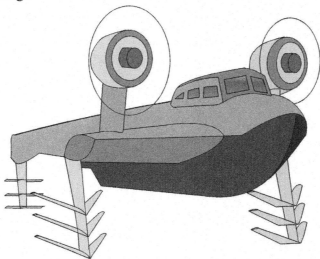

Figure 1-5. The Carl XCH-4.

Four years later, at the Gibbs and Cox boatyard a 25' wooden Chris Craft Cruiser was fitted with foils. It was named Sealegs, Figure 1-6. During open sea runs, the small boat averaged 23 knots in waves 4 to 5 feet. Try that in your Bayliner. This performance inspired the Navy to move ahead with hydrofoil development.

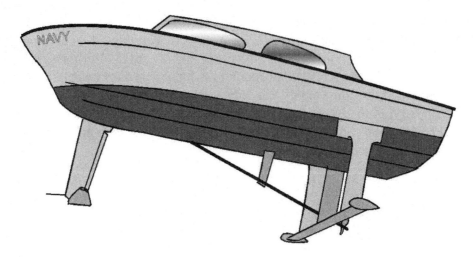

Figure 1-6. US Navy's Sealegs.

In the early 1960s Boeing created the Fresh-1, Figure 1-7, and set the standing speed record of 80 knots. Fresh-1 used submerged foils in its design and influenced the US Navy to move away from the surface piercing Canadian model.

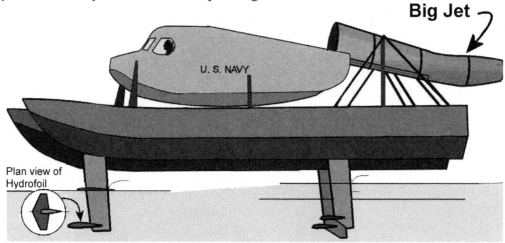

Figure 1-7. Fresh-1, Boeing jet powered boat.

US Navy Hydrofoils. Starting in 1958 the US Navy, Boeing, and Grumman embarked on programs that resulted in the construction of 3 experimental boats and 14 operational ships. They all were fitted with submerged foils. Both conventional and canard configurations were tested. The largest military ship was the Plainview displacing 320 tons. The largest civilian ship is the Boeing Jetfoil that displaces 109 tons and carries up to 350 passengers. Some are still in service.

Here is a list that shows approximate development dates:

Sealegs (R&D)	1958
Fresh-1 (R&D)	1960
High Point, 110 tons	1962
Little Squirt (R&D)	1962
Plainview, 320 tons	1968
Flagstaff, 62 tons	1968
Tucumcari, 58 tons	1968
Swordfish, 60 tons, Italian & Egyptian Navies	1972
PHM-1 USS Pegasus, 235 tons	1975
Jetfoil, 109 tons, civilian ferry	1973
HMS Speedy, 109 tons	1973
Grumman M161, 102 tons, Israeli Navy	1981
PHM-3 USS Taurus, 240 tons, 5 built	1982

Figure 1-8. Dates from Ships that Fly, by John Meyers, IHS.

These were the golden years of military hydrofoils and by 1993 it was all over. On July 30 of that year, all 6 remaining U.S. Navy PHM (Patrol Missile Hydrofoil) Pegasus Class hydrofoils were decommissioned.

Why was the Navy program abandoned? I posed this question to a U.S. Navy Admiral, the keynote speaker at a recent luncheon meeting on the West Coast. He believed that maintenance was the big problem, especially the difficulties with the power transmission systems; and that the lightweight low profile outdrives were the Achilles heels of those high-power machines.

Advice from Lieutenant Vellinga USNR (inactive) to the Admirals of the U.S. Navy: "Build your hydrofoils as flying machines, not as battle ships". It would be inappropriate to mount a 3-inch gun on an F-18 or to build it from steel. The same design rules should apply to hydrofoils that apply to aircraft. Fast, lightweight machines would demand less from their machinery and would therefore have fewer maintenance problems and better performance.

If I ran the Navy it would only have hydrofoils and aircraft. Forget about destroyers and cruisers. There would be a lot less rust and a lot more fun.

Other countries building or operating large military and passenger carrying hydrofoils include the Russia, Switzerland, Italy, Israel and Japan.

Personal hydrofoils. Concurrent with the Navy's program, private industry and individuals developed various small personal hydrofoils, including several prototypes created by the author, Figures 1-9a and b.

Figures 1-9a & b. (a) Early (failed) attempt by author to create a flying motorcycle. (b) 1969 test of SabreFoil. On board is the author, and his intrepid father-in-law, Stanley Altenbernd.

The Hi-Foil, Figure 1-10a, was marketed about 1970 by Anglican Development Ltd on the Isle of Wight. This British personal hydrofoil has 2 seats, motorcycle steering, and is powered by a 25 hp long shaft outboard motor.

Shortly thereafter, in Orange County, California, David Cline was creating the Dynafoil, Figure 1-10b. This flying machine was at the cutting edge of personal water craft development. In fact, the product was successful with over 500 units sold at prices up to $3,500 before production ended in August 1980.

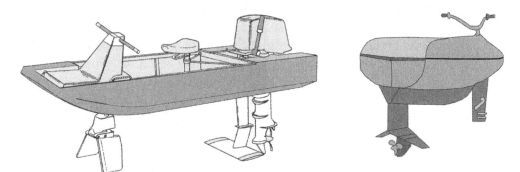

Figures 1-10a & b. Hi-Foil and Dynafoil personal hydrofoils.

A prototype sailboat called the Avocet was the product of a joint effort between Greg Ketterman, an American entrepreneur, and Yamaha Motors's R & D Center led by Kotaro Horiuchi. The Avocet evolved into the TriFoiler and Ketterman's company, Hobie Cat, Co. manufactured them in the 1990s. Both trimarans have two mainsails, one on each outrigger. In 1993 the Avocet boat set a class A record of 50 mph over a 500 meter course in Tarifa, Spain.

In 1998, Dr. Sam Bradford designed the Rave Hydrofoil trimaran for production by Windrider LLC. Two years ago on Mission bay in San Diego I was invited to co-pilot a Rave. With two people it took about 9 mph of wind to become foil-borne. My host reported that his boat sails at 1.5 to 2 times the wind speed. The boat was a real thrill to fly. Dr. Bradfield is also credited with designing the NF2, Neither Fish Nor Fowl. This hydrofoil sailboat held the Class C world speed sailing record between 1978 and 1982.

In Australia, John Ilett's FastaCraft Company and Bladerider International produce complete boats and components for an International Moth class monohull sailing boat fitted with hydrofoils. These boats feature carbon-fiber hulls and foils. Each boat has two inverted "T" foils, one mounted in the centerboard slot and the other in place of the rudder. Under sail-power, their maximum speed is about 35 mph.

About the same time as the Avocet's record runs, human powered hydrofoil boats were pushing the limits. In 1991, a team from MIT led by Mark Drela, PhD. created the Decavitator, Figure 1-11, which set the present record of 21.275 mph over a 100-meter course and won the DuPont prize for the fastest human powered hydrofoil.

Figure 1-11. MIT's Decavitator. The fairing was removed for its record run.

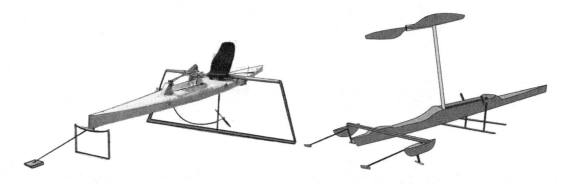

Figures 1-12a & b. Steve Ball's Low Flying Kayak and Dwight Filley's Mach .03.

Today, innovative designs are being brought to life in widely separated parts of the world. In California, my associates are creating human powered hydrofoils, like those in Figures 1-12a and b.

In Australia the Moth class sailboat is evolving into an exciting racing machine, See Figure 18-1. The French Hydroptère, Figure 10-9, and the British Vestas SailRocket are sailing at record speeds. My Hifybe, cover photo, and Harry Larsen's Talaria IV, Figure 8-11, are two examples of the motor-powered hydrofoil evolution.

What about the future? The future starts here. History has shown that hydrofoils are real. They go faster with less power; they cut smoothly through rough seas that bring conventional boats to a crawl, and hydrofoils *fly*. They fly just as an airplane flies, but without the threat of the severe consequences of an unplanned landing.

What is left to discover about aviation? Probably not much, but the hydrofoil, like an underachieving second child, has yet to be pushed to its highest potential. Of course great designs can come from Fortune 500 companies, but experience has shown that they can also come from thinly financed home workshops. Cruising boats like Talaria IV, fun boats like Hifybe, human powered boats like Hydro-ped were all produced by inspired independent innovators.

The challenge is to develop better autopilots, front foil height controls, main foil roll controls, foil retractors, and propulsion systems. These innovations can come from the inspired innovator, the committed experimenter.

Purpose and method. If the purpose of this book were to design and build large aircraft it would not be acceptable to include trial and error in the design process. The costs and danger to life and property would be too great. Boeing, Lockheed Martin, and Airbus employ armies of engineers using supercomputers, wind tunnels, and thousands of years of combined experience to accurately predict the performance of any new design before it is constructed and tested.

Design, build and see if *it flies* could be the subtitle of this book. Probably none of the designs shown in chapters 16, 17, and 18 flew perfectly on the first attempt. The beauty of the hydrofoils proposed in this book is their relatively small size and low cost. This allows for experimentation. The reason for the concepts and formulas is to provide a path to a functioning design. Even Albert Einstein allowed for error. He quipped: "If we knew what it was we were doing, it would not be called research, would it?"

There are ways to reduce the trial and error and increase the likelihood of creating a successful flying machine on the first try. One way is to duplicate the successful designs shown in chapters 16 to 18. Another way is to take a proven design from the military or industry, scale it down and duplicate it. For example, follow the guidelines of chapter 14 on scale modeling and you could modify and create an exciting flying machine using the tested design principles manifested in the surface piercing Canadian Bras d'Or. It might look something like Figure 1-13.

Figure 1-13. Artist's conception of Bras d'Or scaled down to a PWC.

In these ways the path of hydrofoil history could take a turn. It was paved by pioneers and followed by military and industrial innovators. With the heavy work completed, a new direction could come from an army of individual innovators armed with the knowledge gained from these predecessors.

Whether the reader is motivated to create a simple toy or build a hydrofoil empire, this book is written to help take that first step toward innovation, creation and discovery. So taxi into position and hold. Prepare to takeoff on wings that fly through water.

Chapter 2

Theory of Hydrofoil Flight: Aquadynamics

- o Aquadynamics
- o What makes things fly
- o Newton
- o Coanda effect
- o Planing boats

Aquadynamics. "What's in a name? that which we call a rose By any other name would smell as sweet" Shakespeare. Before we move on some confusing terminology needs to be examined. *Hydrodynamics*, would seem to be the natural word to describe the study of hydrofoils. Unfortunately the ancient engineers, who apparently spoke together in Latin, got here first and defined hydrodynamics as "a branch of science that deals with the motion of fluids and the forces acting on solid bodies immersed in fluids and the motion relative to them," *Webster's New Collegiate Dictionary*. This definition includes some of hydrofoil science, but no hydrodynamics book gives enough information about hydrofoils to actually design one. The motion and action of water is relevant, but hydrofoils are really about the science of *flying* through water.

Aerodynamics can teach us many of the things necessary to design hydrofoils, but aerodynamics is defined as "the dynamics of gases, especially of atmospheric interactions with moving objects," *The American Heritage Dictionary of the English Language*. Books on aerodynamics reveal the secrets of how airplanes fly, but these books seldom included much about hydrofoils.

You'd think the word we seek would be "aeronautics", but aeronautics is not about *nautics,* nautical things—it's about aero-*planes.*

The other term we might use is "flying boat". Once again we are trumped by our predecessors. A flying boat is an airplane that floats, not a boat that flies. How fair is that? All the good words have been used, does that leave us to describe the subject of this book as *aerodynamics as applied to hydrofoil boats?*

I propose coining a new word by shortening aquatic-aerodynamics to "Aquadynamics". Put that in your dictionary, Mr. Webster.

Aquadynamics is aerodynamics with a nautical twist. Aerodynamics is the appropriate science because hydrofoils operate under the same principals as airplanes. Both operate in fluids that are incompressible–air is considered uncompressible to aircraft operating at speeds less than mach 1.

There are, however, two significant differences in operations. First, water is more dense and viscous than air. Second, hydrofoils operate at the interface between air and water where excursions in altitude (flying height) are very limited.

Students of aerodynamics might assume, because water is more viscous than air, as expressed in Reynolds numbers, that there are serious operational differences. Reynolds numbers will be examined in chapters 4 and 13. Coincidentally, personal-sized hydrofoils have Reynolds numbers in the realm of model airplanes, i.e., R_N = 700,000 to 3,000,000. This makes it possible to use published airfoil data to predict hydrofoil wing performance. Surprisingly, fluid density does not have a great influence on selection of foil shape. Foil selection is tied to the lift coefficients of a foil's shape. These coefficients are determined by testing and apply to dense fluids (water) as well as non-dense (air). More will be found on density and viscosity in Figure 4-5 and its text.

What makes things fly? Aerodynamics has been studied for over 500 years. Around 1486 Leonardo da Vinci designed a flying machine that flapped its wings like a bird. He also created images of the glider, and the parachute.

My first boyhood academic interest in flying was in making model airplanes. After graduating from university, I was trained in aerodynamics first in the U.S. Navy flight program and again when preparing for my civilian commercial-instrument pilot's license. I learned from my fellow Navy students what makes helicopters fly, "They are so ugly the earth repels them" (The Ugly Theory). If levitating helicopters can be explained so easily can you imagine my surprise when I learned that the experts still disagree about what makes *airplanes* fly?

How does a wing create lift? Most of us had this question answered in grade school, high school, college, or pilot training. It goes like this: the fluid–air and water are both considered fluids–flowing over the curved top side of the wing has farther to go than the fluid flowing under the flatter bottom side. Because the fluid particles on the top and bottom meet at the same time at the trailing edge of the wing we know the top particles, which have traveled farther, have moved faster. Bernoulli's principle, also known as the Venturi Effect, tells us that the faster moving fluid will have less pressure. The effect is lower pressure on the top and higher pressure on the bottom. The wing is "sucked upward", right?

Man, that is sooo last year. Forget all that drivel, get up to date. We now know, because I found it browsing in Barnes and Noble, that lift is created by **Newton's three laws**. Paraphrased they are: 1. If an object is caused to move, it keeps moving. 2. F = MA, Force equals Mass times Acceleration. 3. For every action there is an equal and opposite reaction. In addition we need to know one other law, the Coanda effect.

The **Coanda effect** simply says that, within limits, fluids will conform to a curved surface when flowing around it. When a fluid travels over the curved topside of a wing, it conforms to the curve. This is a function of the *viscosity* of the fluid. The more viscous the fluid, the better it sticks to the wing's topside, and the better it conforms to the curve.

This lift theory, news to old aviators, says that the mass of the fluid is given downward momentum as it follows the backside of the wing's curve. Forcing the particles downward causes an opposite upward force (Newton's third law: opposite reaction), and their *continued* downward motion (Newton's first law, momentum) is in proportion to the force that has been applied to them. Because there are a lot of particles, a lot of mass, there is a significant upward reaction (Newton's second law: F = MA). This upward force is experienced as *lift*. What could be simpler?

Just as I was regaining enough confidence to buy an airline ticket, three other explanations materialized. They are sometimes called: circulation, streamline-curvature, and vortex-based theories. I have some clues as to what these are, but who cares? With 6 theories out there–5 scientific theories plus one ugly theory–the odds are only 1 out of 6 that your favorite theory is the correct one. Of course we hope for better odds when rising from the runway.

Planing boats. All of these theories agree that 2/3 of the total lift is generated by the low-pressure topside of the wing, and that the remaining 1/3 is produced by the bottom side. This is where a hydrofoil and a planing boat are fundamentally different. The planing hull has 100% of its lift generated by the bottom side, so it is important to understand how the bottom side creates lift as well as the topside. Newton's three laws can explain it: The bottom of the hull or foil strikes the particles of water, and they would otherwise remain unmoved but are forcefully displaced by the speeding hull or foil (law 1). This displacement causes an equal and opposite reaction (law 3). The lifting force created is equal to the amount of displaced mass times its acceleration (law 2).

It may come as a surprise to some that hydrofoils are more like airplanes than planing boats, but it is this complexity that makes them more interesting, more efficient and more in need of in-depth study.

Stability, Control, and Trim: a General Discussion

- o Stability, control and trim
- o Maneuverability and stability
- o Computer assisted control system
- o Static and dynamic stability
- o Not all designs fit on the continuum
- o Some fighter aircraft using computer assisted control systems are dynamically unstable
- o The axes of rotation

Stability, control and trim are terms that need to be used with precision. *Stability* is the tendency for a flying machine, without the aid of the pilot, to return to steady flight after something causes the machine to deviate from steady flight.

"Controllability refers to the ability of the aircraft to respond to control surface displacement (as inputted by the pilot) and to achieve the desired condition of flight." From *Aerodynamics for Naval Aviators*, my words in parenthesis. Herein, *controllability* and *maneuverability* will be considered to have the same meaning.

As they are used in this Book, *stability* is built into a craft and *control* is what the pilot can do to influence the craft.

To be in *trim* is the condition where "all moments in pitch, roll, and yaw are equal to zero", also from…*Naval Aviators*. We will examine this later.

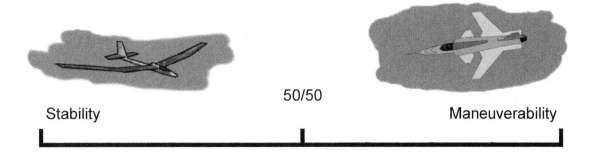

50/50

Stability   Maneuverability

Figure 3-1. The designer's objective lies on a continuum between two extremes. On the left is a stable un-powered glider. On the right is the super-maneuverable experimental X29A.

J. D. Anderson, in *Introduction to Flight*, recognized stability vs. control to be a battle of design philosophy dating back to the French aerodynamicists disagreeing with the Wright brothers. Before the Wright's success at Kitty Hawk, the French created airplanes so stable the pilot could barely make them bank or pitch. The idea was to turn a flat corner. Their designs relied on big rudders to drive around like an automobile.

Famous as contrarians, the Wright brothers invented wing warp to bank, turn, and level the wings. They used a canard elevator to make pitch control a game of skill. The idea was to keep the pilot awake and on the job. The initial test results were superior to those of the French, but as time passed, the dangers of too little stability became apparent as pilots failed to keep ahead of the Wright's lively designs. In fact, five years after the original flight of 1903, Orville was badly injured and his passenger, Army Lt. Thomas Selfridge, was killed in a crash at Fort Meyer, Virginia.

Maneuverability and stability, as designer's objectives, are at opposite ends of a continuum. Relatively speaking, a cruising aircraft is stable but has weak pilot controls, and a fighter plane is unstable but has strong pilot controls. The Cessnas 152 and 172 will easily cruise with hands off until the gas is gone, but the F117 Nighthawk stealth fighter is inherently unstable and could not be pilot controlled without its **computer assisted control system.** To quote Wikipedia, "the loss of all flight control computers could immediately render the aircraft uncontrollable". The Cessna is impossible to snap roll but the fighter planes routinely do acrobatic maneuvers, including snap rolls. It is not a question of which is better, stability or maneuverability, it is a question of what type of craft the designer hopes to realize. Obviously no object in motion will be absolutely stable or totally maneuverable.

Some modern aircraft do seem to defy this concept. Consider, for example, the F-18s of the Navy Blue Angels. While flying in their diamond formation, 18 inches apart, they are demonstrating obvious stability. When they do snap rolls and rapid pitching movements they are demonstrating high maneuverability. But without computer assisted control systems the F-18, as well as the F-117 and others, could not perform the precision maneuvers, and merely controlling the aircraft would be beyond the capabilities of the pilots.

The concept can be demonstrated with two dissimilar bowls, each containing a ball. The narrow steep sided bowl rigidly confines its ball, whereas the flattened bowl allows its ball more freedom. The ball in the steep bowl is very stable but is difficult to maneuver. The ball in the flattened bowl is not as stable and is easier to move (maneuver).

Figures 3-2a & b. More and less stable balls in bowls.

Likewise, hydrofoil handling qualities may be plotted on this continuum. Too much stability and the craft will resist pitching, turning, or banking. Too much controllability and the pilot will have an impossible struggle to prevent the craft from leaping, turning and rolling. "In fact, a high degree of stability tends to reduce the controllability of an aircraft". From *Introduction to Flight*.

Static and dynamic stability are defined as follows:

Static stability. A displaced object is said to be statically stable if it has a strong tendency to return to equilibrium when displaced. An example of a statically stable condition would be a ball bearing in a bowl filled with molasses, Figure 3-3a:

Static and dynamic Stability is demonstrated in Figure 3-3b with the ball in the bowl without fluid:

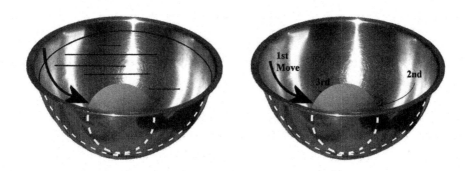

Figures 3-3a & b. (a) Ball in a bowl of viscous fluid demonstrating static stability.
(b) Ball in a bowl of no fluid demonstrating static stability and dynamic stability.

The difference between *static* and *dynamic* stability is the oscillation over a period of time. *Static stability* is the tendency to return directly to equilibrium, Figure 3-3a. *Dynamic stability* is when equilibrium is reached through a series of oscillations over a period of time, Figure 3-3b. All dynamically stable systems will have static stability. Not all statically stable systems will have dynamic stability.

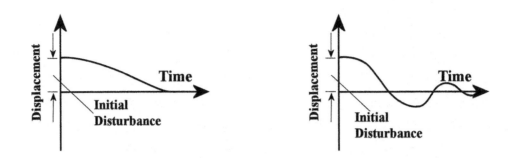

Figures 3-4a & b. The Graphs represent *static* and *static plus dynamic* stability.

Maneuverability and controllability in flying machines describes handling characteristics where the craft is easily displaced from its condition of equilibrium.

Neutral static stability, for banking or rolling, is found in some private aircraft. They tend to remain at their present modest angle of bank. It takes control input from the pilot to level the wings of such an aircraft, whereas a very stable airplane will be more likely to return to straight and level flight without pilot input. Figures 3-5a and b illustrate neutral static stability.

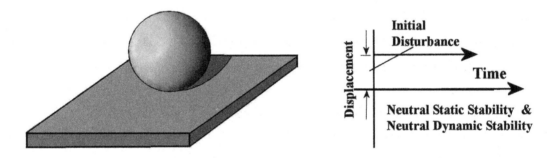

Figures 3-5a & b. Neutral stability shown as a ball on a *level* table.

Notice the ball on the level table, Figure 3-5a. If the ball is moved it will keep moving, but if it is stopped, it will stay stopped.

For example, assume a hydrofoil is flying at 6 inches of submersion and is displaced to 4 inches. If it stays at 4 inches, it is displaying neutral static stability.

Not all designs fit on the continuum. It would be unusual, but not impossible, for a craft to have very high stability as well as very high maneuverability. Likewise it can have very low stability and very low maneuverability. An example of high stability along with high maneuverability would be a boat with an adequate keel and a large rudder. This boat could progress in a very straight line and would be directionally stable. If it were designed so that the rudder and the keel could be rapidly deflected—one to the right, the other to the left—the boat could be turned rapidly. In this hypothetical example there is high stability and high maneuverability.

A more typical case would be a sailboat with a long deep keel and a small trailing rudder. This type of boat easily maintains course (high directional stability) but resists turning (low directional control).

An example of low stability and low maneuverability, is a sailboat with no rudder or keel. This boat would be at the mercy of the winds. It neither could follow a steady course, nor be turned at will.

Static instability is illustrated with a ball on a bowl:

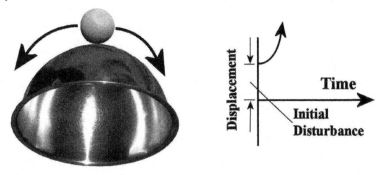

Figures 3-6a & b. Unstable ball on a bowl. The arrow diverging upward represents an increase in displacement over time.

Any displacement of the ball and it falls off the bowl. The farther the ball is displaced from the balance point the more force is required to return it to the balance point. This is generally an undesirable quality for anything that floats, flies or is on the dinner table.

There are 3 modes of oscillation as graphed in Figure 3-7. The three modes are:

    a. Positive static and positive dynamic stability
    b. Positive static and neutral dynamic stability
    c. Positive static and negative dynamic stability

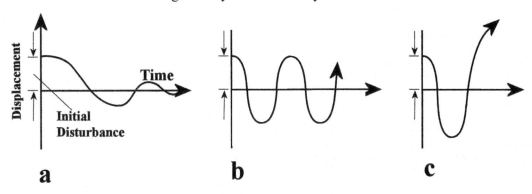

Figures 3-7a, b, & c. The three modes of oscillation.

Positive static and dynamic stability is illustrated by the ball in an empty bowl, Figures 3-3b and 3-7a. When displaced it rolls to the point of equilibrium, past it, and up the other sided. It oscillates like this, losing energy with each cycle, until its energy is dissipated. This is generally a desirable action in boats, planes, and hydrofoils, but it is not always an easy thing to achieve.

A perpetual motion machine, if such a thing existed, would have a chart like Figure 3-7b. Oscillations of constant magnitude could only exist if energy equal to resistance were introduced to the moving object on each cycle, or if there was zero resistance. It would be unnatural if a disturbed object, without additional power inputted, continued to oscillate at a constant intensity. That would suggest a frictionless condition, and that is not normally encountered on earth.

Dynamic instability is illustrated in Figure 3-7c. This is caused by outside energy entering into the oscillation with each cycle, and it is evidence of a positive feedback loop. It is seen in some pitching speedboats and sometimes in landing seaplanes. In a motorcycle it is called speed-wobble. In some conditions the oscillations are exacerbated by human input. All of these examples can have disastrous consequences.

As mentioned, some modern **fighter aircraft using computer assisted control systems are dynamically unstable**. The aircraft's instability is controlled by a sensitive and rapidly responding autopilot. This system is often inaccurately called "fly by wire" which has to do with replacing the mechanical and hydraulic control systems with electrical wires. The wires are necessary, but it is the computerized autopilot that represents a revolution in control technology.

If the autopilot fails, the aircraft goes out of control because pilot's response time is too slow to correct for the quick and intensifying oscillations of the aircraft. The pilot's late response sometimes synchronizes with the wrong peak of the cycle and thereby augments the intensity of the cycle. This is called a positive feedback loop. Within a few augmentations a violent divergence may result. Depending on the craft, the proper pilot technique might be to hold the controls steady to encourage the cycles to dampen. Modest inputs at a cycle speed slower than the machine's will hopefully dampen the wild excursions. Other craft do better if the pilot releases the controls. It is important to read the manual before advancing the throttle.

Imagine a dynamically unstable front foil. Let's assume you are flying at cruise height. The slightest disturbance upward would be followed by a magnified correction downward causing a greater correction upward. Within a few cycles the bow will either crash to the surface or fly into the air. Bow foils that lack height controlling systems naturally behave this way when combined with badly timed pilot input. Controlling this natural instability is a big part of what this book is about.

A boat floating on its hull must be statically and dynamically stable. If tipped, a boat must return to its upright position. If hydrofoils are attached, the boat must continue to be statically stable. In general, foils deployed below the center of gravity will contribute to static stability, provided they have a density greater than water.

The axes of rotation. Hydrofoil boats, like aircraft, rotate around three axes. The point where these axes meet is called the *center of rotation*. For now, we will assume it is located at the *center of gravity*. There will be more on center of rotation in chapters 8, 9, and 10. Rotation around the lateral axis is called *pitching*. Rotation around the longitudinal axis is called *rolling*. Rotation around the vertical axis is called *yawing*. A *moment*, as used in Figure 3-8, is a "quantity that represents the magnitude of force applied to a rotational system at a distance from the axis of rotation" from Wikipedia.org.

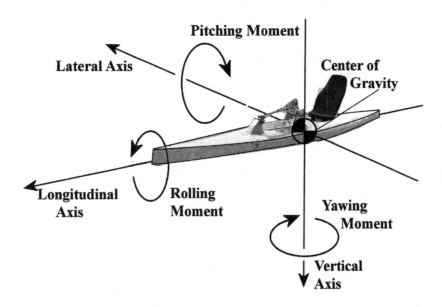

Figure 3-8. Three axes of rotation. The foils have been removed from this human powered hydrofoil boat for clarity.

What does this mean to the designer? A flying machine must be stable and controllable around all 3 axes. The management of moments around these axes is the subject of chapters 8, 9, and 10.

Lift, Area, and Speed Calculations

- Hydrofoil wing
- Calculating lift
- Aquadynamics is more aviation than boating
- Reynolds number
- Submergence factor
- Aspect ratio
- $V_{MAX} \approx 2*V_{TO}$
- Adjusting the lift

From the previous chapters you should have an idea of what a **hydrofoil wing** is and what it should look like. This chapter takes a closer look at those characteristics.

The *profile*, or cross section, of a foil should resemble other wings, like those of birds or airplanes. Some examples of those used on hydrofoils are the NACA 63-412, NACA 4412, or Ogival sections. These wing profiles can be seen in Figures 13-1, and 13-2. A profile is selected based on its lift, drag, and stall characteristics as well as its ease of fabrication.

The path of fluid over the wing must be as flawless as possible and follow a consistent curve with no pits, waves or dips, and the wing's surface should be as smooth as practical. This is particularly critical on the top surface of the foil and less critical on the bottom side. It is also more critical on the leading 1/3 of the top of the wing, and less critical on the trailing 2/3. The surface of the bottom side is the least critical.

The thickness of the wing should be appropriate. 10 to 15% of the chord is common. *Chord* is the distance between the extreme leading edge and the extreme trailing edge. Thickness is the maximum vertical measurement. The wing must be thick enough to have adequate strength and thin enough to have relatively low form drag. The geometry of a thicker wing allows a larger radius on the leading edge, resulting in improved lift, drag and stall characteristics.

For efficiency, the deeper the foil runs below the surface, the better. This depth is appropriately measured in chords. See Figure 4-7 to visualize the effect.

Air must not be allowed to enter onto the upper, low-pressure side of the wing (ventilation). The foil should not exceed its stall angle of attack during normal operations (stall). A high-speed foil needs a profile designed to control water vaporization (cavitation). We will revisit these conditions in chapter 6 as well as Figure 13-4 and its text.

The main foil should be at an angle of attack where the lift / drag ratio (L/D) is highest, either at cruise speed or top speed, depending on design objectives. See chapter 5 for more on L/D. Where power is critical, as with human powered or sail powered boats, it may be necessary that the foil be at its most efficient angle of attack at takeoff speed; in other words, at the AOA with the highest L/D. Otherwise takeoff power may not be sufficient to overcome drag.

In hydrofoils, because of high wing loads and thin foil sections, strength and stiffness are critical. Foil materials must be carefully selected. Wingspans should be calculated and limited so as to not exceed the material's strength. See chapter 11.

The axis of balanced lift, the line connecting the *centers of pressure*, on a foil will be 25 to 33% back from the leading edge for most common foil sections. This is the lateral line where the forces of pitch forward and pitch backward are equal. The balance point will move with changes in angle of attack. This movement will be greater in cambered foil sections than in symmetrical ones. Cambered foil sections can be modified to reduce the change in torque around the center of lift by curving up the trailing edge slightly.

Except for front foils that pitch independently of the hull's pitch, such as the Shutt Strut, which can be seen in Figures 8-6a and b, the front foil should have a higher wing loading, lift/area, than the rear foil. Read the text associated with Figures 8-14 and 8-15 for an explanation.

Calculating lift. Now that we have some idea *how* lift is created let's think about *how much* lift is created. To do this we are going to use some math.

The lift formula is the mathematical cornerstone of hydrofoil design. We will use numbers from Hifybe as an example. The formula is borrowed from aerodynamics and is shown:

$$\mathbf{L = \tfrac{1}{2}\, \rho * V^2 * S * C_L}$$

We can calculate the value of ½ ρ, Where ρ (rho) = density of the fluid. The density of seawater is 1.99 slugs and when multiplied by ½ the result rounds off to 1.00. (Fresh water is 3.5% less dense, thanks for asking).

Because ½ ρ = 1, we can simplify the formula to:

$$L = V^2 * S * C_L$$

L = Lift, pounds. Lift equals weight when flying straight and level.
V = Velocity, ft / sec (1 mph = 1.47 ft / sec)
S = Surface area of foil, projected vertically in square feet, ft^2.
C_L = Coefficient of lift, this is a dimensionless number found in tables of wing profiles as in *Theory of Wing Sections.*

Even without calculating this equation we can use it as a logical guide to create design rules:

Lift is in proportion to:

1. The area of the foil. Doubling the area doubles the lift
2. The coefficient of lift. Increasing the angle of attack to double the coefficient of lift will double the lift. Using a foil section with 10% greater C_L increases the lift 10%.
3. The square of the speed. Doubling the speed increases the lift by 4 times. Tripling increases by eight times.

Remember that lift will equal weight when flying straight and level. The importance of controlling weight cannot be over emphasized, because every pound of weight gained must be matched by a pound of lift. That means the area, C_L, or the speed must be increased to compensate.

Because this is a book on nautical craft it is natural that many readers will have a boating orientation. Displacement boats, whether wind or motor powered, have little concern for weight. Their lift is provided by displacing water and if the boat is a little heavy it simply displaces a bit more water. Want an extra anchor? No problem. Bring it onboard and don't forget the chain.

Conversely, a planing boat is a little more sensitive because it partially depends on dynamic forces to raise its hull to the surface where it skims. Leave the extra anchor on shore.

A hydrofoil depends entirely on aquadynamic forces to raise its mass above the surface. Like with all flying things, hydrofoil weight is critical. Leave both anchors on shore.

Lift, Area, and Speed Calculations

For the guy who just wants to build a boat without suffering brain damage, the simplest expression of the formula would be a table such as in Figure 4-1:

Determine Surface Area of Foil in Square Feet

Velocity in mph	6	8	10	12	14	16	18	20	22	24
100	3.25	1.83	1.17	0.81	0.60	0.46	0.36	0.29	0.24	0.20
200	6.49	3.65	2.34	1.62	1.19	0.91	0.72	0.58	0.48	0.41
300	9.74	5.48	3.50	2.43	1.79	1.37	1.08	0.88	0.72	0.61
400	12.98	7.30	4.67	3.25	2.38	1.83	1.44	1.17	0.97	0.81
500	16.23	9.13	5.84	4.06	2.98	2.28	1.80	1.46	1.21	1.01
600	19.47	10.95	7.01	4.87	3.58	2.74	2.16	1.75	1.45	1.22
700	22.72	12.78	8.18	5.68	4.17	3.19	2.52	2.04	1.69	1.42
800	25.96	14.60	9.35	6.49	4.77	3.65	2.88	2.34	1.93	1.62
900	29.21	16.43	10.51	7.30	5.36	4.11	3.25	2.63	2.17	1.83

(Lift, lbs — row labels in leftmost column)

Figure 4-1. Table determines area in ft^2. Foil profile is NACA 63-412. AOA = 4°.

With this table you can take the target speed and weight of your boat and determine the required surface area of the foils. Noodle out some system for controlling height and pitch with a small front foil and roll control for the large rear foil and, *voila*, you have a plan.

Incidentally, multiples or divisions of the inputted lift and area can be used. For example, to calculate the area needed for 3,000 lb lift at 10 mph, find the area corresponding to 300 lbs. lift on the table and multiply this area by 10. The answer is 35 ft^2. Multiples of speed cannot be directly inputted, because area is inversely proportional to the square of the speed. Doubling the speed reduces the required area to 1/4th the previous area. Intermediate area values can be approximated by extrapolating between two lift or speed values.

Ironically, over-simplifying the design problem like this can really complicate the results. A table with a few inputs and one output requires so many assumptions that the designer gives up too much control of the process. For example, in the table are the assumptions that the angle of attack is a constant 4°, flying is in salt water, $R_N <= 1,000,000$, the depth is greater than one chord, the wing span is infinite, and the wing profile is a NACA 63-412. To change any of these assumptions requires–guess what–recalculating the table using the underlying formula. My advice is to use the method that is the most comfortable. I prefer, after estimating the variables, to use a Microsoft Excel spreadsheet do the calculations. Spreadsheets are harder to construct for the first calculation, but it is simple to change inputted values, and it is easy to make legible hard copies using the computer's printer.

Aquadynamics is closer to aerodynamics than to boating science. The essential difference is characterized in the lift formula. The lift formula has no meaning to displacement or planing boats but it is the heart of hydrofoil performance calculation.

The energy required to create flight is proportional to the lift. In level flight, lift equals weight. So an extra pound of weight requires an additional pound of lift. This lift is created by increasing speed, foil area or coefficient of lift. In general, those changes increase drag, and added drag demands added horsepower. A more powerful, heavier motor requires a stronger transom, larger gas tank, etc. Furthermore, the strength of the foils and struts may require augmentation to carry the extra weight. See where this spiral goes?

Later we will be discussing specific design and construction methods, some taken from aviation experience, oriented to minimizing foil-borne weight. Forget about making your houseboat fly. If you want to adapt foils to an existing hull start looking for a lightweight aluminum Jon boat, a fiberglass runabout, or a carbon-fiber kayak. You are limited only by your imagination–and weight.

Human powered boats require particular attention to weight, and this includes the rider. So, step away from the cheese cake. Getting in shape won't do much to compensate for an overweight boat, and a slimmed down boat will not fly if the pilot is 90% *graisse matérielle*, pardon my French. In a human-powered boat, a pilot with a high power to weight ratio is essential. Getting strong and weighing less is essential. Bicycling is an excellent preparation.

Meanwhile, back at the formula. We can solve this equation for any part that may be unknown (you can only solve for one unknown at a time).

$$L = V^2 * S * C_L$$

$$S = L / (V^2 * C_L)$$

$$V = \sqrt{ L / (S * C_L) }$$

$$C_L = L / (V^2 * S)$$

The parameters for the rear foil of Hifybe (my "High Flying Banana") *at takeoff speed* (V_{TO}) are:

L = 281 lbs.
V = 11.8 ft. / sec. (8 mph)
S = 1.95 ft^2.
C_L = 1.04 at 7° takeoff.

There are 4 values to the formula. We need to know three values to determine the fourth unknown value. This requires us to make some assumptions. The assumptions made for Hifybe are: 16mph is the fastest your conservative author is willing to go on a high-flying banana. Very light outboard motors between 50 and 60 lbs. are available up to about 8 hp. We know 8 hp will push a light planing boat and pilot to low double-digit mph, at least 16 mph. Takeoff speed is about half the maximum speed when simple foil systems, without flaps, slats, etc., are used. Go to the last page of this chapter for an explanation of why $V_{MAX} \approx 2*V_{TO}$.

Lift, Area, and Speed Calculations

Let's try an example using the lift equation to determine the size of foils that will be built. Takeoff speed is a critical condition. This is where the hull and the foils are creating maximum drag. On the drag charts it is called the *drag hump* (not to be confused with the drag bucket described earlier and seen in Figure 5-5). See Figure 5-4 for an illustration of the drag hump.

With a fixed pitch propeller, motor rpms will be below the level of maximum hp. In addition, at takeoff available lift is at its lowest because takeoff speed is the lowest flying speed. After takeoff the hull drag goes away, the wetted strut area declines, the boat accelerates quickly, the motor speeds toward maximum power, and the available lift increases with the square of the increase in speed. So lift at takeoff-speed is critical and this is a good place to begin our calculations.

After these assumptions, we have 3 values existing at takeoff:

$L = 281$ lbs. for the rear foil.

$V = 11.8$ ft. / sec. This is half the target top speed of 23.6 ft. / sec. or 16mph.

$C_L = 1.04$ The C_L is determined from Figure 4-2, NACA 63-412 at 7° is the sum of 3° (highest lift drag ratio) plus 4° bow high takeoff attitude.

$S = L / (V^2 * C_L)$

$S = 281 / (11.8 * 11.8 * 0.9)$

$S = 281 / 125$

$S = 1.95$ ft^2 or

$S = 280$ in^2 (multiply ft^2 by 144 to convert to in^2)

Assuming that your wing section has a chord of 4.75in., divide 4.75 into 280. The result is 59. Fifty-nine inches is the span of the main foil.

The results from this formula are based on foils that were long ago tested in some laboratory. Use the following sources for lift tables or further information on airfoil profiles:

Theory of Wing Sections, Airfoils at Low Speeds, NASA, Google: NASA airfoil sections, University of Illinois airfoil sections. See bibliography for details.

The C_L is for a deeply submerged, infinite span wing under ideal conditions. The C_L table for our three wing profiles is shown in Figure 4-2:

AOA	NACA 63-412 Aft foil Coefficient of Lift	NACA 4412 Front foil Coefficient of Lift	Ogival Coefficient of Lift
-8	-0.600	-0.45	
-7	-0.491	-0.34	
-6	-0.382	-0.23	
-5	-0.273	-0.12	
-4	-0.164	-0.01	0.007
-3	-0.055	0.10	0.100
-2	0.054	0.20	0.192
-1	0.163	V$_{MAX}$ 0.30	0.278
0	V$_{MAX}$ 0.272	0.40	0.375
1	0.381	0.50	0.445
2	0.490	0.60	0.525
3	0.599	0.70	0.590
4	0.708	0.80	0.675
5	0.817	0.90	0.770
6	0.926	1.00	0.835
7	1.035	1.10	0.900
8	1.144	V$_{TO}$ 1.20	0.987
9	1.253	1.30	1.050
10	1.362	1.40	1.085
11	V$_{TO}$ 1.460	1.48	C$_{LMAX}$ 1.090
12	1.520	1.53	1.080
13	1.560	C$_{LMAX}$ 1.55	1.040
14	C$_{LMAX}$ 1.580	1.51	0.950
15	1.550	1.45	
16	1.450	1.40	
17	1.270	1.35	

Figures 4-2a & b. (a) This is the C_L table for the three wing profiles used in this book. The V$_{TO}$ and V$_{MAX}$ is for Hifybe. For a more complete table go to Figure 13-3. (b) As velocity increases CL must decrease. Recall: $C_L = L / (V^2 * S)$.

Airfoil data: NACA 63-412 and NACA 4412, Theory of Wing Sections, R_N = 3,000,000. Ogival, thickness ratio = 7%, "Report #E-79-6", Calif. Institute of Tech, Wade, R_N = 750,000. See bibliography for source details.

For greater accuracy the lift formula can be expanded. There are three conditions that may significantly affect the performance of the foil: aspect ratio, depth of submergence, and Reynolds number. The remainder of this chapter is primarily devoted to explaining these three conditions.

Reynolds number (R_N) to quote from Wikipedia: "is a dimensionless number that gives a measure of the *ratio* of inertial forces…to viscous forces…and, consequently, it quantifies the relative importance of these two types of forces for given flow conditions." It is important whenever there are differences in size, speed or fluid. Another approach is taken in this quote from Hoerner's *Fluid-Dynamic Drag:* "According to Reynolds' similarity law…flow pattern (including boundary layer) and force coefficients of two similar bodies (identical in shape, but different in size), or those of one and the same body in different mediums—are similar if their Reynolds numbers are identical."

Its primary significance has to do with the boundary layer. The lower the R_N, the greater the tendencies for the boundary layer flow to be laminar. The higher the R_N the more the boundary layer flow will tend to be turbulent.

Laminar flow tends to consume less energy, which is another way of saying it creates less drag. Conversely, turbulent flow creates more drag. Unfortunately laminar flow is difficult to maintain and when it converts to turbulent flow there tends to be a dramatic separation of the flow from the foil's surface.

Figure 4-3 illustrates the differences in performance. Figure 4-4 interprets the previous two charts. Observe that a low R_NS wing has lower maximum coefficient of lift, lower maximum AOA, but higher L/D due to reduced drag.

The opposite effects go with a high R_N.

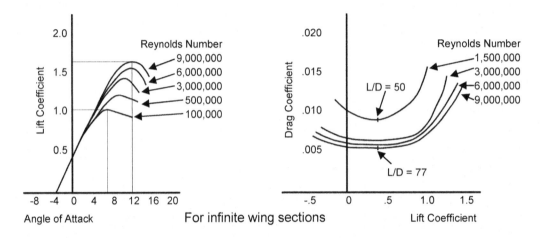

Figures 4-3a & b. A lower R_N results in a lower C_{LMAX} (bad), and a lower AOA_{MAX} (bad), but a higher L/D_{MAX} (good). The data is from *Aerodynamics for Naval Aviators*. Wing section profile is a NACA 4412.

High R_N	Low R_N
Higher maximum C_L	Lower maximum C_L
Higher maximum AOA	Lower maximum AOA
Higher drag	Lower drag
Lower L/D – higher lift but much higher drag	Higher L/D – lower lift but much lower drag

Figure 4-4. Effect of high and low R_Ns based on observations of the previous figures.

In Figure 4-3b, observe the absence of a depression, or *drag bucket,* in the L/D curve. This indicates a non-laminar-flow wing profile.

Figures 4-5a and b illustrate a laminar flow wing profile, in this case the NACA 63-412. Laminar flow wings, when operating in the realm of a low R_N, have L / D charts that show a dramatic drop in drag in a narrow range of coefficients of lift. In the curve of R_N = 3,000,000, it is between C_L = .1 and C_L = .7. A second graph of the so called *drag bucket* of the NACA 63-412 is seen in Figure 4-5b. Observe that the drag bucket is only pronounced at lower R_Ns. Departure from the drag bucket indicates the AOA where the flow separates from the airfoil or hydrofoil. Smaller, slower hydrofoils are operating in the realm of low R_Ns. This is the realm where large birds and typical radio controlled model airplanes operate.

A higher R_N can be a good thing, because this indicates that a higher angle of attack and a higher C_L are obtainable before there is turbulent flow and flow separation (stalling). Unfortunately, drag is also higher, and that lowers the maximum L/D.

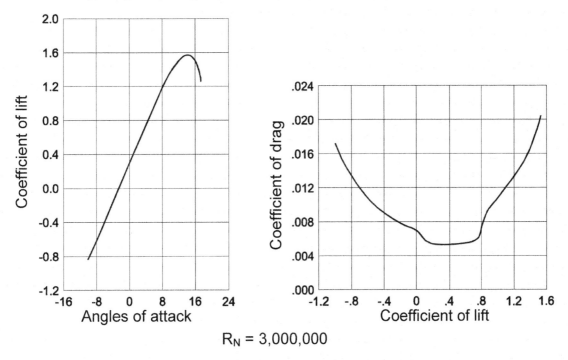

R_N = 3,000,000

Figures 4-5a & b. Tables of NACA 63-412, showing: (a) C_L vs. AOA, and (b) C_L vs. C_D. Data is from *Theory of Wing Sections*.

We use the Reynolds number to select the appropriate coefficient of lift curve, and that particular lift curve then serves as the source of the coefficients of lift. In this way the Reynolds number affects the results of the lift calculations.

Lift, Area, and Speed Calculations

The R_N is determined by using the following formula:

$R_N = \rho V d / \mu$

Where:

ρ = the density of the fluid—water
V = velocity of the free-stream flow
d = mean chord
μ = fluid viscosity

The units used in this formula may be unfamiliar to some. For example, viscosity is measured in centipoise. Fortunately the classic formula, used in aerodynamics, can be simplified for hydrofoil applications. Unlike air, water remains fairly constant in density and viscosity, at least within the realm of a hydrofoil's normal operating conditions. Because of this, the formula can be abbreviated by computing a factor to replace the density and viscosity values:

For water flight:
$V_{mph} * C_{ft} * 121{,}000 = R_N$ Or $V_{ft/sec} * C_{ft} * 83{,}000 = R_N$

For air flight:
$V_{mph} * C_{ft} * 9{,}300 = R_N$ Or $V_{ft/sec} * C_{ft} * 6{,}300 = R_N$

Where:
V_{mph} = Velocity in miles per hour
$V_{ft/sec}$ = Velocity in feet per second
C_{ft} = Chord of foil in feet

For Hifybe:

V_{MAX} = 16 mph = 23.6 ft. / sec
C_{ft} = 4.75in / 12 = .4 ft
Hifybe's R_N = 83,000 * 23.6 * .4 = 800,000 (rounded)

From observing the formula for R_N we can determine, even without doing calculations, that R_N is proportional to:

1. The density of the fluid.
2. The velocity through the fluid.
3. The length of the body passing through the fluid. For a foil this would be its *chord*.

Furthermore, R_N is inversely proportional to the viscosity of the fluid.

Incidentally, lift and drag increase by a factor of 800 when an aerodynamic shape is taken from air and operated in water. This is because the density of water is 800 times that of air, and density is a term in both the lift and drag formulas.

However, the R_N is affected by a factor of only 16 because 800 / 50 = 16. 800 is the increase in numerator, density, and 50 is the increase in the denominator, viscosity.

It may be possible to avoid R_N computation all together by using the table in Figure 4-6:

Determine Reynolds Number, R_N, in millions

Speed, mph:		6	8	10	12	14	16	18	20	22	24
	1	0.07	0.09	0.11	0.14	0.16	0.18	0.20	0.23	0.25	0.27
	2	0.14	0.18	0.23	0.27	0.32	0.36	0.41	0.46	0.50	0.55
	3	0.20	0.27	0.34	0.41	0.48	0.55	0.61	1.68	0.75	0.82
	4	0.27	0.36	0.46	0.55	0.64	0.73	0.82	0.91	1.00	1.09
Chord, inches	5	0.34	0.46	0.57	0.68	0.80	0.91	1.02	1.14	1.25	1.37
	6	0.41	0.55	0.68	0.82	0.96	1.09	1.23	1.37	1.50	1.64
	7	0.48	0.64	0.80	0.96	1.12	1.27	1.43	1.59	1.75	1.91
	8	0.55	0.73	0.91	1.09	1.27	1.46	1.64	1.82	2.00	2.18
	9	0.61	0.82	1.02	1.23	1.43	1.64	1.84	2.05	2.25	2.46
	10	0.68	0.91	1.14	1.37	1.59	1.82	2.05	2.28	2.50	2.73

Figure 4-6. Reynolds number look-up table.

Hifybe has a rear foil chord of 4.75 in. rounded up to 5 in. and it flies between 8 and 16 mph. The table shows its Reynolds number to be from 460,000 to 910,000, about the same as the wing of a pheasant or seagull. Looking up the lift table in *Theory of Wing Sections* we find the lowest R_N for the NACA 63-412 wing section is 3,000,000. Short of lugging our foil section to the nearest wind tunnel for testing, we are forced to use the closest data available, so let's go with R_N = 3,000,000. But keep in mind, with our lower R_N, our stall AOA , the $C_{LMAX,}$ and the drag will be slightly less. The lower drag (while in the drag bucket) will result in a higher L/D than the available charts indicate.

Submergence factor, or operating depth's effect on lift, is next to be considered. The shallower a foil runs, the more it will be influenced by the atmosphere and the surface. Because less depth corresponds with a shorter air path along the strut, air is more likely to find its way into the relative vacuum on the upper side of the foil. In addition, because there is less fluid mass over the top of the foil, there is less mass to be vertically accelerated. The reduction of lift can be explained within the context of one of the five theories of lift (excluding the Ugly Theory) and I am still not going to go there. Also, the closer the foil is to the surface, the more the surface will be disturbed in the form of waves. This means an increase in wave drag.

Lift, Area, and Speed Calculations

The relationship between foil lift and submergence is expressed as the *submergence factor*. Here is the formula for a submergence factor, F_S, as determined empirically by Beason and Buckle:

$$F_S = 1 - .222 \left(\frac{((1.5 * \text{Chord}) - \text{Submergence})}{\text{Chord}} \right)^2$$

The submergence factor is used by multiplying it by the values of the lift formula, introduced earlier in this chapter: $L = V^2 * S * C_L$.

The resulting formula is: $L = V^2 * S * C_L * F_S$

The following graph, 4-7, represents the F_S for various fractions of submergence expressed in chords. For example, when a foil with a 10 inch chord is submerged 5 inches (.5 chords), it will produce 78% of the lift of a deeply submerged foil.

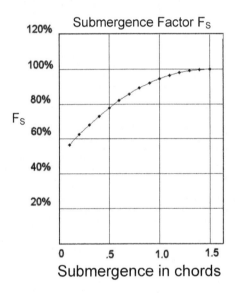

Figure 4-7. Submergence factor, F_S, vs. Submergence.

The surface effect can contribute to pitch stability, but a really good and versatile design will still depend on a surface sensor coupled with variable area or variable lift foil. Operating within one chord of the surface is a very limiting. Running that close to the surface risks ventilation and the need to maintain a consistent depth is incompatible with all but the smallest waves.

As shown in Figure 4-7, the surface effect on lift is not very significant at depths exceeding 1 chord–in Hifybe's case that is 4.75 inches. With less than one chord of depth the lift drops quickly until the *top* of the foil provides no aquadynamic lift because no water is passing over. It is fair to conclude that as long as the design provides for foil depth always being more than one chord, this effect need not be calculated.

There are, of course, some exceptions where it will be necessary to calculate the effects of submergence. With special designs the submergence depth effect can be used for height stability. Some Russian riverboats use low aspect ratio foils with very wide chords so one chord depth is a significant measurement. Their fore and aft foils are widely spaced front to back and the struts are short. This limits the AOA changes resulting from hull pitching. The Russian design, named after its creator, Dr. R.Y. Alexeyev, dates back to the mid 1940s.

In the Alexeyev design, to aid in takeoff and bow height maintenance, the front foil system gets part of its lift from a planing foil placed above the primary front foil. The vertical distance between the planing foil and the foil below it is about one foil chord. The planing surface is large enough to resist penetrating the surface. At cruising speed this planing foil creates a portion of the total lift. Because it resists submergence, it augments the stiffness of the bow's height maintenance. Within a narrow range of speed and depth, this simplified system can find its flying height without the aid of complicated variable lift devices.

Another example of using the F_S for height stability is in human powered hydrofoils (HPH). Due to power limitations some of these fly in a very narrow range of speed. There are HPH boats that fly at a stable height when the speed is held steady and the front foil is carefully trimmed to fly below the surface a fraction of a chord measurement.

A small hydrofoil could conceivably be designed around this characteristic, but there are at least two problems. Any surface following mechanism needs an adequate range of depth excursion. If one anticipates 6-inch waves, a 6-inch chord would be needed to limit the range of submergence to one chord. That is a big chord for a small foil. Take Hifybe for example. Its front foil area is just 48 square inches, so the indicated span would be 8 inches (6 x 8 = 48) resulting in a low aspect ratio. Such a low aspect ratio foil would be very inefficient, as you will see later in this chapter.

The second problem is the depth correctional force of the submergence effect is too weak in comparison to the changes in lift due to hull pitching. Hifybe can pitch nose up 3° and pitch down 3°. See chapter 8 for calculations on converting flying height excursions into changes in pitch angle. A 3° change in angle of attack could radically change the C_L. If the bow is high and our front foil is flying at AOA= 3° the $C_L = .60$. If the bow drops or the stern rises to change the AOA to 0° then the $C_L = .40$. This is a 33% reduction of lift $(.60 - .40) / .60 = .33)$.

Incidentally, drag is increased as the foil flies nearer to the surface. This is mostly because the passing of the foil will cause a deformation of the surface, in other words, a wave is created that trails behind the disturbance. The energy expended in creating this wave is measured as drag and is called, appropriately, *wave drag*. See chapter 5 for more on drag.

Aspect ratio (AR) is a measure of fineness of the wing. In constant span wings it is the ratio of *span / chord*. In tapered wings, it is the *span squared* divided by the wing *area*. AR affects lift and induced drag, especially induced drag. A high aspect ratio wing–a long fine wing–has less of a wing tip influence due to the tip's small size relative to the wide span. Therefore it creates less induced drag.

Of the three conditions affecting the coefficient of lift–aspect ratio, depth of submergence and Reynolds number–aspect ratio is usually the most significant. The higher the aspect ratio the closer the wing is to having an infinite span.

It can be seen from Figure 4-8, based on data from *Theory of Wing Sections,* that lower aspect ratios (but above AR = 1) increase the stall angle of attack, and the maximum coefficient of lift is slightly affected. In this chart, the slope of the lift curve is reduced with lower aspect ratio wings. In other words, the necessary angle of attack to achieve a given C_L is increased. Think of the supersonic Concord with its long chord and narrow span. As it flares for landing the pitch up is so extreme that the nose must be hinged downward to permit visibility to the runway.

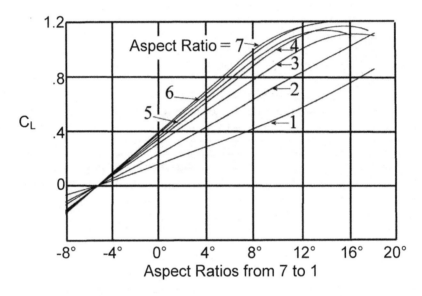

Figure 4-8. Aspect ratio affects the slope of the C_L.

The aspect ratio influence is greatest below AR = 4. The performance of a wing with a very low aspect ratio is dominated by the wing tip vortex effect. To provide for the difference, an aspect ratio factor, F_{AR} can be incorporated into the lift formula. The revised formula looks like this: $L = V^2 * S * C_L * F_{AR}$. Referring to Figure 4-9a, one can see that for a wing with an aspect ratio of 3 the factor would be: $F_{AR} = .65$. By including this factor in the formula the effect is to reduce lift, L, to 65% of its uncorrected lift. We will revisit wing tip effect when discussing induced drag in chapter 5.

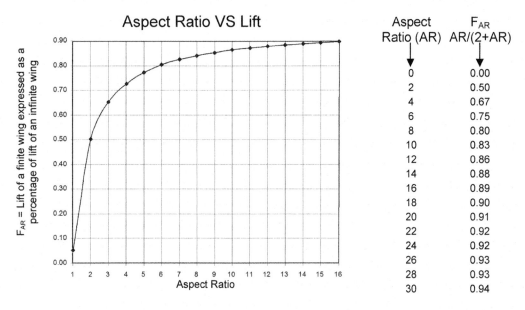

Aspect Ratio (AR)	F_{AR} AR/(2+AR)
0	0.00
2	0.50
4	0.67
6	0.75
8	0.80
10	0.83
12	0.86
14	0.88
16	0.89
18	0.90
20	0.91
22	0.92
24	0.92
26	0.93
28	0.93
30	0.94

Figures 4-9a & b. Low aspect ratio wings have reduced lift for a given V, S, and C_L. The percentage shown on the Y axis equals F_{AR}.

$V_{MAX} \approx 2*V_{TO}$. This rule of the thumb needs examination before leaving the subject of lift, area, and speed calculations. Simply accepting this rule will save the reader some thinking, but for you doubters the rule can be proven by using the lift formula, $L = V^2 * S * C_L$, which was introduced earlier in this chapter.

In steady flight, lift equals weight, but lift increases with the square of the velocity. Lift exceeding weight will be rapidly created as speed increases. To bleed off excessive lift on the main foil, the C_L may be reduced as speed increases, and this is typically done by reducing the angle of attack, AOA. See Figure 4-2b. However, if the AOA at takeoff is only 4°, there is not much room for reduction, so let us assume that by raising the bow 3° the AOA at takeoff is increased to 7°. Using the C_L chart for the NACA 63-412 foil section we see that C_L at 7° is 1.035 and the C_L at zero degrees is .272. Zero^o can be obtained by flying in a -3° (nose down) attitude. In the next step, we apply the formula:

$$V = \sqrt{L/ (S*C_L)}$$

Using the formula, we find the velocity at 7° AOA to be 8 mph, and at 0° to be 15.7mph. In other words, for the lift to remain constant while the speed doubles, it will be necessary for the AOA to be reduced from 7° to zero^o. See Figure 4-2 to lookup the C_L.

We can use Hifybe as an example to apply the formula. At takeoff, the calculation for its main foil looks like this:

$V_{TO,}$ AOA = 7°:

$V = 11.82$ ft/sec $= \sqrt{282lbs/(1.95 \ sqft * 1.035)} = 8.06$ mph

Lift, Area, and Speed Calculations

and:

$V_{MAX,}$ AOA = $0°$:

$V = 23.06$ ft/sec $= \sqrt{282\ lbs/(1.95\ sqft * .272)} = 15.69$ mph

In practice, the reduction in AOA needed might be slightly less than $7°$. As speed increases the stern rotates upward around the height stable bow foil, reducing the angle of attack of the aft foil. As the aft foil approaches the surface it becomes less efficient (submergence effect) and lift is reduced until a balance is found. On the other hand, raising the bow $3°$ for takeoff may not be feasible especially with a boat who's hull extends aft of the main foil. Raising the bow of such a boat will cause "tail squat" and the additional drag may prevent the boat from obtaining V_{TO}.

The point is: V_{MAX} is limited to about twice V_{TO}, because above the maximum speed too much lift is generated, and the rear foil will breach the surface. The way around the rule is to reduce the C_L or the foil area while in transitional flight.

Adjusting the lift of the rear foil in order to accommodate an increase in speed can be done in these ways:

- ➢ Reduce the angle of incidence by using an on-the-fly adjustment mechanism.
- ➢ Use flaps as most aircraft do. Figure 4-10 illustrates the aircraft solution.
- ➢ Use a surface piercing dihedral foil like Hydro-ped's, Figure 17-3. Ladder foils may also be used. Both systems reduce their wetted area as speed increases.
- ➢ Reduce the wetted area with partially retractable foils, as Decavitator, Figure 1-11.
- ➢ Invent something, like telescoping winglets.

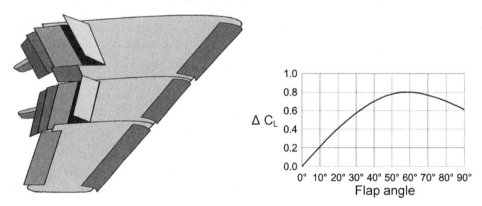

Figures 4-10a & b. (a) Variable lift devices deployed on a modern aircraft wing. (b) The effect of a single trailing edge flap. With a flap deflection of $50°$ the C_L increases by 0.8. From NACA TR 677, see bibliography. The delta symbol, Δ, means "difference in or change in."

This discussion of excessive lift with increasing speed is primarily a problem with the rear foil. The front foil's lift will be regulated by the height finding system, and this will better accommodate changes in speed.

40

Drag and Power Calculations

- Induced and parasite drags
- Friction and wave drags
- The theoretical maximum hull speed
- Form, spray, air, pressure, interference, and induced drag
- Drag hump
- Drag bucket
- Streamlining
- Formula for induced drag
- Formula for parasite drag
- Common shapes with their C_D
- Caveat
- Drag $\approx$ square of velocity
- Power $\approx$ cube of velocity
- Overall propulsive coefficient
- Determining power at the drag hump
- Towing method
- Factor for boat, strut, and foil drags
- Lift / Drag

If the Grinch took all the fun from hydrofoils, they'd still compare favorably to other boats because they have a smoother ride, and they create less drag at higher speeds. To understand why there is less drag, let's look at the types of drag, what causes each type, and how they are reduced in hydrofoils.

Induced and parasite drag are broad categories. There is only one type of induced drag, but several types of parasite drag; they are friction, wave, form, interference, and spray. Induced drag, also called lift drag, is a direct result of creating lift. Parasite drag in its various forms describes all other types of energy wasted as an object passes through a fluid. We will discuss the various parasite drags first.

Friction drag affects all vessels. It is the effect of an object's surface moving through a viscous fluid. The fluid closest to the boat's surface clings to it and moves as if attached to the surface. As the distance from the surface increases the fluid moves slower than the speed of the surface and more like the speed of the slipstream. This area of transition is called the boundary layer. Energy is lost in accelerating the fluid within the various levels of the boundary layer. There are two patterns of flow within the boundary layer: laminar and turbulent. This subject is covered in detail in the text associated with Figures 5-1, and 13-6 through 13-12.

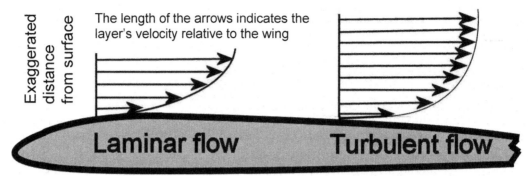

Figure 5-1. Profiles of laminar and turbulent flow.

In Figure 5-1, the arrows represent the difference in velocities between the moving wing's surface and the fluid surrounding it. Notice that fluid touching the surface moves at almost the same speed as the wing's surface. The speed of the fluid far from the surface is unaffected, and has the same velocity as the free stream.

Aerodynamics for Naval Aviators states that the characteristics of the flow profiles are:

Laminar profiles

- ➢ Low thickness
- ➢ Low velocities next to surface
- ➢ Gradual velocity change
- ➢ Low skin friction

Turbulent profiles

- ➢ Greater thickness
- ➢ Higher velocities next to surface
- ➢ Sharp velocity change
- ➢ Higher skin friction

Wave drag is the most visible of any of the drags. It can be observed whenever a boat disturbs the surface. The vertical displacement of water is a wave, and the energy expended is called drag. The bigger the wave is, the greater the energy wasted. As graceful sailboats demonstrate, wave generation can be minimized—at least up to speeds approaching *hull speed,* V_{HULL}.

The **theoretical maximum hull speed**, *hull speed*, or V_{HULL}, is the maximum speed that a displacement boat can go without climbing high on its own bow wave. A displacement hull is one that moves *through* the water. Most sailboats and all conventional ships have displacement hulls.

Because the bow is deep-set in the water it creates a serious disturbance aptly called a "bow wave". Unfortunately, the water being passed through is limited in how fast it can get out of the way and return to where it was. As the speed of the ship increases the newest bow wave climbs on top of the previous one creating a continuous form. The mounting water causes the bow to buoy upward. Behind the wave a trough is created. As the bow is lifted on the mounting wave the stern settles into the following trough. The ship is climbing continuously up hill, and the power consumed increases geometrically with increases in speed. As power increases, the boat quickly becomes unstable as the stern continues to drop and the bow points skyward. In this condition, some boats will violently roll, skid or dive off to the side with disastrous results. The hull has exceeded the limits of its maximum displacement hull speed, V_{HULL}.

A shore-bound observer can make some estimate of the power required to propel a boat by observing its wake. Compare the wake of a displacement sailboat to that of a planing boat when both are operating near V_{HULL} but below planing speed. Assume their speed and weight are equal, but the sailboat is long and slender and the speedboat is shorter, wider and has a sharp break at the transom. You observe the tranquil water being parted by the sailboat's bow and quietly joined at the stern. At this slow speed the planing boat struggles to climb onto its bow wave. The stem rises and the stern squats. A large diagonal wave is created at the bow and another amidships. Collectively these are called a *wake*. It's easy to see that low power is needed in the sailboat, and that high power is required of the planing style boat. The advantage ends there. The sailboat stops accelerating when it reaches its V_{HULL} whereas the planing boat accelerates past its V_{HULL}, gets up on its step and speeds away.

The hull speed of a displacement boat can be estimated with the formula:

$$V_{HULL} \cong 1.5 \sqrt{L}$$

Where,
V_{HULL} = Maximum hull speed in mph.
L = Water line length in feet.

This means that my 10 ft. dinghy climbs onto its bow wave at 4.5mph[a], but your 100 ft. yacht (that cost you a million bucks more) starts mega-sucking gas at just 15 mph[b]. You wasted your money. Here's the math:

a) $1.5 * \sqrt{10}$ = 1.5 * 3 = 4.5 mph
b) $1.5 * \sqrt{100}$ = 1.5 * 10 = 15mph

Smaller powerful boats exceed their hull speeds by using a relatively flat bottom, a bow that lifts with speed and a stern that has a clean break with the water it passes over. These are planing boats. For more see chapter 12, "Hull and Motor Selection". For a table of V_{HULL} vs. length see Figure 12-1 and its associated text.

Form or profile drag is important to all boats and ships. It is created by forcing the frontal area through the water. Streamlining allows the water to gracefully flow around the moving vessel, but the effect of pushing a mass through the water cannot be completely avoided. This drag increases with the square of the speed.

Spray drag shares some similarities to form and wave drag but spray drag is associated with higher speeds, whereas form drag is evident at all speeds, and wave drag becomes significant at relatively low speeds. Spray drag represents the energy needed to accelerate and hurl water from one place to another. It is not associated with hull length. Any design that reduces spray will, of course, reduce spray drag.

Four things determine the amount of energy lost to parasite drag: frontal area, speed, surface smoothness, and fluid viscosity. The first three are self evident, but let's look at viscosity. Water pours quickly but molasses doesn't. It is the viscosity of the molasses that puts the brakes on the fluid. Whenever you apply the brakes, energy is consumed. Water is 50 times more viscous than air and this will influence our comparisons to things aeronautical. In chapters 4 and 13, this comparison is quantified by referencing the object's Reynolds number.

Air drag might be mistakenly thought of as a problem only for *high-speed* hydrofoils. However, testing a human powered hydrofoil on a windy day will quickly demonstrate that low speed hydrofoils are affected as well. Air drag should always be considered, but it is outside the scope of this book to go into depth here. Suffice it to say that the principles of streamlining applied to wetted areas may be applied to the upper structures as well. One caveat can be gained from the trials of Decavitator, Figure 1-11. The MIT team chose to do their record-breaking runs without the use of the extensive fairings shown in the illustration. They found the added structure caused instability at speeds approaching 20 knots.

Pressure drag. This type of drag has to do with the distribution of pressure around a moving object. When a shape, like a foil or a strut, moves through a fluid the pressure on the leading portion will be greater than on the trailing portion. The amount of pressure on the trailing portion is variable depending on its flow separation patterns. These patterns are dependent on the Reynolds number (R_N), surface smoothness, etc. We address an example of flow separation in our golf ball example in Figure 13-12 and its associated text. At very low R_N, like in a falling snowflake, one third of the total drag can be attributed to pressure drag, but in the realm of hydrofoil boats it is not so significant. For more on this subject, consult Hoerner's *Fluid-Dynamic Drag*, chapter 3.

Interference drag. When two or more submerged moving bodies are close to each other they will lose lift and have more drag than if they are far apart. The increase in drag due to proximity is called *interference drag*, and it should be kept to a minimum. If a biplane configuration is used, one wing above another, the distance between wings should be greater than 1 chord. The top wing should not be directly above the bottom one. Take a hint from the Boeing-Stearman PT-17 Kaydet biplane or the Beech Staggerwing, and place the top wing roughly one half chord forward of the bottom.

The exact placement is an art requiring examination of the pressure patterns on both wings to be followed by some experimentation. If the vertical separation is less than one chord, the interference drag and loss of lift will increase geometrically as the wings are positioned closer to each other.

To further minimize interference drag the junction between struts and wing should be faired and the junction should be at the greatest angle possible. In the case of a "T" junction, 90° is good, but a 120° "Y" junction is slightly better. Figure 1-10b shows the Dynafoil's rear foil intersects its strut at an angle of 105°. The "T" foil at the stern of the Hi-Foil, Figure 1-10a, intersects its strut at a 90° angle. Incidentally, the rear foil anhedral of some hydrofoils, including the Dynafoil's, allows sharper banking without the foil breaching the surface.

The following figure shows the importance of fairing:

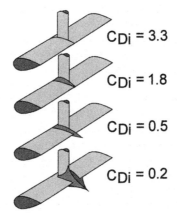

$C_{Di} = 3.3$

$C_{Di} = 1.8$

$C_{Di} = 0.5$

$C_{Di} = 0.2$

Figure 5-2. Faired struts and their coefficients of interference drag.

Adding fairings to the above strut junctions reduced the coefficient of interference drag to less than 10% of the non-faired junction. The bottom fairing extends one strut chord behind the trailing edge. These struts have a thickness ratio of 43%. The data is from Hoerner.

Induced drag is associated with wings when they are flying at high angles of attack, like on airplanes and hydrofoils at takeoff and slow flight. It is the result of the pressure differential between the top of a wing (partial vacuum) and the bottom (slight pressure). At the wing tips the pressurized air tends to move into the vacuum. Because the wing itself is moving, this movement of fluid from the bottom to the top comes off the back of the wing in the form of a vortex or spiral. Looking forward, the spiral is clockwise on the left wingtip and counterclockwise on the right.

At high speed, low angle of attack, and low C_L this pressure differential is relatively low, and there is not much induced drag. At takeoff and low speeds the angle of attack is high, the pressure differential is elevated, and the C_L is high. Therefore, for a given configuration induced drag is highest at low speeds and lowest at high speeds. This is the opposite of the other types of drag.

At low speeds induced drag dominates. As speed increases, induced drag diminishes, and the parasite drags (wave, form, and spray) become dominant. Generally we will be using the word *drag* to indicate the total of all forms of drag. The interaction between induced and parasite drags is illustrated in Figures 5-3 and 16-4.

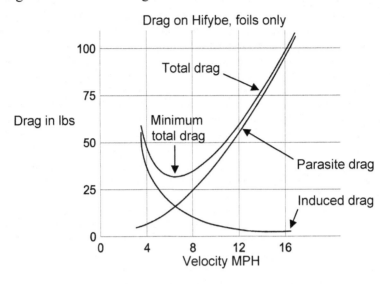

Figure 5-3. The interaction between induced and parasite drags.
This is adapted from *Aerodynamics for Naval Aviators*.

Drag hump are not dirty words–shame on you. Drag hump is a condition common to aircraft as well as hydrofoils. See Figure 5-4. It occurs during the transition from non-flying to flying. As an aircraft rotates for takeoff, it is in a condition of high induced drag, rising parasite drag, and low flying speed. Contributing to drag are partial flaps, landing gear, and high angle of attack. In addition there is rolling resistance from the wheels on the runway. This configuration is called "dirty" but that too is OK to say around the kids. Conversely the craft's configuration while cruising is called *clean*.

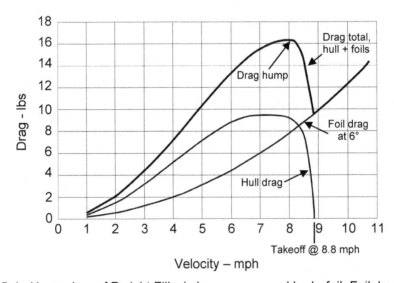

Figure 5-4. Hump drag of Dwight Filley's human powered hydrofoil, Foilplay, showing the combined drag of the hull and foils. This boat is designed to have a large wing, low speed, low power, and long endurance. The chart is by Ray Johnsen.

Similarly, the hydrofoil at takeoff is in a condition of high drag. The foils are at a high angle of attack, extra lift devices such as flaps may be in use, extra foils may be deployed, ailerons may be deflected and, most of all, the hull and all the struts are dragging deep in the water. The craft is operating in a condition of low speed and high drag. It is riding the drag hump, like in Figure 5-4. It is a critical condition and it is particularly critical for limited powered craft such as human or wind-powered hydrofoils. With the Foilplay, it is essential that the pilot hold the bow down so that the hull's tail does not drag. Just prior to takeoff the main foil is deflected to a high angle of attack while the hull runs at an attitude of low drag. If the nose were lifted prior to takeoff it might create enough drag to make it impossible to accelerate to V_{TO}.

Except when changing speed, propulsion equals drag. The two places where this little equation becomes critical is at takeoff and at maximum speed. As stated, to takeoff, enough propulsion must be created to overcome the hump drag. Before and after, parasite drag increases with the square of velocity, but the propulsion is limited. At some point in acceleration, the drag will have increased to the point that it equals maximum *overall propulsion* available (see OPC later in this chapter). This point is called maximum velocity or V_{MAX}.

Drag Bucket. Operating in the drag bucket simply means operating at the angle of attack where there is the lowest drag / lift or the highest L/D. This area of operation is easily identified in many charts showing drag vs. lift. The bucket shape is a phenomena associated with laminar flow wing sections operating at relatively low Reynolds numbers. The charted drag values take a dip as the lift increases, and the chart line takes on the appearance of a bucket. Usually the bucket spans 3 or 4 degrees AOA before it takes a sharp turn upward. It's ok to operate, some of the time, outside the protection of the bucket; but if the boat is designed for cruising, then the cruising speed should fall within the bucket. Boats designed for speed, or endurance, or easy takeoff, will want to be "in the bucket" during these points of performance. Power is proportional to drag, of course, so this will also be within the realm of lowest power for the assumed speed.

Unfortunately, no matter how beguiling the drag bucket may be, it is usually impossible operate in it over a wide range of speeds and varied conditions. To achieve it, laminar flow is necessary, and laminar flow requires ideal conditions such as smooth, clean surfaces with no cavitation or ventilation. In addition, the drag bucket exists only at lower R_N, and the R_N increases with speed. For example, Figure 5-5 shows how sensitive the formation of a drag bucket is under various Reynolds numbers.

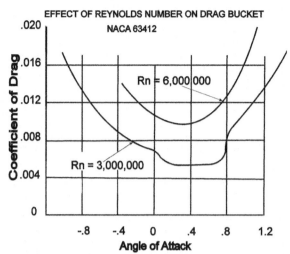

Figure 5-5. The Drag bucket in a laminar flow wing section occurs at the lower R_N. Data acquired from *Theory of Wing Sections*.

The importance of **streamlining** has not always been fully appreciated. Early airplanes, sailing ships, and motorcars are ungainly things. Through experience all these vehicles evolved graceful lines to reduce drag, but some of the big drag creators are easily overlooked. Howard Hughes' H-1 racer used flat-headed rivets to achieve skin smoothness never before seen. This contributed to the H-1's record-breaking performance.

An earlier, more significant discovery was streamlining and then eliminating the wires. Early biplanes depended on exposed wires to connect the top and bottom wings to create truss-like structures. It was believed that thin wing sections had superior lift / drag characteristics. Unfortunately designers used exposed wires to make these thin wing combinations strong. How much drag could there be in a little wire? Plenty, they soon found. Round wires were replaced with flat rods with the cross sections of tiny symmetrical-profile wings. This simple change reduced the wire drag to a small fraction of its original drag.

Refinements in wing sections permit greater design freedom. Thicker wings with good aerodynamic characteristics allowed for thicker, stronger internal spars. Monoplane wings replaced biplane wings and exposed wires were relegated to history.

Incidentally, biplane wings suffer from another problem. Simply stated, the bottom surface of the upper wing creates local pressure in the free stream. This higher pressure diminishes the relative vacuum being created by the upper surface of the lower wing. The result is reduction in efficiency or a lowering of the lift / drag ratio. Check post WWI biplanes and you will usually see a staggering of the wings. The top wing will be slightly larger and forward of the lower wing.

To calculate drag, all parasite drags use the same formula, but induced drag has its own formula.

Induced drag, or lift induced drag, is calculated differently because its changes are inversely proportional to speed. In other words, induced drag is highest at a low speed, a high angle of attack, and a high C_L. Unlike a typical aircraft, which can operate with an extreme nose high attitude, most hydrofoils cannot operate with the bow pointing upward and, in normal operation, cannot experience extremely high angles of attack. This is because hydrofoils commonly extend their hulls aft of the main foil to provide sufficient displacement (support) near the center of gravity, and because in hydrofoils, the length of the front strut limits the pitch-up angle.

There are exceptions, of course. The Dynafoil, Figure 1-10b, has a short hull with very little of it extending aft of the rear foil. The line of thrust is low and when power is forcefully applied, it will freely rotate around its pitch axis and do a "wheelie", that is, stand on its tail with the nose pointing to the sky. Its pitch-up is not limited by the length of the front strut that becomes un-wetted and does not provide lift during the wheelie. Skillful management of the throttle will allow the boat to continue forward, balancing on its stern. This extreme attitude is just for fun and probably stalls the rear foil with most of the lift coming from the thrust of the propeller.

Induced drag may be significant at the lowest operational speed, V_{TO}, but not at V_{MAX}.

The **formula for the coefficient of induced drag,** from NACA, is:

$$C_{Di} = \frac{C_L{}^2}{\pi * AR * e,}$$

Where:

C_{Di} = Coefficient of induced drag
C_L = Coefficient of lift
π = 3.14
AR = Aspect ratio
e = Efficiency factor based on plan form of the wing, where an elliptical wing is e = 1 and all other shapes have e < 1.

From the equation it can be concluded that the coefficient of induced drag increases in proportion to the square of the coefficient of lift. Of course, the C_L is inversely proportional to the square root of the velocity. See Figure 4-2b.

Parasite drag will be the limiting factor in determining V_{MAX}. The formula for *parasite drag*, which is total drag *excluding Induced Drag*, is the same as the formula for lift except the coefficient of drag, C_D is substituted for the coefficient of lift, C_L.

The **formula for parasite drag** is:

$D = \frac{1}{2} \rho * V^2 * S * C_D$

Drag and Power Calculations

As with the lift formula of chapter 4, we again calculate the value of ½ ρ, where ρ (rho) = density of the fluid. The density of seawater is 1.99 slugs and when multiplied by ½ the product rounds off to 1.00.

Because ½ ρ = 1, we can simplify the formula to:

$$D = V^2 * S * C_D$$

If V is in ft / sec, and S is in square feet, then D, the result, will be in pounds.

Parasite drag is in proportion to:

1. Surface area of the foil, usually frontal view, but see caveat following Figure 5-7. Doubling the area doubles the drag.
2. The Coefficient of drag. Changing the angle of attack to double the coefficient of drag will double the drag. Using a foil section with 10% greater C_D increases the drag 10%.
3. The square of the speed. Doubling the speed increases the parasite drag by 4 times. Tripling increases it by eight times.

If V is in ft / sec, and S is in square feet, then D, the result, will be in pounds.

As stated, drag is proportional to the C_D. If a round plate is forced, blunt end first, into the free stream, the C_D is a whopping 1.2. Whereas in a streamlined shape such as the NACA 0033, the C_D is .04, or just 3% of the blunt plate. Incredibly the two shapes in Figure 5-6 have the same drag despite their size difference.

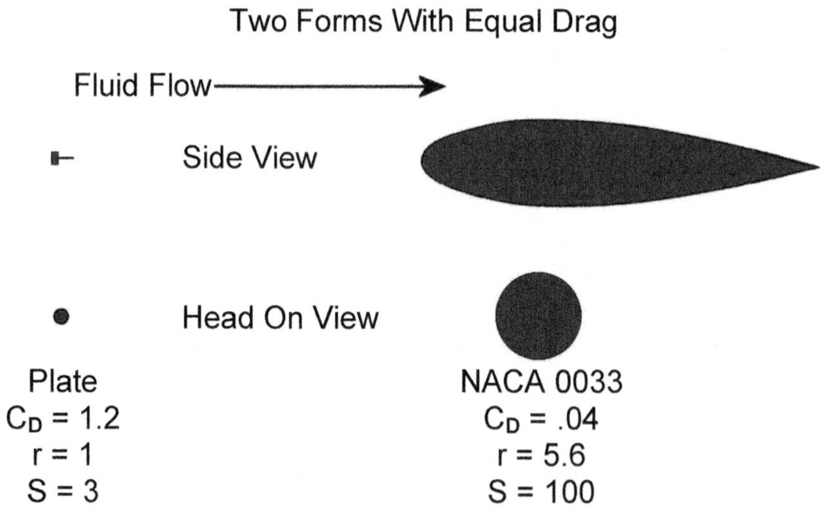

Two Forms With Equal Drag

Fluid Flow⟶

Side View

Head On View

Plate
C_D = 1.2
r = 1
S = 3

NACA 0033
C_D = .04
r = 5.6
S = 100

Figure 5-6. Drag in flap plate vs. streamlined shape.
Where r = radius, and S = Surface area.

The fact that they have equal drag can be easily proven (The formula for the area of a circle is: $A = \pi * r^2$).

Use these values, round off results:

Assume that V = 10 ft/sec,

r_{PLATE} = 1 ft radius
S_{PLATE} = 3.14 ft^2 = frontal surface area
$C_{D-PLATE}$ = 1.2 coefficient of drag
r_{NACA} = 5.6 ft radius
S_{NACA} = 100 ft^2 = frontal surface area
C_{D-NACA} = .04 coefficient of drag

We calculate drag for both the plate and the NACA shape using the formula,
$D = V^2 * S * C_D$:

D_{PLATE} = 10 * 10 * 3.14 * 1.2 = 377 lbs., round to 400 lbs.
D_{NACA} = 10 * 10 * 100 * .04 = 400 lbs.

In this calculation we used V = 10, but V could be any value and the two shapes would still have equal drag (ignoring Reynolds number differences, etc).

Here are some other **common shapes with their Coefficients of Drag**:

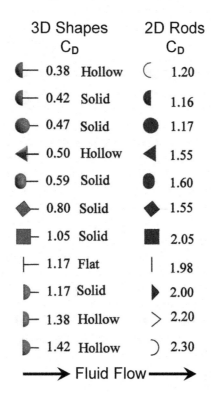

3D Shapes C_D		2D Rods C_D	
0.38	Hollow	1.20	
0.42	Solid	1.16	
0.47	Solid	1.17	
0.50	Hollow	1.55	
0.59	Solid	1.60	
0.80	Solid	1.55	
1.05	Solid	2.05	
1.17	Flat	1.98	
1.17	Solid	2.00	
1.38	Hollow	2.20	
1.42	Hollow	2.30	

→ Fluid Flow →

Figure 5-7. Drag Coefficients of various 2 and 3 dimensional shapes. The data is from Hoerner.

Each C_D as shown above was calculated on conditions of $R_N = 10,000$ to $R_N = 1,000,000$ based on its diameter. When using these coefficients in the drag formula, use frontal area—area projected into the free stream—for the S value. See Hoerner's *Aerodynamic Drag* for other examples of C_Ds and their calculations.

There is a little **caveat** about using an unfamiliar C_D. To do drag calculations, some coefficients of drag are to be used with *frontal* area and others, *planform* area. In Hoerner's book the difference is indicated by a tiny dot next to the coefficient. Usually, with parasite drag, the frontal area will be used, but for lift-induced drag the planform area (viewed looking straight down) will be used in the calculations.

Before leaving the subject, it should be mentioned that rods may still be exposed to the slipstream if special conditions exist. Rods and wires that are presented *diagonally* to the slipstream have improved drag characteristics, because the path of the fluid will be similar to the path around an oval. Figure 5-8 shows how an observer sees a rod from the side and how fluid sees it when passing by. The approximate C_D is indicated.

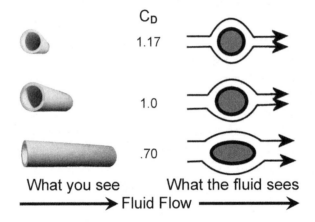

Figure 5-8. Fluid flow around a tube or wire changes with orientation to the flow. The viewer's perspective is perpendicular to the flow.

Boats with their power source in the bow exploit this principle with their inclined propeller drive shaft. The upper portion of the shaft is un-wetted at flying height and the lower portion presents itself diagonally with the fluid-stream.

So far we have been talking about *drag*. To estimate the required *power*, we need to increase the influence of velocity in our equation. Let's take it logically:

Drag, parasite, increases with the *square* of the velocity (Hoerner):

$$D = C_D * S * V^2$$

The *power* required increases with the *cube* of the velocity:

P = D * V (J. D. Anderson) and by substituting the above equation for D, we find:

$$P = (C_D * S * V^2) * V$$

Therefore $P = C_D * S * V^3$

Repeat, parasite drag increases with the *square* of velocity, whereas power increases with the *cube* of velocity. This explains why it is so difficult to break speed barriers using raw horsepower, and why streamlining and other drag-reducing techniques are critical.

To express power as horsepower (from iProcesSmart, Horsepower formulas, *www.iprocessmart.com/*):

$$Hp = (C_D * S * V^3) / 33{,}000 \text{ or } Hp = (P * V) / 33{,}000$$

To do the calculations, remember never mix units. For English units, use ft/sec and ft².

The **Overall Propulsive Coefficient**, OPC When the power requirement is known, an appropriate engine can be selected. There will be more on engine selection in chapter 12, but for now, don't forget to provide for the inevitable inefficiencies between the motor and the propulsion. The horsepower claimed by the engine's manufacturer is usually *brake horsepower*, BHP. This is power measured at the flywheel. The power at the end of the coupling flange is called *shaft horsepower*, SHP, and that will typically be about 97% of BHP. The propeller shaft bearings on a straight drive line, or gears and U joints of a Z drive, will reduce the available power to perhaps 95% of BHP. Now brace yourself, stock propellers waste as much 50% of remaining available power, according to Dudley Dawson writing for *Yachting* magazine. The total power lost, therefore, can be as much as 55% of the BHP of the engine. At certain speeds, a 100 hp engine might be delivering only 45 or 50 hp in propeller propulsion and even less in water jet propulsion. The curves of propellers and water jets show how speed affects efficiency in Figure 5-9.

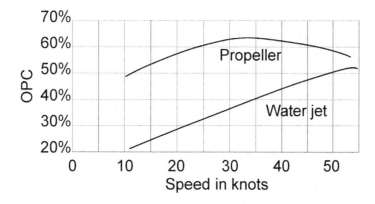

Figure 5-9. This chart shows Overall Propulsive Coefficient, OPC, of a water jet vs. an efficient propeller. The data is from Capt. Robert J. Johnson, USNR (Ret), *Naval Engineers Journal.*

Custom propellers with low gearing can deliver as much as 60 to 70% in propulsion, according to Dawson; nonetheless, these inefficiencies are too large to ignore. It will be necessary to include a power loss factor in our power calculations. More on this later.

Determining power consumed at the drag hump. Power consumed will be at its highest at V_{MAX}; however, the craft will never reach V_{MAX} unless it can pass through the drag hump. In other words, in the realm of the drag hump there must be more power *available* than is *consumed*. Because of this, it is particularly important to know the power consumed at the drag hump. When this figure is known, the minimum horsepower required for flight is known.

To calculate the power, it is first necessary to determine the drag. It is fairly easy to calculate the drag of a simple hydrofoil wing, but this number is not of much value in determining the critical drag hump. We need to know the *overall drag*. This is the combined drag of all the wetted components: hull + motor shaft+ struts+ foils. After takeoff we need to know the drag for the portions of these elements that remain wetted. Some designers refer to this as *drag accounting.* It requires adding up the calculated drag of each of these components to give us an approximation of total drag. To do this it is necessary to make so many assumptions that the results are difficult to rely upon. We are not going to pursue this method, but if the reader wishes to do so, a good place to start would be Hoerner's book on drag (see the bibliography).

The **towing method** is most direct, and it panders to one's impulse to get out and play in the water. For example, if you already have your hull selected, why not tow it behind another boat and use a linear hanging scale on your towline to determine how much drag the hull creates at various speeds, loads, and flying configurations? For this test, we need to include the pilot's weight and a dummy motor to provide weight and drag similar to the final configuration. The motor needs to be only roughly similar to that of the motor you are going to select. The propeller should be removed because in a boat underway, the propeller provides propulsion, not drag. Our primary goal is to find the drag at V_{HUMP}. For the boat towed without foils, V_{HUMP} would occur at what would be V_{TO}, if there were foils in place. V_{TO} is determined by calculation.

When using one boat to tow another, avoid the impulse to tie the towrope around the outboard motor of the towing boat. Attaching the towrope aft of the longitudinal center of rotation will cause directional instability in the lead boat. Of course controlling the two boats is then a chore, but obtaining a stable and accurate tow pressure reading will be impossible. Plan on rigging an attachment point for the towrope on the towing boat about one third of the boat's length forward of the transom. The ski-boat shown in Figure 5-10 is typical for water skiers, and would probably an excellent towing boat. Notice how far forward the towrope attachment point is. The height of the tow point is simply to provide headroom for the crew.

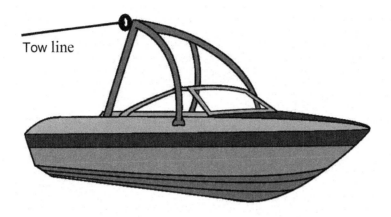

Figure 5-10. This is a typical towboat for water skiers.

There is a commercially available device called a *transom harness* that is designed to pull a water skier. It attaches two straps to the outboard ends of the transom to form a V shape. This might stabilize the towboat, but the hanging scale would be well aft of the stern at the bottom of the V and therefore, difficult to read.

Another established way of determining the drag of a boat with its foils attached is to bring it to flying speed, cut the power, and measure its deceleration. The boat can be brought up to speed by towing or by using the boat's power, if available. This method is really outside the scope of this book, but the formula is no secret. It was first published by Isaac Newton as his second law, and it is: F = M * A. Where F = Force (drag), M = Mass (weight), and A = Acceleration. The calculations are simple enough, but there is a problem. To use the formula, a boater needs an accelerometer to measure deceleration (equal to the acceleration required to speed up the boat). The drag at any selected speed is calculated by cutting the power and multiplying the *deceleration* by the *weight* of the boat. The result will be *drag* at the selected *speed*.

We can however, create a **factor to estimate the drag** of the hull, motor, hydrofoils, and struts. This factor will be multiplied by just the drag of the hull and motor. How will we determine this factor?

Luckily we have some examples to work with. Refer to Figure 5-4. Foilplay takes off at 8.8 mph (12.9 ft/sec.). The maximum hull drag prior to takeoff, with foils removed, is slightly more than 8 lbs. With foils in place the total drag is 16 lbs. The hull contributes 50% of the total drag. (8 / 16) * 100 = 50%. The foils and struts contribute the remaining 50% of drag.

Now look at Figure 5-11. Shutt's Hydro-ped takes off at 6.8 mph (10 ft / sec.). Just prior to takeoff, with foils, struts and hull wetted, the drag peaks at 20 lbs. This is total drag. As soon as the hull becomes airborne the drag drops to 8 lbs—this is foil and strut drag. The foils contribute 40% of the total drag. (8 / 20) * 100 = 40%. The hull eats up the other 60% of total drag.

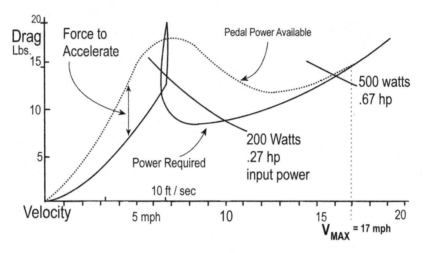

Figure 5-11. Graph by Sid Shutt representing Hydro-ped.

Because these two examples fall in a narrow range, 50% to 60% of the drag being created by the hull, we can construct a rough rule of thumb that total drag from hull, struts and foils, will be about twice the drag of the hull alone. Look, we are just trying to select an outboard motor, not earn the Noble Prize in mathematics.

We are going to apply the derived factor to Hifybe in the following calculations. If a clean planing hull and motor create 100 lbs. of drag at takeoff speed, we can estimate that the drag of the combination of hull, foils, etc. will be 200 lbs.

Let's once again design Hifybe using the following assumptions:

> Drag, hull & motor determined by tow tests: $V_{MAX} = V_{TO}$ = 94 lbs.
> Lift = Total weight of hull, foils, motor, rider, etc: L = 365 lbs.
> Velocity at takeoff: V_{TO} = 8 mph = 11.8 ft/sec.
> Velocity maximum: V_{MAX} = 16mph = 23.5 ft/sec. For this determination we used the rule-of-thumb: $V_{MAX} \approx 2V_{TO.}$
> Area, surface: S = 2.28 ft^2.

Applying these parameters to the formula for determining required *delivered* horsepower:

$$P_{hp} = (D_{lbs} * V_{ft/sec}) / 550$$

$$4 \text{ hp} = (200 * 11.8)/ 550$$

We have calculated that for Hifybe, 4 hp is the required *delivered* horsepower (the overall propulsion expressed in hp). To determine the *nominal* hp we divide by the delivered hp by the overall propulsive coefficient. This is the OPC graphed in Figure 5-9 and explained in the associated text. In this case we are going to assume OPC = 50%, or .50. This includes *all* losses between the nominal (published) hp and actual propulsion.

4 hp / .50 = 8 hp. Luckily, I just happen to have an 8 hp outboard available for Hifybe.

By the way, if in Figure 5-11 you noticed that the funny little bump in the "power required" curve exceeded the "pedal power available", move to the head of the class. Up to this point in the acceleration of the Hydro-ped, the front foil is retracted and the hull and main foil are at low angles of attack. To takeoff, Shutt pedals extra hard, speeds the boat faster than the hump speed, forces the front foil down into the free stream. That raises the bow, rotates the hull, and increases the rear foil's angle of attack. This converts the extra speed into a surge of lift that forces the hull away from the surface and into the air. For an instant, momentum is traded for lift, so the velocity decreases slightly, but the boat is now flying and the power required has dropped dramatically. Once airborne, Shutt can relax a little and enjoy the reduced power requirement, or he can continue to input full power and accelerate to 17 mph, V_{MAX}.

Lift to drag ratio. For now, we will ignore the calculations for drag and go directly to the result. We can compare some aircraft and birds shown in Figure 5-12a to the hydrofoils in 5-12b.

Airplanes and Birds	L / D			Hydrofoils	L / D
Modern Sailplane	60			Plainview	15.7
Rutan Voyager	27			Swordfish	14.2
Albatross	20		Military	Tucumcari	12.3
Boeing 747	17			Pegasus	10.1
Common Tern	12			Bras d'Or	9.2
Herring Gull	10			Fresh-1	6.7
Concorde--Mach 2	7.14			Hydro-ped	14
Cessna 150	7		HPH	Dragonfly	10.5
Concorde--Approach	4.35			Foilplay	7.9
House Sparrow	4			Talaria IV	5.6
Apollo CM--Reentry	0.37		Non-military,	Hi-Foil	3.7
			Engine-powered	Hifybe	3.5
				Dynafoil	2.9

Figures 5-12a & b. (a) The L/D of some aircraft and birds.
(b) The L/D of hydrofoils. The hydrofoils drag was
calculated using the formula D = ((P * 550) / V).
The lift is equal to the weight.

Drag and Power Calculations

The data comes from various sources:

> http://en.wikipedia.org/wiki/Lift-to-drag_ratio
> Declassified performance data of US Navy ships in documents like the *Advanced Naval Vehicle Concept Evaluation*
> Jane's *Surface Skimmer Systems*
> Promotional data on production hydrofoils
> Personal observations

Notice that the hydrofoil examples of Figure 5-12b are divided into three classes: military, human powered, and personal engine powered hydrofoils. The *military* hydrofoils compare to personal hydrofoils like airliners compare to Cessnas. They both fly, but the military craft have big budgets, are created by Boeing and Grumman, have enormous horse power, have deep draft, fly fast, and literally weigh tons. They must have very efficient foils, struts, drive trains, and propellers to support their great weight, be speedy, and not exceed the power of their engines. As a result, they have high L/D. For example see Figure 5-13 showing the L/D of three such hydrofoil ships:

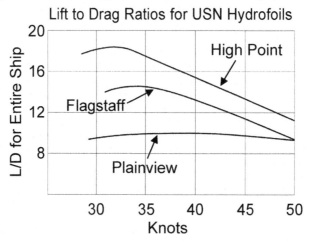

Figure 5-13. L /D plotted against speed, for three Navy hydrofoils. The data is from Capt. Robert J. Johnson USNR (Ret), *Naval Engineers Journal.*

The other class with high L/D ratios is the *human powered hydrofoil*, HPH. Boats in this class must be efficient because their power source is limited. All of these machines must create high lift and low drag, or they will not fly.

The boats in the next class are smaller than Navy ships and larger than HPHs. These are personal engine powered, PEP. They may be designed like Navy hydrofoils, but don't have armor plate or big guns. These boats typically use some form of "Z" drive to allow rational placing of the power unit. To support the weight of engine and drive train, they often have an extra strut in line with the Z drive to support the mid section of the aft foil. To deliver a lot of power without allowing the diameter of the propeller to exceed the space available, they use low aspect ratio props. The boats listed all use mass-produced propellers. As a safety measure some PEPs, like Hifybe, use wetted propeller guards. Some boats, like the OU32 use the inefficient jet pump. The result is a relatively low L/D.

It is useful to know the typical drag of the various types of hydrofoils because a boat being planned can be compared to existing boats and thereby approximate its future L/D.

In order to use L/D we need to understand it and know how it is computed. Obviously if one knows the lift and the drag of a hydrofoil, he need only divide one by the other to obtain the ratio. *Lift* is easy to determine because it is equal to weight–while in steady flight. The problem is determining *drag*, as we discovered earlier in this chapter, but if a boat is already operating the following simple formula will calculate D by using lift, power, and speed:

$$D = L / ((hp * OPC * 550) / V)$$

Where:
L = Lift = Weight, lbs.
V = Velocity, ft / sec.
hp = horsepower, nominal
OPC = Overall Propulsive Coefficient.

To estimate the OPC, we will be examining the three classes of propeller driven hydrofoils:

Military	60%
HPH	80%
PEP	60%

For a water jet, reduce the efficiency by 10 percentage points at fifty knots, 20 points at 30 knots and 30 points at 10 knots. Refer to Figure 5-9.

Sid Shutt's boat, Hydro-ped – to be studied and illustrated in chapter 17 – will be used as another example of an efficient human powered hydrofoil. Fortunately, due to his careful analysis and willingness to share, we have a reliable model to learn from. Shutt's boat sets a high standard, but it will serve as a starting point or goal for estimations. As Figure 5-11 shows, Hydro-ped has lift /drag ratios of 13 (225 / 18 = 12.5) at the drag hump and 15 (225 /15 = 15) at top speed.

Drag and Power Calculations

Knowing something about how drag is created can help us understand how it is reduced, but it's not essential to know the theory to implement good design practices. Simply stated, to reduce drag, do the following to all parts underwater:

> If possible, operate in the "drag bucket", that is, the bottom of the drag vs. lift chart. See Figure 5-5. If not possible, avoid high angles of attack or extremely low AOA.
> Use high aspect ratio foils and struts
> Make the wing planform elliptical (best) or tapered; otherwise, use wing tip fences.
> Streamline everything.
> Minimize the number of struts.
> Avoid self-standing power struts like in "Z" drives and outboard engines.
> If possible, integrate the power strut with the foil strut located in the center.
> Make fairings at the junctions between foils and struts.
> Make junctions with the most oblique angle possible.
> Use torpedo shapes at junctions when possible, even though the torpedo shape increases the frontal area. Fairings as shown in Figure 5-2 are also acceptable.
> Avoid wires and rods especially if perpendicular to the path of travel.
> Polish all surfaces. Avoid surface pits, bumps, and waves.
> Keep free of seaweed, barnacles, etc.
> Control ventilation.

Ventilation, Cavitation, and Stalling

- o Ventilation
- o Preventing or reducing ventilation
- o Stall
- o Avoiding stalling
- o Cavitation
- o Cavity collapse
- o Supercavitating propeller
- o Speed vs. cavitation
- o Summary

Ventilating, cavitating, and stalling all destroy lift, but they are three distinctly different conditions affecting hydrofoils.

Ventilation is the easiest to explain: it is the introduction of air into the low pressure, upper-surface of the lifting hydrofoil. In normal flight the passage of fluid over the curved upper side creates a reduction in pressure. The reduced pressure and smooth water flow over the top is part of the lift creation process. If the reduced pressure is allowed to suck air into itself, the pressure differential is compromised, the flow is disturbed, and lift suffers. A cavity filled with air is created and lift is lost in proportion to the ventilation.

Air can enter into the foil's low-pressure side in several ways. A surface piercing foil may allow air to travel along its span. Air can flow down the outside of a supporting strut or a hollow strut can allow air to flow from within. Foil and strut ventilation possibilities increase with an increase in angle of attack of either the foil or the strut. Anything near the surface is more vulnerable than deeply submerged components. In all cases, turbulent air replaces smooth flowing water and the suction is broken.

Lift killing ventilation can occur at relatively low angles of attack. Indeed Breslin and Skalak tests showed examples of how the horizontal lift of surface piercing struts is affected, see Figure 6-1. In this example their strut ventilates at 4° and 75% of lift is lost. Similar lifting-foil ventilation can be anticipated as the air finds a path down the strut.

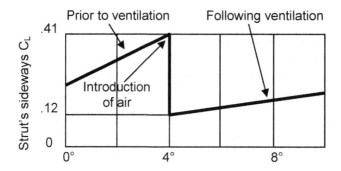

Figure 6-1. Ventilation causes a dramatic drop in lift.
Data from Breslin and Skalak.

There are several design ideas to **prevent or reduce ventilation**. Ventilation is reduced in foils that run deep, foils that are located ahead of their struts, and struts or surface piercing foils that have fences. It is helpful to use streamlined pods or fairings at the intersections to act as fences. The struts may be slanted forward from the top down so that the path of ventilation is opposed by the water's flow. Finally, foils and struts should have their leading edges rounded to discourage flow separation.

It may surprise some that when the leading edge of a foil is knife sharp it is more prone to ventilation than when rounded. It is tempting to guess that a sharp leading edge would cut through the water and make less spray and have less separation than a rounded leading edge. This may be true at very low angles of attack, but at a higher AOA the fluid separation at the sharp edge is more pronounced. The result is a narrower range of useable angles of attack followed by more violent stalling and ventilation. Roderick Barr states that the foil sections are more likely to ventilate if they have nose radii of less than one percent of the chord.

Once it occurs, even after the path of air is cut, ventilation can persist momentarily. Air introduced to the flow around a foil or strut may be reluctant to detach itself and be replaced with lift-creating water. The result is a measurable amount of time until lift can be fully restored. To speed up the shedding of the air bubble, try anything that will promote the smooth flow of water including: using a sweptback wing, fairing the wing-strut joint, staggering the wing mounting ahead of the strut, inclining the strut, increasing the smoothness of the foil surface, rounding the leading edge, and reducing the angle of attack.

Stall is the same condition in a hydrofoil wing as in an aircraft wing. It is primarily a function of angle of attack. With too high an angle of attack, the fluid passing over the wing can no longer maintain a smooth flow, so the fluid separates from the wing. The difference between a stall and cavitation (to be defined below) or ventilation is that in a stall the fluid remains attached but in a turbulent state. The water flow changes from smooth to tumbling and chaotic. A stall can occur even when no vapor or air enters into the area of turbulence.

A coefficient of lift curve will show lift increasing as the angle of attack increases until the curve no longer slopes upward, but levels and then drops. This sudden decrease in lift marks the stall.

Avoid stalling by not exceeding the maximum angle of attack as shown in the lift curves of Figures 4-5a and 13-3. The point of stall is marked by shading in the C_L columns of Figure 13-3. Notice how lift begins to fall off rapidly around $12°$ to $14°$. Careful selection and skillful replication of an appropriate foil profile is important.

Cavitation affects only hydrofoils, not aircraft. Cavitation is a function of speed, foil shape, ambient pressure, and temperature. It occurs when the pressure reduction on the upper surface is great enough to cause the flowing water to vaporize. This creates a cavity filled with gasified water. The water actually boils. At sea level the pressure is 14.7 lbs / in^2 and water boils at $100°$ C. At 1 lb / in^2 boiling temperature is reduced to $40°$ C or slightly above body temperature. The pressure on the topside of a foil can be so low that the boiling temperature can be reduced to less than that of the water temperature. Another way of saying the same thing is that cavitation occurs where the pressure of the liquid falls below its vapor pressure. At that point water turns to gas, the foil experiences cavitation and most lift on the upper foil surface is lost. Ambient pressure can be assumed to be sea level pressure, with some obvious exceptions—avoid Lake Titicaca at 12,580 feet altitude. Deep running foils will have increased pressure of about ½ lb /sq in for each foot of submergence.

A serious side effect occurs when the gas filled **cavity collapses** farther down the chord causing the water to strike and damage the foil's surface. This collapse has such force that the hardest of materials, including stainless steel, can be eroded by the millions of rapid fire implosions.

Increased temperature will also contribute to the onset of cavitation, but the big variable is speed. The incipient speed is high–perhaps 40 or 50 mph. Figures 6-2 and 13-4 show some foil profile examples designed to fly while partially engulfed in a cavity. The sharp leading edge encourages flow separation on the upper surface at modest angles of attack. The resultant cavity is filled with water vapor at a pressure that is much lower than the bottom side pressure. The greatest lift results from the positive pressure as the underside strikes and deflects the fluid it is forcing its way through. The lift is an opposite and equal reaction to the fluid displaced, and is in proportion to the mass and velocity of the fluid displaced (see Newton's laws, chapter 2).

Under normal operation, 2/3rds of lift is created by the upper surface of the wing. But, in a supercavitating wing the upper surface lift is virtually eliminated, so lift is greatly reduced. This would seem to be a big problem, but these foils operate at high velocities, and lift increases with the square of velocity. Recall $L = V^2 * S * C_L$ from chapter 4.

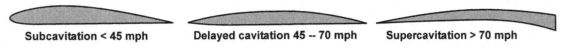

Subcavitation < 45 mph   Delayed cavitation 45 -- 70 mph   Supercavitation > 70 mph

Figures 6-2a, b, & c. Profiles of three foil types. Adapted from Eames and Jones.

Cavitation affects propellers as well as the wings of a hydrofoil–a propeller is a rotating wing. The blades of a propeller travel much faster than the boat it propels. This is logical because not only is the propeller moving at the speed of the boat, but it also has a rotational velocity that is added to its forward progress.

At high speeds, a **supercavitating propeller** will be necessary if the blades will be going faster than subcavitating speeds. Examples of supercavitating propellers would be found on the USN hydrofoils, Denison or Flagstaff. This type of propeller has the cross section required to create lift under high-speed conditions where cavitation prevails. These blades are typically in the form of a cupped wedge with the sharp end serving as the leading edge. A water vapor cavity forms quickly on the front side of the blade. This vapor side creates little lift (propulsion). The aft-side creates the lift as water is forced backward resulting in an opposite reaction. In effect, the blade is planing.

Supercavitating hydrofoil propellers and wings are less efficient, but besides operating at higher speeds, there is an additional advantage that is sometimes exploited. When operating near the surface, the lift lost from breaching is less than with a subcavitating propeller or foil because there is no topside vacuum to destroy when air is allowed to reach the lifting surfaces (ventilation). Unlimited hydroplane propellers, like the one on Miss Budweiser, for example, operate half submerged and fully ventilated. They have more consistent propulsion because they never develop lift-creating vacuum on the fully ventilated forward side of the propeller, so less propulsion is lost as the propeller emerges from the surface or when it reaches the speed of cavitation. In addition, because only the bottom half of the propeller is normally wetted, the inclined power shaft is above the surface and not creating drag.

Supercavitating foil profiles have been employed for height finding front foils, such as on the Rich Miller Hydrofoil Sailboard (see bibliography). The supercavitating profile foil, in effect, planes on the surface and provides stiff and effective height control.

In both of the above examples, it is important to distinguish between ventilation and cavitation. When air is entering the lifting surface (at any speed) the foil or propeller is ventilating. When air is *not* entering, yet a vapor cavity is formed, we have cavitation. Cavitation is a function of high speeds. **Reducing speed reduces cavitation**.

In **summary**, ventilation goes away when air is prevented from entering into the low pressure area on the upper side of the foil. Stalling is avoided by not exceeding the maximum angle of attack as shown on the appropriate lift curve. Cavitation is avoided by not exceeding subcavitation speeds. The cavitation speed can be increased by flying in cold water at sea level pressures or lower, and by avoiding foil and strut sections that have sharp leading edges. Compared to ventilation and stalling, cavitation is not primarily linked to excessively high angles of attack.

Foil Configuration: Distribution of Weight and Lift

- o Three foil configurations: airplane, canard, and balanced
- o Determining the weight distribution
- o Wing loading
- o Determining the waterline

At the beginning of any project, a hydrofoil designer must answer key questions: What will be the boat's configuration? What will it weigh? How will the weight be distributed? Where will the foils be located, and how much weight will be carried by each of the foils?

The size of the foils, fore and aft, depends on the total weight and the weight distribution. The location of the engine, crew, payload, etc. will determine the center of gravity, CG. With that information the designer can locate the foils and calculate the load to be carried by each foil.

Based on these distributions there are **three foil configurations**–airplane, canard, and balanced.

Airplane, or conventional configuration. For conventional airplanes, science and evolution favor having their large wing up forward where most of their weight is concentrated. For stabilization, they have a smaller wing at the extreme aft end. The smaller wing, or *horizontal stabilizer*, provides pitch stability by exerting downward force to the tail, and it acts like the tail feathers on an arrow, correcting for disturbances in pitch.

What is conventional for airplanes is not conventional for hydrofoils. In an airplane, pitch and altitude stability depends partially on altitude excursions. Pitch down and the aircraft descends. Speed and lift increase causing the nose to pitch up. The speed then decreases causing lift to decrease and the nose to settle. This is static stability. If the amplitude of the excursions decreases with each cycle, it is dynamically stable, as well.

Hydrofoil boats, as will be explained more thoroughly in chapter 8, "Height and Pitch Management", operate in a very narrow range of heights above the water's surface. The front foil performs the task of height control, and the rear foil follows in a way that stabilizes pitch. It works like the way the rear wheels of a car follow the steerable front wheels. To be most effective in height control, the front foil operates in the realm of higher angles of attack and is therefore less efficient. If the inefficient front foil is required to carry a large proportion of the craft's weight, the overall efficiency of the craft will be diminished. In the interests of creating an efficient design, the front foil should be smaller than the rear foil and the rear foil–the more efficient foil–should provide the majority of lift.

A **canard** flying machine has the large wing near to and aft of the CG and a smaller wing forward. Mysteriously, ducks–which call themselves *les canards* when in France–are not configured like this. In flight their lightweight necks and tiny birdbrains extend far forward giving them the appearance of having their CG ahead of their big wing. It might be confusing that the authentic *canard* has a conventional configuration, but it's simply another example of French contrary thinking. With hydrofoils, since the Canadian experiments with the Bras d'Or, Figure 1-4, the canard configuration has become the most common.

The canard configuration is generally the best for engine and human powered hydrofoils. The larger foil, carrying the majority of weight, will then be assigned the task of roll control. Small changes in lift at the tips of the large aft foil will be effective in starting or stopping a rolling moment. Later in this chapter we will do some calculations to show just how important span (the width from tip to tip) is for roll control. The smaller, narrower forward foil would not be as effective in roll control, so its task will be limited to the exacting task of pitch control. Additionally, the front foil's strut usually serves as a rudder.

Sailboats are an exception to the logic of the canard configuration. Because the center of effort (source of propulsion) is located on the sails high above the center of resistance (created by the foils and struts), there are strong tipping forces. Tipping to the side, *heeling*, is usually managed by having a wide foil array. Trimarans and catamarans use this principle of roll control. Tipping aft is not a problem because sailing directly into the wind is not possible. Tipping forward, *pitchpoling*, can be a problem. Pitchpoling occurs on a fast downwind course that overruns waves and that runs perpendicular to them. Under these conditions a substantial amount of lift must be provided by the bow or, in hydrofoil boats, the front foils. This is generally done by placing two large height finding foils ahead of the CG and at the gunnels of outrigger hulls. A smaller rear foil and strut are usually mounted at the transom to create both lift and steering force. The rear foil may also be required to create a downward force to prevent pitchpoling.

Also, a potential structural problem is reduced by having the sail's center of effort approximately in the same lateral plane as are the main foils. If they were significantly separated, such as having the sail forward and the main foils at the stern, there would be significant twisting forces that would act on the length of the hull.

There is another sailboat with a conventional airplane configuration that has recently emerged–the Moth class single-track hydrofoil. We will be designing one of these in chapter 18.

In many boats, the canard configuration comes naturally after the logical placement of the heaviest components of the craft.

For example, if the plan is to retrofit hydrofoils to a conventional outboard motor boat and the pilot and crew are to be located near the transom-mounted engine, the weight distribution is predetermined. Assume you attach the rear foil to the transom and the front foil to the bow. You might find 80% of the weight supported by the rear foil and 20% by the bow.

The **Balanced** configuration is…well, balanced. The forward wing and the aft wing are about the same size. Few aircraft have this configuration. One of this small group would be the French home built aircraft of the 1930s named the *Pou du Ciel* , often called the *Flying Flea,* but literally translated as the *Louse of the Sky*. This charming little buzzer may have killed more Frenchmen than Absinthe. But enough about the French.

Figure 7-1. Pou du Ciel. The French Flying Flea has a balanced wing configuration.

The surface piercing hydrofoils made by Supramar, Rodriquez, and the Russians are generally balanced with even fore and aft weight distribution and roughly equal foil areas. See Figure 1-2 for an image of the Rodriquez.

Sometimes the special requirements of hardware and crew placement will outweigh hydrodynamic considerations and dictate the conventional configuration. In a hydrofoil, a balanced or conventional configuration will be necessary, and the use of the canard system will be eliminated, if the engine, payload, and/or crew are located forward. For example, assume a goal is to avoid installing a complex Z drive by using a simple straight shaft extending aft to a deep running propeller. In this case, to limit the inclination of the shaft, the engine will be placed well forward and the canard configuration will not be possible.

Physically **determining the weight distribution** can be done by using a scale and blocks. Begin by placing weight, equal to the pilot's, at the seat location. Place other weighty components at their intended locations. Then support the bow with blocks at the forward foil attachment points. Use a suitable scale to weigh the hull at the point of aft foil attachment. Next, switch the blocks to the aft attachment point; and move the scale to the forward point. The two weights added together will equal the total boat weight. Divide the weight of each foil attachment point by the total weight to determine the ratio of weight supported by that foil. Multiply the result by 100 to convert the ratio into a percentage. For example, if the front foil's load is 54 lbs and the rear's is 311 lbs, then the total weight is 365 lbs. The portion of weight supported by the front foil will be 15%. (56 / 365)* 100 = 15%. This happens to be Hifybe's weight and balance, and that is covered in depth in chapter 16.

Logically the individual area of each foil should be exactly proportional to the percentage of the load each foil will support. However, for improved pitch stability, the front foil should have a **wing loading** greater than the rear foil. *Wing loading* is another term borrowed from aerodynamics. It refers to the amount of supported weight divided by the area of foil. In other words, the front foil will be proportionally smaller than the fraction of weight it supports. Speaking in percentages, if the front foil provides say 15% of the lift it may only contribute 12% of the total foil area. To compensate, it will operate at a higher angle of attack. Chapter 8 goes into more detail.

To **determine the waterline** location without actually putting the boat in the water, we can get help from Archimedes principal. About 212 BC he declared that an object immersed in a fluid is buoyed up by a force equal to the weight of the fluid displaced by the object. Dwight Filley, my associate in California, applied this principal in a way that was novel to me.

He places his hollow hull on two scales and fills it with water equal in weight to the total of the boat and rider. In calculating the waterline, he excludes the weight of the hull because the hull is already on the scale. The amidships waterline created inside is at the same level as the waterline that will be on the outside.

Prior to this exercise, Dwight calculates the boat's weight and balance and places the two scales equal distances fore and aft of the calculated center of gravity. To determine the hull's pitch when floating, he adds shims between the scales and the hull, thereby shifting the water until each of the scales carries the same weight as the other. He then marks the waterline at the bow and the stern. He connects the three marks, fore, amidships, and aft. This will be the waterline when the boat and rider are afloat.

The principles shown in this chapter will work on existing boats. What if you don't already have a boat and you are going to plan it and *then* build it? This will require some other calculations. Perhaps the best explanation of how to calculate weight and balance is by example. Jump to Figure 16-1 and the text following it for a demonstration on how the distribution of components was done for Hifybe.

Height and Pitch Management

o Height and altitude
o Height control vs. altitude control
o Surface proximity
o Variable lift front foil
o Variable area foils
o Surface piercing: dihedral, ladder, truss, or combination
o Trimming the running height, front foil
o Trimming the running height, rear foil
o Submerged foils
o Manual pitch control
o Height sensor
o Submerged front foils vary their CL
o Flaps, ailerons, and elevators
o Variable incidence winglets or flippers
o Flippers, stabilators, and tailerons
o Symmetrical wing profiles
o Center of pressure
o Spoilers
o Height sensor and surface follower
o Meacham brothers
o Shutt Strut
o Surface follower reports flying height and hull pitch information
o Surface follower ahead, behind, or on the strut.
o Unconventional solutions
o Contouring and platforming
o Water's movements within the wave
o Rear foil?
o Differential wing loading
o Gain is Δ lift / Δ height, height, and Gain/inch
o High CG

Height and altitude, for our purposes, are the same except for scale. Both indicate the distance between the bottom of a craft and the surface it is passing over. In aircraft we usually say *altitude* and it is measured in hundreds or thousands of feet. In hydrofoils we will be using *height*, or *flying height*, and it will normally be measured in inches or feet. Height will depend on the size of the hydrofoil boat and the length of its struts.

Height control in hydrofoils differs greatly from altitude control in aircraft. In a cruising aircraft relatively large excursions in altitude are normal. Hydrofoils operate in a narrow range of height, inches from the surface. Let's take a flight in a typical airplane and see how cruise altitude is maintained.

OK, you be the pilot, I'll serve the peanuts. You are in the left seat, you have just taken off and are almost finished climbing to your cruising altitude. To stop climbing you push the stick forward, allow the craft to accelerate to cruise speed and then pull back the throttle. You reduce power to the cruise setting and lower the nose to a point on, or slightly above, the horizon. While holding the control stick so the nose does not rise or fall you adjust the trim so that there is no pressure on your hand from the stick. A good pilot like you can now take your hands off the stick. The plane will continue straight and level.

However, it does not remain exactly at altitude. Natural disturbances cause the nose to fall or rise, the altitude to decrease or increase, and the speed to increase or decrease. Speed is *coupled* with altitude, and these changes are called *excursions*. You are flying a stable aircraft so you now lean back and open a beer…I mean a cup of coffee. The nose rises and so the airplane climbs. The speed is reduced and this causes the nose to settle. As a result, the speed increases creating more lift and the nose rises…and so on. You report to Air Traffic Control as being on altitude, but in fact you are oscillating up and down through your reported altitude. This is an example of dynamic pitch stability and it is built into properly designed cruising aircraft.

Hydrofoils are not afforded the luxury of altitude excursions. If you settle toward the water you can only settle a very small amount–perhaps inches–before running out of height. There is virtually no change in speed so there is no corresponding change in lift. A hydrofoil cannot use this altitude vs. speed coupling to oscillate around the designated altitude.

Hydrofoils have the advantage of **surface proximity**. Their closeness to the interface between the air and water makes it possible for their height sensors to receive precise height information from the water's surface. The height sensors are linked to a system that increases or decreases lift. Fly too high and the lift decreases. Fly too low and the lift increases. In this way, precise height control is maintained. The front foil is assigned the task of height control. Height control is essential to all hydrofoils, regardless of size or speed.

Without height control a front foil can be maniacal or, technically speaking, dynamically unstable. Take this example: the boat is at rest and the front foil is fully submerged. In an attempt to take off, power is applied and speed increases. Lift increases with the square of the speed and soon lift exceeds weight. We are assuming that the stern stays on the surface. The front foil rises, rotating the hull, and as it does the Angle of Attack (AOA) increases causing lift to increase. This causes the foil to rise more, the AOA to increase more and the foil to rise more. This is a self-amplifying and is called a *positive feedback loop*.

This will continue until the front foil stalls or leaps out of the water. Lift collapses and the foil crashes back. In crashing back from a breach, the foil brings with it a bubble of air on the top or vacuum side (this is ventilation previously examined in chapter 6). We are experiencing dynamic instability. With the orderly fluid flow disturbed and the relative vacuum broken, lift is reduced by 50 to 70%.

We have assumed for the moment that the rear foil is not interested, but usually when the front foil is misbehaving the rear foil will begin to compete for attention. Its AOA has been increased with the bow rising, so it to starts flying. Now the stern is high and, as described in the previous paragraph, the front foil is diving. The more the front foil descends, the more the rear foil's AOA decreases and the more its lift is diminished. Possibly the AOAs of both the foils become very negative, and the total lift becomes negative. The boat dives to the surface causing a rapid slowdown and possible *submarining*. The result may be damage to the foils, struts, hull, crew, etc. Our goal is to tame this bad behavior through good design of the front foil system.

What is needed is a **variable lift front foil**, and the lift must be linked to the flying height. There are several ways of designing this. Spoilers can reduce lift. The wetted area of the foil can be changeable. The angle of attack can be changeable, or the flap angle of the foil can be variable. In addition, differential wing loading between the fore and aft foils can contribute to pitch stability.

Wing loading is normally higher in the forward foil than in the aft foil. We will be going into detail on this in Figures 8-14 and 8-15 and their associated text.

Variable *area* foils are either surface piercing dihedral foils, Figures 8-1a and 10-12a; anhedral foils, Figure 10-12b; ladder foils, Figure 8-1b; or a combination thereof, Figure 8-1c. When cruising, part of the foil is above the surface and part is below. If a disturbance pitches the bow up, the lifting area is reduced and the lift decreases. The bow settles. Any disturbance pitching the bow down submerges more hydrofoil and lift increases. The bow rises. In this manner the bow foil finds equilibrium at its design height for its current speed. The wetted area, and therefore height, varies with speed. As speed increases, lift increases, and the foil rises in the water until the wetted area is reduced enough to create a state of equilibrium. Equilibrium is where lift at the bow equals the weight at the bow. Equilibrium should occur at the appropriate height for the trim speed. *Trim speed* and *trim height* are those at which the hydrofoil will remain without further control inputs. *Trim attitude* of the hull can be shortened to *trim,* meaning the hull's pitch or roll angle in relation to the horizon.

At a specific speed, the equilibrium height of a surface piercing hydrofoil boat is trimmed by increasing or decreasing the angle of incidence, AOI, of the foils. The angle of incidence is the angle between the foil and the longitudinal axis of the boat. Changing the AOI naturally changes the angle of attack, AOA, the angle between the foil and the fluid flow. Changing the AOI of a foil allows the pilot to change the AOA and the lift of the foil without changing the trim attitude of the hull.

Surface piercing dihedral foils can be designed to be simple, economic, and strong. Because they operate near the surface, they are less efficient and more susceptible to ventilation than submerged foils. On the other hand, surface piercing foils are often designed into boats that set speed records. This is because at maximum design speed, there is a reduced area of foil remaining in the water. This permits the speed to exceed the $V_{MAX} \approx 2*V_{TO}$ rule explained in chapter 4. Two examples of such boats are Sid Shutt's Hydro-ped, Figure 17-3, and the HD-4 by Alexander Bell and Casey Baldwin, Figure 1-1. The fastest human powered hydrofoil, Decavitator, shown in Figure 1-11, used a partially retractable main foil to reduce wetted area during its fast runs.

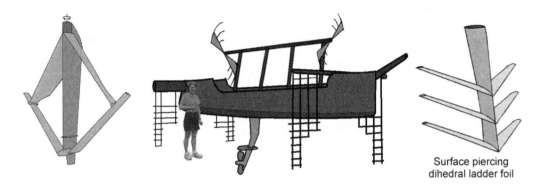

Surface piercing
dihedral ladder foil

Figures 8-1a, b, & c. Examples of surface piercing hydrofoils: (a) The front foil of Bras d'Or.
(b) Enrico Forlanini's boat from 1910. (c) One of two front foils on the Carl XCH-4.

A **ladder foil** *looks* like a ladder. Each foil is a rung and the vertical struts are stringers. The strut-stringers connect the foil-rungs to the hull. At rest, all rungs are submerged. As speed and lift increases, the hull rises. The upper rungs rise out of the water and therefore no longer contribute to lift. As a stable speed is reached the ladder settles into the water until the correct area of lifting surface is submerged and equilibrium between lift and weight is achieved. The Forlanini hydrofoils of Figure 8-1b are a good example.

A variation of the ladder foil is the **truss foil**. An example can be seen in Keiper's Williwaw style boat, Figure 1-3. This looks like a ladder foil made by a drunken carpenter. Ladders are similar to parallelograms, the stresses are bending stresses at the joints, and the assembly is subject to collapsing onto itself. By replacing parallel elements with triangular shapes, the irregular angles stiffen and strengthen the foil structure to reduce flexing and breaking problems at the joints. The bending stress at the joints is superseded by tension and compression of the rungs and stringers. Keiper understandably chose this rugged foil structure for his 20,000 miles of Pacific Ocean sailing.

Dihedral and anhedral foils enter the water at an angle. Dihedral foils can be joined to form a V or anhedral foils can be joined to form an inverted V. See Figures 8-17a and b.

The ladder and the dihedral types can be used in **combination** to smooth the lift transition from one rung to another as in Figure 8-1c. Observe that for any one of these 3 types to control height it must be surface piercing with part of the area above the surface while flying in a state of equilibrium. The portion that is out of the water is necessary to serve as a reservoir of lift to be put into effect as needed.

Incidentally, with submerged foils, dihedral can also be used to manage roll, but not to manage pitch. Unless the dihedral foil pierces the surface, they are not height setting. A submerged dihedral foil would generally be the main lifting foil. There is more about this in chapter 9, "Steering and Roll Management: Solutions".

The choice between submerged and surface piercing systems depends very much on the objective. The Russians have chosen surface piercing foils for their river cruising passenger hydrofoils, while the U.S. Navy has chosen submerged foils (more on submerged foils below) for their sophisticated fleet of 13 high speed deep water hydrofoil ships of the 1960s, 70s and 80s.

The riverboats deal with hidden obstacles, shoaling water, small waves and frequent docking. Simplicity and economy are important in keeping the ticket costs low. On the other hand, the faster U.S. Navy vessels operate in an environment of high waves, long swells, blue water and big budgets.

Trimming the running height of the front surface piercing foil is done by altering its AOA as explained back under "variable area foils".

Trimming the running height of the rear foil is usually done by adjusting its AOI. Moth class sailing hydrofoils, Figure 18-1, do this with a twist of the tiller. The AOI of Hifybe's rear foil can be changed only when hull-borne, prior to takeoff. The difference is, Moths are constantly trimming to adjust for changing points of sail, wind speed, location of the crew, etc. Hifybe has a predictable power output, always flies at $V_{MAX,}$ and is not bothered by normal winds. Therefore, only occasional trim change is needed.

Decavitator, Figure 1-11, is able to reduce the area of its main foil by retracting one of its biplane wings to accommodate an increase in speed. In effect, this is a gross change in rear foil trim. Retraction more than doubles the wing loading of the remaining wetted foil.

A similar system is found in Shutt's Hydro-ped, Figures 17-1a and 17-3, which uses a surface piercing dihedral main foil. The wetted area at the extreme outboard sections of the wing decrease as speed increases. This automatically trims the aft foil height while providing roll stability.

Submerged foils are more adaptable to extreme sea states. If properly designed, they are more sophisticated and efficient. They are less susceptible to crash diving due to ventilation because air is less likely to follow the long path down the struts to the deep running foils. However, they are more complicated because they need moving parts to regulate their lift, so they lack the rugged simplicity of surface piercing foils.

To provide information to the height controlling mechanism, the submerged front foil must have some type of height measuring system. This can range from the human eyeball to high tech electronic gizmos.

Eyeball? Yes, **manual pitch control** can work for slow moving hydrofoils such as those powered by humans. An alert pilot can control the bow height by observing and responding– see Dwight Filley's Bandersnatch in Figure 8-22 (showing an extreme and unlikely attitude change). This type of system relies on a carefully balanced design with the pilot trimming the front foil so that it rides close below a calm surface. In this case, *close* means within about one chord of the surface. In this realm lift is dominated by the surface proximity effect–lift is reduced as the foil approaches the surface. The percent amount of change in lift is called the *submergence factor* (F_S). The key elements here are smooth water, slow speed, and a relatively long separation of the front and rear foils (foil-base). For example, Bandersnatch is 10 ft. long and flies at 10 mph. Conceivably a longer boat of this type could be designed for greater speeds. Return to Figure 4-7 and its text for a deeper discussion on submergence.

In case you are wondering how length ties into speed, here's the answer. The longer the foil-base, the fewer degrees of angle of attack change will result from each unit of bow-height change. Look ahead to Figure 8-21. The boat shown there has a 12 foot foil base and its foils increase their AOA 4.8° for each 12 inches of elevation of the bow. If the foil base where 24 feet, the AOA would increase only 2.4° for each 12 inches of elevation change. By lengthening the foil-base the designer can reduce pitch sensitivity so that the pilot can remain in control at higher speeds.

While the surface effect can contribute to pitch stability, in practice it does not provide sufficient control on its own. Operating within one chord of the surface risks ventilation. Any waves but the smallest will briefly change submergence, which in turn changes lift. A really good and versatile design will rely on a surface sensing system coupled with a variable area or variable AOA foil to achieve much greater control than can be achieved when relying on just the submergence effect.

A **height sensor** tells the front foil when to increase or decrease lift. The sensor can be as simple as a wand hinged at the front strut, with the wand's free end skiing on the surface. A pushrod links the sensor to the hinged foil or to the foil's flap so that lift changes in the opposite direction that height changes. If the bow goes up, lift goes down and that lowers the bow.

Regardless of design, all **Submerged front foils vary their C_L** as depth changes. Lift is proportional to C_L. The equation is $L = C_L * S * V2$. We did the math in the chapter 4. The C_L changes with the foil's angle of attack (AOA) or with the flap/aileron deflection.

The following chart, Figure 8-2, demonstrates the difference. Assume straight and level flight with a C_L of .4 (Point A). Now assume that a wave encounter forces the bow up.

After passing the wave, the bow descends and its momentum causes the bow height to decrease below its trim height. The bow foil needs additional lift to recover to its trim height. Let's say that the foil needs a C_L of 1.0 to recover. This increase could be designed to occur in one of two ways. The flap may be deployed to its maximum (maximum deflection = 30° is typical) and thereby shift the entire lift curve upward. This will increase the C_L to 1.0 (Point B). Otherwise, the AOA could be increased to 12° from 5° thereby increasing the C_L to 1.0 (Point C), just what you need to recover from the nosedive.

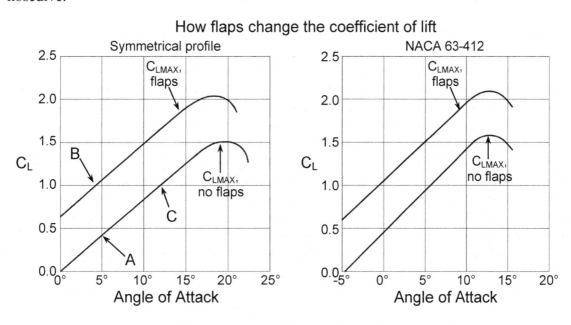

Figures 8-2a & b. (a) This shows the effect of flaps on a symmetrical profile, from *Aerodynamics for Naval Aviators*. (b) Extrapolated data for the NACA 63-412 profile.

There are three similar lift-altering devices that are hinged to the horizontal lifting surfaces: **flaps, ailerons, and elevators.** *Plain flaps* are attached to the trailing edge of a wing and deploy only down, thereby increasing lift and drag. They are normally located near the wing root, away from the tips. They are used to augment lift. *Ailerons* are likewise attached at the trailing edge of a wing but away from the root and closer to the tip. They rotate downward to increase lift and drag, and up to decrease lift and slightly increase drag. They are deployed asymmetrically to induce a rolling moment. Elevators are flaps on the tail wing of a flying machine. Elevators control the pitch of the hull or fuselage.

Figures 8-3a, b, & c. Wing flap or aileron in operation. Only ailerons hinge up as in (c).

A flap, aileron, or elevator can be replaced by a **variable incidence horizontal winglet,** also known as a **flipper.** The flipper is a small wing or wing extension that rotates along the axis running parallel to the leading and trailing edges; see Figure 8-4. Similar devices are the **stabilator,** and **taileron.** All are aerodynamic units that rotate around their lateral axis to vary the lift they create. If used in the tail in place of the horizontal stabilizer and elevator combination, it is called a *stabilator*. Indeed most supersonic aircraft use stabilators, for example, the F-14 Tomcat, F-15 Eagle and the F-18 Hornet, but it is also used in the Piper Cherokee and many modern airliners.

A *taileron* is an *elevon* that is not part of the main wing, but instead is a separate tail surface. An elevon is an "aircraft control surface that combines the functions of the elevator (used for pitch control) and the aileron (used for roll control). They are frequently used on tailless aircraft such as flying wings. These definitions, rearranged to fit our purpose, are from: en.wikipedia.org/wiki/Elevon.

Figures 8-4a, b, & c. This is a variable incidence horizontal winglet, or flipper. In this application they are being used for roll control. They could be used for pitch control if the port and starboard flippers rotated in unison, instead of opposite rotations as these do.

Variable incidence winglets, or flippers, control roll on Hifybe. They are shown above in Figures 8-4a, b, and c. They often use **symmetrical wing profiles**, where the top curve is a mirror image of the underside curve. This type of foil section has a **center of pressure** that moves less than that of a cambered foil section. "The center of pressure of an aircraft is the point where all of the aerodynamic pressure field may be represented by a single force vector with no moment", to quote Wikipedia. The less the center of pressure migrates, as in a symmetrical foil section, the less change in control pressure will be experienced.

An aircraft's elevators must generate negative as well as positive pitch forces. For this, a symmetrical wing section creates down forces as efficiently as up forces. Another use for negative lift is in any hydrofoil that has a tendency, when accelerating quickly, to stand on its stern and point the bow skyward. This maneuver is called a *wheelie* when done on a motorcycle. Wheelies can be controlled with a front foil that produces negative lift. A symmetrical foil section is appropriate for this purpose.

Likewise, catamaran and trimaran hydrofoil sailboats often have a need for negative lift on their outboard foils. When sailing on a reach the windward hull is un-weighted, and capsizing toward the leeward hull becomes a possibility. A downward force on the windward foil may keep it from breaching. Similarly, pitchpoling may be prevented by the negative lift generated by the aft foil. For generating positive and negative lift, a symmetrical foil profile is appropriate.

If the design calls for running at zero lift, symmetrical sections have the shape of the classic streamlined form and therefore have less drag under no-lift conditions. Unlike asymmetrical foil profiles that generate some lift at zero degrees angle of attack, symmetrical foils generate no lift unless they have a positive AOA.

Incidentally, non-symmetrical foil profiles can also generate negative lift, but to do so they must run at a pronounced negative angle of attack.

Spoilers are the least common device used to control lift in hydrofoils, see Figures 9-26a and b. A spoiler can be used on a foil that is designed to be oversized and create excess lift. A mechanical spoiler is a fence that rises from the upper surface of a foil to disrupt the fluid flow over this lift-creating area. A less common design is the air spoiler, Figure 9-26b, that permits air to enter into the relatively low-pressure area on the upper surface of the foil. This kills local lift. Both types create excess drag, and tend to switch between full on and full off. The ventilation spoiler creates an air bubble that may be difficult to shed when attempting to restore full lift. These idiosyncrasies could result in problems when trying to create a fine balance between lift created and lift required. Porpoising may result as front foil lift alternates between too much and too little. Incremental deployment along the span may be a solution, albeit, complicated.

The mechanical **height sensor** in the form of a surface follower that skis along the surface has been around for a long time. They were first used on a craft built by the Chicago based **Meacham brothers** sometime prior to 1906. See Figures 8-5a and b. Their old design is flyable, but apparently they knew little about hydrofoil wing profiles. In their 1913 patent (see bibliography), they described the front lifting system as a hydro*plane*. Except for the poorly formed front lifting surface, the one-piece combination of a front *pseudo-foil* and surface follower looks remarkably like the front foils on Decavitator, Hydro-ped, and Hifybe. The Meachams where many decades ahead of their time.

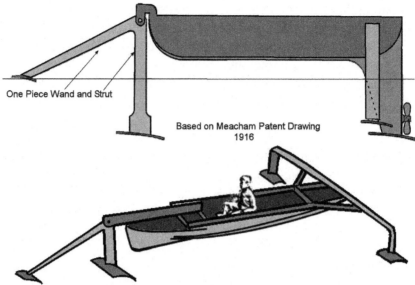

Figures 8-5a & b. (a) top, is from the Meacham patent.
(b) bottom, is based on *Ships That Fly*, John Meyers.

Figures 8-6a and b show the eloquently simple, yet effective front foil system designed in the 1960s by Sid Shutt for his record setting Hydro-ped. Like the Meacham brothers device, the height finding unit is one piece combining foil, strut, forward facing arm and surface follower. This combination is commonly known as the **Shutt Strut**. The top of the strut is attached to the boat with a simple transverse hinge pin that allows fore and aft rotation. At the end of the arm is a buoyant planing surface follower. In Figure 8-6a you can see that prior to takeoff the surface follower is at its highest elevation. The foil is at its greatest AOA and, therefore, its greatest C_L. Speed increases until sufficient lift is created and the bow lifts-off. In Figure 8-6b as the bow rises, the surface follower descends, and the foil's AOA is reduced. In this fashion the front foil finds equilibrium and flies at its design height. Within limits it adjusts automatically for the boat's speed and weight.

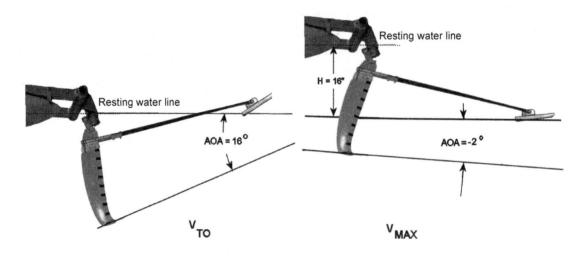

Figures 8-6a & b. The Shutt Strut, a modern variation of the Meacham brothers height finding foil. Figure 8-19 shows AOA and C_L values.

This clever system is economical, simple, efficient, and reliable. However, it operates in a narrow range of conditions, is not robust and does not do well in large waves. On occasion the surface follower will pop-up or tuck-under. At low speeds this is annoying, at high speeds it is disastrous. Shutt Struts are appropriate for human powered hydrofoils and slower, smaller, motor-powered hydrofoils, like Hifybe.

With the Meacham foil or Shutt Strut, the fore-aft location of the pivot hole on the strut also affects the load on the surface follower. Moving the pivot back reduces the load in the surface follower. Too light a load and it will pop up sometimes, too heavy a load and it may tuck-under. A cable can be rigged to limit strut rotation and prevent tuck-under if necessary.

 Notice that the rate of lift change, or *gain*–to be discussed in depth later in this chapter–is dependent on the length of the wand, and is independent of the length of the strut. The wand on Hifybe is a 40 inch carbon fiber golf club shaft that is living a more glamorous life than in the hands of a duffer.

Incidentally, the Shutt Strut does not follow the rules concerning hull pitch as in Figures 8-7 and 8-8. The Shutt Strut has the surface follower ahead of the variable lift foil, but the unique thing is that the pitch of the hull does not affect the information collected by the surface follower. This is because the one piece wand and strut combination hinges at the point it attaches to the hull so that no information about the pitch of the hull is communicated from the hull to the wand, strut or foil. See Figures 8-6a and b. The Shutt strut is isolated from the pitching of the hull and the only information the surface follower sends to the variable lift foil is *how high* the bow is flying. Because of this, the full range of angles of attack can be exploited and the front foil can have the same wing loading as the rear foil. Read on for more on differential wing loading.

It is important to recognize that some **surface followers collect two types of information,** *flying height* **and** *hull pitch*. The amount of front foil lift must vary with pitch as well as depth. Unless properly designed, the follower can return contradictory signals. Most height finding systems have their surface follower attached to a wand or rod connected to the hull or stationary strut. If it extends ahead or behind the foil it will sense more information than just height. The wand will also give hull pitch information. The information given will be affected by the hinge location of the surface follower. See Figures 8-7 and 8-8.

The timing of wave encounters is also affected. If ahead of the foil, the follower will give height information about the waves about to be encountered. If behind the foil it will give information about the waves just passed.

There are three possible longitudinal locations of the surface follower: **ahead, behind, or on the strut.** For example, assume that the bow is displaced from its cruise height, resulting in the boat being in a bow high or a bow low condition. The table below indicates that the height sensors positioned *forward of* or *at* the strut will create the most accurate input to the variable lift front foil.

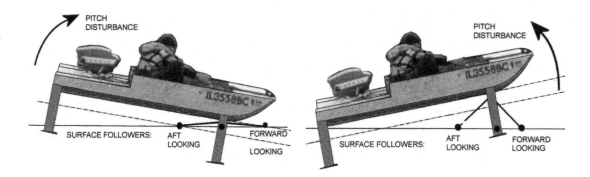

Figures 8-7a & b. Surface followers looking forward gather different information
than those looking back. Each boat shows different orientations of
the wand and follower: forward, aft, and on the strut.

Follower position	Bow pitch down	Bow pitch up	Weathervane effect?	Appearance	Subject to roll-under?
Forward of strut	Exaggerated	Correct	Unstable	Ungainly	Yes
On strut	Correct	Correct	Neutral	Compact- looks good	No
Aft of strut	Understated	Understated	Stable	Partly hidden	No

Figure 8-8. This table shows how three surface followers
perceive and report height changes due to hull pitching.

In Figure 8-8, Column 1 indicates the followers are located forward of, on, or aft of the strut. Columns 2 and 3 show the hull pitch information, as indicated by the surface follower, to be exaggerated, correct, or understated. *Roll under*, column 6, is a structural failure of the wand resulting it bending backward to trail in the slipstream.

Figures 8-7 and 8-8, indicate that the orientation of the surface follower in relation to the strut affects the amount of pitch change the follower senses. Assume the boat is flying at a height of 8 inches and something causes the front foil to take a dive. The cause might be a reaction to a wave or another boat's wake. The wave or wake encounter could rapidly pitch the bow up. The pitch-up would be followed by downward momentum that could bury the bow foil.

The surface follower should report to the front foil that not only has there been a reduction of flying height, but the hull is pointing seaward as well. In our diagram, if the follower extends forward of the strut it perceives the actual drop of 8 inches plus a false drop of 8 inches. The forward follower will report a total drop of 16 inches. This should result in a maximum increase in lift of the front foil—just when maximum lift is needed.

On the other hand, if the surface follower is operating at the same location as the strut, it will accurately measure the bow drop of 8 inches. Depending on the *gain* of the front foil, there may or may not be an adequate increase in front foil's lift to stop the descent and elevate the bow.

Go to Figures 8-19 and 8-20 and their text for the explanation of *gain*.

What about the trailing surface follower? The diagram shows that it will be caught snoozing. The bow of the boat is crashing, increased lift is needed and needed NOW and the surface follower thinks everything is OK. The response of the variable lift front foil will be inadequate and the bow will crash to the surface.

Take note that in the absence of pitch all three followers accurately report low height, such as would be experienced prior to takeoff. Each one would send information to the front foil that more lift is needed and thereby initiate an increase.

Of the three configurations, the forward follower gives the best information. It tells the front foil to increase lift if level flight is too low and it sends a panic signal if the height is too low along with the bow being pitched downward. In addition, it accurately reports high flying. But the forward-looking follower looks ungainly and is relatively delicate, making it subject to bending backward from the force of the free stream. It projects out the front of the boat looking for trouble.

The aft looking follower is more robust because it weather vanes in the passing water. However, it inaccurately measures pitch changes.

One answer is to mount the surface follower on the front strut like it is on the Dynafoil. This compact design senses height information accurately whether it was the result of either pitch or height changes. See Figures 1-10b, 8-16, and 10-3a and b. The functioning of Dynafoil's front foil is examined in more detail in Figures 8-10a, b, and c and its text. More on this in the following pages.

Perhaps the best solution is to mount the hinge point for the surface follower forward of the front strut. The follower itself will trail aft to about the location of the front strut. This configuration can be seen on the human powered boat, Phoenix. It apparently worked for this well designed craft when it set international speed records and won races in Japanese competition. The disadvantage is in the complicated linkage between the surface follower and the front foil.

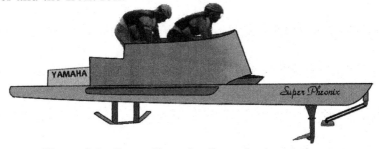

Figure 8-9. Super Phoenix. Propeller is not shown.

There are some **unconventional solutions** to the height finding problem that deserve examination. One promising idea is described in a 1963 report created by Grumman Aircraft Engineering Corp, entitled, *Development and Testing of Fully Submerged Hydrofoils with Drag Vane Control Installed on 15 foot Runabouts*. They designed and tested a depth-sensing vane that is attached directly to a flap trailing the front foil. The vane projects upward toward or through the surface. See Figure 8-16, for the artist's depiction of the report's grainy black and white photos that defy accurate interpretation.

As the submergence of the foil and flap increases, more of the vane is pulled down into the free stream. This deflects the vane downstream and in turn the flap is levered downward. The deflection of the vane is balanced by the hinge moment created by the hydrodynamic pressure on the flap. The deflected flap increases the lift, the foil rises, the wetted area of the vane decreases, the rearward force on the vane decreases, the flap hinge moment becomes dominant, and lift vs. submergence equilibrium is achieved.

Using this system, a 15 ft aluminum boat was able to smoothly negotiate 1 1/2 ft. waves at 31 mph. Grumman heralded the system's simple construction, efficiency in rough water, and good lift recovery after breaching. Why didn't Grumman put this promising design into production?

Perhaps Grumman's engineers had difficulties focusing on a 15 ft. boat when the Apollo landing module and the F-14 Tomcat fighter jet were competing for their attention. Still, this could prove to be the best height finding system ever. Maybe all that is needed is exposure to the world of innovative hydrofoilists to work out any remaining bugs.

Another clever device for regulating the front foil's height is found on the Dynafoil, as shown in Figure 8-10. At first glance its looks like the front strut is a simple variable incidence tri-plane delta wing at the bottom of the strut combined with a delta wing shaped surface follower mounted high on the strut. Thanks to Scott Smith, who owns and enjoys a Dynafoil, we have insight on how it really works.

The unique thing about this device is that the height-finding surface-follower doubles as another lift-creating delta-shaped foil. When hull-borne, prior to takeoff, the three small lower foils are at their maximum angles of attack, AOA. In this condition, the upper foil-follower is forced by the free stream to have its lowest AOA, but due to its large size it is providing significant lift.

As speed and lift on both foils increases, the bow rises, and the foil-follower begins to breach allowing it to pivot its trailing edge downward. It is linked internally to the lower tri-foils and they reduce their AOA as the upper foil-follower increases its AOA. The link can be adjusted to alter the gain. The increase in upper foil's AOA has little effect though, because it has risen above the surface and only its trailing edge is wetted.

This system works, in part, because of the configuration of the upper foil-follower. The upper foil-follower has the shape or a cupped delta wing, slightly resembling the wings on the Concord supersonic transport. Delta wings stall at high AOA, so lift is created even though the foil-follower rotates through a wide range of AOAs. The lower delta-shaped wings are not cupped.

In this clever design, another important factor is at work. Because the bow is lightly loaded (about 10% of total weight), the foil base is short in relation to the depth of the propeller, and the powerful engine's line of thrust is very deep, application of high power will result in a significant upward rotation of the bow. This boat will do wheelies at the twist of the throttle. Scott Smith claims his Dynafoil will rotate onto its back if the throttle is not treated with respect when accelerating. More on wheelies in chapter 19.

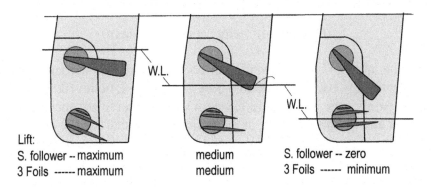

Figures 8-10a, b, & c. Functioning of the Dynafoil
surface follower (top) and triple foil.

A significant innovation can be seen on the 58 mph Hydroptère. To reach these speeds, the Hydroptère must sail in high winds and rough seas. To reduce the shock to the boat and crew, the inward-pointing surface piercing hydrofoils are hinged at the top. The axis runs fore and aft, and allows the foil to rotate upward in response to wave encounters. The hinge is spring loaded and shock absorbers dampen the movement. See a sketch of the boat at Figure 10-9. Hi-Foil has a similar feature that is patented (expired). See the front foil in Figure 8-17b.

Another design feature to be seen on the Rave and some Moths is the spring loaded surface following vane. A shock cord is belayed in its jam cleat to adjust the tension applied to the vane. This insures that it remains in contact with the surface under all conditions.

Winning the prize for clever adaptation of hydrofoils onto a conventional boat is Harry Larsen of Seattle, Washington. He converted a single engine 24 ft. Bayliner into a hydrofoil, Talaria IV. Talaria uses a surface follower attached to forward extending parallel control arms, that are linked to the submerged variable angle of incidence front foil. See Figure 8-11 for a photo I took of Harry and his boat in 2006 at Vashon Island, Washington.

Figure 8-11. Harry Larsen's Talaria IV.

Christopher Hook and A. C. Kermode in their book, *Hydrofoils,* advocated surface following wands trailing back from double bowsprits. Hook believed that if the surface follower was in front of the boat, the foil system would receive advanced warning of upcoming waves and troughs. A look at the numbers puts that idea in doubt. Hydrofin, Figure 8-12, was designed to reach a top speed of around 53 knots, or 90 ft. /sec. Judging that Hydrofin's wand extended forward 10 feet, the advanced warning Hydrofin would receive would be 10/90 of a second. If the waves are 5 feet apart the front foil will be changing its lift 12 times a second (90 / 5 = 12). If the front foil is given enough pitch authority to conform to these oncoming waves, there is going to be a very bumpy ride. Don't leave the dock without a barf-bag.

Figure 8-12. Artist's conception of one of the many
variations of Christopher Hook's Hydrofin.

The surface follower mechanism must be detuned to average out the small waves and effectively respond only to the consistent changes in height. Because the boat will not be making big lift changes in anticipation of these oncoming waves, it appears that for height control only it doesn't matter if the surface follower is ahead of, behind, or at the location of the front foil.

This brings up the general question of how a hydrofoil boat should negotiate disturbed water. If the bow will not be pitching up for every wave and diving down for every trough, a flight path called **contouring**, how else will it travel in rough water? Contouring is shown in Figure 8-13b. The alternative is to maintain a constant pitch angle of the hull and allow the length of the struts to smooth out the choppy water. The highest wave nearly touches the keel and the deepest troughs nearly expose the foils. In this way the short waves are smoothed. Concurrently the vessel may follow the contour of larger swells. On a larger boat, this is how a well-designed height finding system should work. This type of flying is called **platforming**, as seen in Figure 8-13a. Of course the wave negotiating system must be tailored to the size of the vessel. Ultimately, the longer the strut, the more potential a vessel will have for level flight through choppy seas. Hifybe with its 30 inch struts cannot aspire to the sea keeping characteristics of Boeing's Jetfoil with its 120 inch struts.

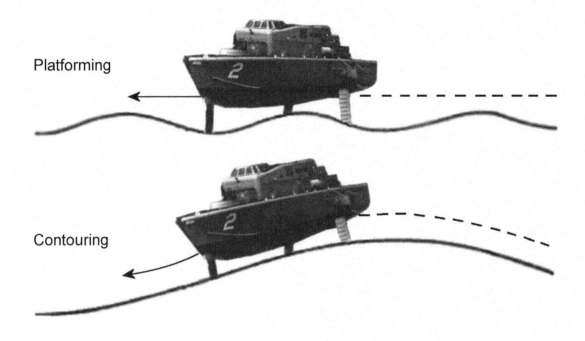

Figures 8-13a & b. Platforming and contouring.

Complicating the task of the height setting system is the **water's movement within waves.** Non-turbulent *currents* that move the entire body of water should not be a factor, because the vessel moves within this system as if it were a part of it. An aircraft flying into a head wind does not experience reduced air speed, nor does flying downwind increase the airspeed. The wind adds or subtracts from the ground speed but not the airspeed. So it is with all watercraft. The currents add or subtract from the speed over the bottom, but they do not affect the speed in relation to the water.

The water's movement *within* the waves will affect the way a hydrofoil flies. It is a challenge to describe, and the best explanation comes from Scott Smith who has plenty of experience traversing waves in his Dynafoil and Grumman hydrofoil boats. He has permitted me to blend his comments with mine as follows: There are a few things to know about the effect of waves. One is what happens in the trough between waves. The second is the difference between rolling swells and breaking or near breaking waves. The third is an effect caused by the distance from the bow of the boat to the front foils (on most configurations).

As far as how it affects lift on the foils, one can think of the water's movements within a wave as having four directions: up, down, approaching, and receding. With a hydrofoil, the horizontal movements are more important than the vertical movements in creating lift, this is because the foil's lift changes with the *square* of the horizontal velocity; whereas, vertical water movement will simply add or subtract from a level trajectory. However, the movement of a particle of water within the wave will almost always be moving partly horizontally and partly vertically, and it is best described as circular or orbital.

Let's picture a head sea first. The first horizontal movement begins just after the middle of the trough, and extends up the face of the wave almost to the crest. This is where water is 'pulled' into the wave, decreasing apparent speed and therefore hydrofoil's lift. Somewhere just before the crest that horizontal movement dissipates even though there is still vertical movement. Next, there is a lull in horizontal movement approaching and slightly after the crest of the wave, where the forces on the foil return to 'normal'. Then, from a point just after the crest and extending down almost to the center of the trough there is significant horizontal movement, an increase in apparent speed and therefore lift. Last of all, there is a period beginning before the center of the trough, and ending just after, where horizontal forces are again 'normal'.

In a following sea, when the boat is contouring, it can 'surf' a bit on the face of a following swell. It only tends to happen with small boats in big waves, but it does happen.

Part of the visualization becomes confusing because of the difference between breaking waves and swells. Standing in the water at the beach, facing the approaching surf, you feel the pull of the wave on the back of your legs before it reaches you and before it builds vertically. You still feel the pull as the wave face hits you, but then it instantly pushes you backward as the crest passes. That is because in a breaking wave the 'lull' at the top of the wave is almost nonexistent. The water in the crest isn't carried over to the back of the wave, it is pushed out in front of the wave where gravity pulls it down. In rolling swells the horizontal components are spread out more evenly. Ever watch a piece of seaweed floating just beyond the breakers? It seems to orbit for a long time–in and out, up and down–with each wave while not really coming any closer. Then it finally gets caught in a breaker, and gets driven all the way to shore in just a few moments.

For conventional hulls, the vertical components have the highest importance. As mentioned, with hydrofoils, the horizontal forces are most important. Because of this difference, one book may seem to contradict another. It depends on the orientation of the author (hydrofoil guys are a different breed).

The final point is, a conventional hull tends to respond immediately to the crossing of the wave under the bow. In a head sea, if the bow strikes a wave, it tends to rise instantly. But because the foils on a hydrofoil vessel are usually significantly *behind* the bow, the action is different. When the bow hits the wave, the front foils usually haven't gotten there yet, they are still in the 'low lift' area of the wave. Even though the hull may want to rise, the foils tend to hold the bow down, forcing it through the wave. It's hard on the hull, struts, and foils. The hull tends to slow with each impact, but not rise significantly. Ironically, as the boat suffers, it slows and the ride becomes more comfortable. This is because the vertical movements of a boat distress passengers the most.

Scott further shares this observation: "I rode in a Volga in 3 foot seas. Even though it is only designed to rise a few inches above the water, this foil-bow relationship kept the ride quite comfortable at about 20 knots (faster than the open-fishermen boats going the same direction). This dramatizes one of the unanticipated dangers of hydrofoils. Passengers get used to the smoother ride, they get complacent, they walk around, turn sideways in their seats, etc. If the foils do hit something solid or breach dramatically, the passengers get thrown suddenly and may be injured."

He continues: "In the first few hours of running my Grumman, I had two people (on different occasions) slide off their seats onto the floor when the boat went hull-borne unexpectedly. Both times they had turned askew to look over the side of the boat at the front foil. Both of them were warned in advance, but fell anyway. It is enough of an issue that I decided to put seatbelts in the boat and make people wear them."

We can conclude that even thought hydrofoils can fly above the waves, the waves are still a problem–in a complicated way.

In demanding situations, the ability for a height finding system to average out the surface disturbances may be beyond the reach of a mechanical system. This is why electronically controlled systems are so beguiling. Wrap your mind around this: an ultrasonic range finder mounted at the bow sends a digital signal to an onboard laptop computer. The software in the computer sends micro-current impulses to transistors and the amplified impulses go to either electrical step motors or solenoid powered hydraulic valves. These servomechanisms move flaps on the front foil and thereby adjust to changes in height.

In-flight adjustments to ride characteristics are made with digital inputs by keyboard. You are doing quick maneuvers and want a stiff ride? Enter 10 into the computer. Does Mother-in-law in the back seat want a soft ride? Enter 5. If you want to design a control system like this for all extreme sea states, it is best if you actually own a country, hire Boeing and let them work out the details. On the other hand, compact and inexpensive digital components are commercially available more than ever before, and undoubtedly there are electronic innovators behind closed garage doors working to create the next generation of bow height control systems.

What about the **rear foil?**

If the front foil functions properly and maintains the correct height, the rear foil, without sensors, will find its level for its speed and angle of incidence. The AOI in a rear foil is fixed except for trim adjustments, but AOA will change as the bow rises and falls.

The rear foil works like a weathervane. If the bow rises, the AOA of the rear foil increases. This causes the lift of the rear foils to increase and the foil rises to reestablish the previous vertical relationship between the fore and aft foils. The reverse is true if the front foil takes a dive. The rear foil looses AOA, lift decreases and the foil sinks down. As the boat rotates around the height setting front foil, the aft AOA adjusts until equilibrium is reestablished.

Again, think of the fore and aft foils working in combination as a weathervane. If the weathervane is turned sideways to the wind, the aft, feathered portion will have more corrective force created than the forward slender part. The weathervane points back toward the wind. Likewise the aft hydrofoil must adjust its path–determined by it's up and down pitch orientation–toward the direction of travel. The foil with the smaller percent change in lift corresponds to the slender end of the weathervane. The rear foil, with its larger percent change in lift, corresponds to the feathered back end of the weathervane. The weathervane swings into the wind and our hydrofoil swings into the direction of travel. Except for the difference in axis of rotation, vertical in the weathervane and horizontal in the hydrofoil, the two function much the same.

When applied to hydrofoils, the weathervane effect is the result of *differential wing loading*, defined earlier as lift divided by area. Normally the front foil would have a higher wing loading than the rear foil and this allows the vessel to weathervane. Figure 8-14 is a typical chart of the Coefficient of lift (C_L) vs. AOA for the NACA 63-412 foil. An extreme example is chosen to demonstrate differential wing loading. Assume your front foil, with its high wing load, is cruising at 8 degrees AOA and the rear, with its low wing load, is at 0 degrees. A two-degree pitch up would cause the C_L of the rear foil to increase from .25 to .50, a 100% increase. The front foil C_L increases from 1.20 to 1.40, a 16% increase. The percentage increase in lift on the front foil is much less than on the rear, and this makes the foil system act as a weathervane.

Coefficient of Lift vs. AOA – NACA 63-412

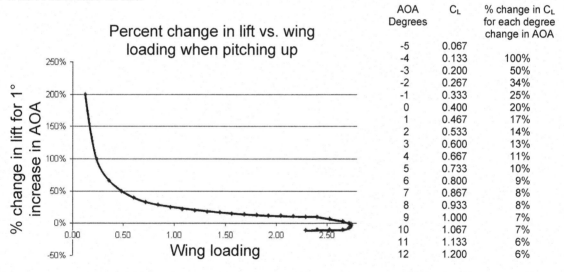

Figure 8-14. Lift vs. AOA showing percentage of lift changes more on the wing with the low wing loading (low C_L) despite equal changes in AOA.

Another way to illustrate this principle is shown in Figure 8-15. Using the chart, let's compare two foils, one with a light wing loading of .25 lbs / in^2 and another foil with a heavier wing loading of 1 lb / in^2. If the angle of attack on the first foil is increased 1°, the lift will increase by 100%. The same change in AOA on the second foil will result in a 25% increase in lift.

AOA Degrees	C_L	% change in C_L for each degree change in AOA
-5	0.067	
-4	0.133	100%
-3	0.200	50%
-2	0.267	34%
-1	0.333	25%
0	0.400	20%
1	0.467	17%
2	0.533	14%
3	0.600	13%
4	0.667	11%
5	0.733	10%
6	0.800	9%
7	0.867	8%
8	0.933	8%
9	1.000	7%
10	1.067	7%
11	1.133	6%
12	1.200	6%

Figures 8-15a & b. (a) Wing loading affects relative lift change when pitched up. The hook in the curve reflects the stalling of the wing at maximum AOA. The horizontal scale is in lbs / in^2. (b) is similar, but it is in table form and shows AOA in place of wing loading.

Unfortunately, **differential wing loading** is not enough for pitch stability in hydrofoils. Consider, for example, our hydrofoil flying straight and level with no height stabilizing mechanism. Assume something disturbs the pitch and the bow is displaced upward two degrees. We have seen that the much higher percent increase in the rear foil creates the weathervane effect and points the craft into the slipstream. But both foils still are pitched up creating lift greater than the assigned load. Unless that is corrected quickly, the craft will *breach* (fly out of the water). The weathervaning has served to partially correct the pitch disturbance, a revised angle of hull pitch has been established, and the path–although stabilized by weathervaning–has been altered. To return to a cruising height and pitch, an additional stabilizing device is needed. This is where a height sensing wand, or semi-submerged foil configuration, or some other type of surface sensor is needed.

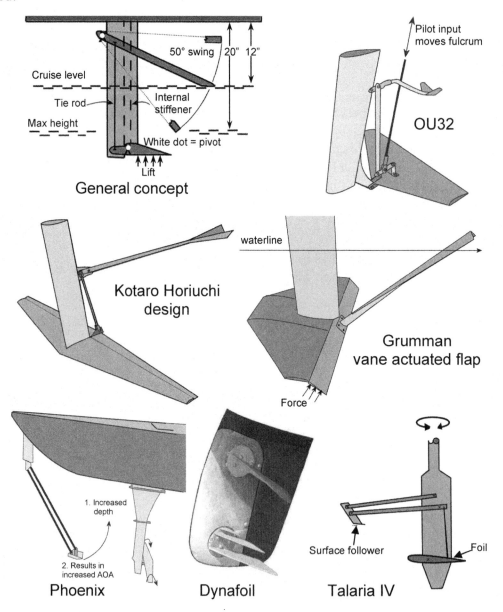

Figure 8-16. Examples of height finding submerged front foils.

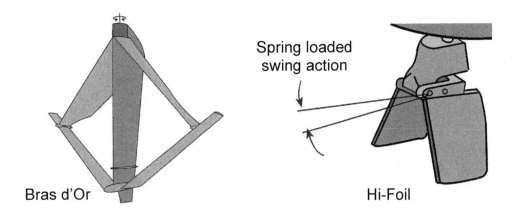

Spring loaded
swing action

Bras d'Or   Hi-Foil

Figures 8-17a & b. Examples of height finding surface piercing front foils.

Incidentally, two height controlling foils positioned wide abeam can also control roll, especially in hydrofoil boats designed to make flat, non-banked turns. For more see chapter 9 on roll control.

How much correction is necessary? Too much height control by the front foil will result in an uncomfortably stiff ride and the increased possibility of stalling or ventilating the foil. Too little and the bow will be subject to uncontrolled excursions, aka, porpoising. The bow will leap and dive. To allow comparison of one boat to another, we use a measure of stiffness called **Gain**, which is a ratio of **Δ lift** divided by **Δ height**, where the symbol **Δ** means the difference between two values.

Height, H, is flying height, expressed in inches. There are three heights of interest. They are all measured from the resting water line down to the flying water line below the attachment point of the bow strut.

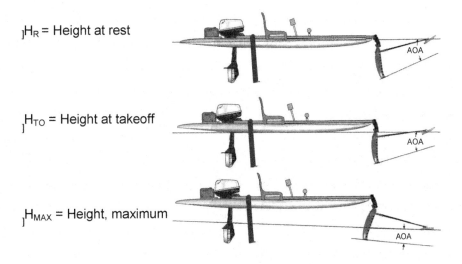

H_R = Height at rest

H_{TO} = Height at takeoff

H_{MAX} = Height, maximum

Figures 8-18a, b, & c. The three heights and their symbols.
The AOA is shown as well.

H_{MAX} occurs at V_{MAX} (in Hifybe, this is roughly equal to V_{CRUISE}). It may seem like an unnecessary complication to indicate three flying heights, and indeed for Hifybe we can ignore H_{TO} for the most part because it is so close to H_R. H_{TO} gains importance in boats that have deep and slender keels, like the Dynafoil's, Figure 1-10b. The Dynafoil can be flying quite high and very little "air" will be showing under the keel. It is built like this for two reasons. The high chine allows the boat to bank sharply before it touches the water, and the deep-V keel reduces the shock of wave encounters.

Gain/inch (gain per inch) is an example of height finding stiffness tailor-made for this book. It is the percent difference in lift (or C_L) of the front foil caused by decreasing its flying height from H_{MAX} to one inch below H_{MAX}. We will use Hifybe's "Shutt Strut" as an example, Figure 8-19. Here is the equation:

$$\frac{\Delta C_L / in}{C_L @ H_{MAX}} = \text{gain / inch (gain per inch)}$$

$\Delta C_L / in$ is the C_L change that occurs when the height is reduced 1 inch from Height, maximum (H_{MAX}). It stands for: "the difference in coefficient of lift per inch of height reduction".

The *slope* of the lift curve is found in Figure 13-3. This is how much the C_L changes for each *degree* of AOA change. The slope for the NACA 63-412 is .109 and the slope for NACA 4412 is .100. The slopes of the two NACA profiles are nearly constant from C_L = zero to C_L = maximum. This is indicated by the straight line on their C_L charts.

The $\Delta C_L / in$ is found by multiplying the *slope* by the *AOA change per inch of height change*. Figure 8-20 shows us Hifybe's Shutt Strut with a 40" wand changes its AOA 1.4° per inch of height change (this is Δ AOA / in). Here is the math:

1.4 * .100 = .14.

To save you from this calculation, column 3 of Figure 8-20 also shows the $\Delta C_L / in$.

Now divide the inch-slope by $C_L @ H_{MAX}$ to arrive at the Gain / inch of 47%.

.14 / .300 = .47 or 47%.

Next we review the way the Shut Strut functions. Basically the higher the boat flies, the lower the foil's AOA. In Figure 8-19, for example, at V_{MAX} and H_{MAX}, the bow will be 11" above the surface, and the AOA will be -1°. Detailed functioning of the Shutt Strut is explained in Figures 8-6a and b and their accompanying text.

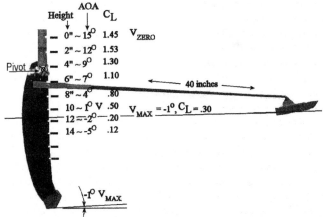

Figure 8-19. This is Hifybe's modernized Meacham front foil, called a *Shutt Strut*. The diagram shows that the angle of attack of the foil varies with the height of the bow. Its profile is the Clark Y, which is much like the NACA 4412.

Incidentally, to decrease the gain on any height finding mechanism with a near-horizontal wand, simply lengthen the wand. This applies to the Meacham foil, Shutt Strut, Talaria IV height finder, etc. The lengthening also affects the load on the surface follower and reduces its minimum required size. Boats with a linkage between the surface follower and the front foil would change the bell-cranks or other parts of the linkage geometry to decrease the ratio of movement between the two.

The gain / inch can be also be increased by decreasing the C_L @ H_{MAX}. A direct way of doing this would be to increase the area of the front foil. Increasing the foil size without other changes decreases the foil loading. The lift of a lightly loaded foil has a greater percent change of lift for a given change in the AOA. Review Figure 8-14 for a better understanding.

The table on the following page, Figure 8-20, shows various wand lengths for a Shutt Strut. It demonstrates how a one-inch decrease in flying height from H_{MAX} will increase the AOA and C_L. The last column shows the increase in C_L as a percent of the C_L at H_{MAX}.

Wand length, inches	Δ AOA / inch	Δ C_L / inch	Gain / inch, %C_L / in
10	5.7	0.57	192%
15	3.8	0.38	128%
20	2.9	0.29	96%
25	2.3	0.23	76%
30	1.9	0.19	64%
35	1.6	0.16	55%
40	1.4	0.14	48%
45	1.3	0.13	42%
50	1.1	0.11	38%

Figure 8-20. This shows how the wand length of a Shutt Strut affects Δ AOA /in, Δ C_L /in, and Gain/in.

Height and Pitch Management

The Assumptions for Figure 8-20 are:

- NACA 4412 profile.
- One-inch decrease (change) in flying height from H_{MAX}.
- H_{MAX} AOA = -1°.
- C_L at -1° = .30. See Figure 13-3.
- C_L change for each degree change (slope) = .10. See Figure 13-3.

Some general guidelines for gain, in general are:

- Faster boats need less gain to avoid excessive stiffness.
- To keep the ride smooth, boats in choppy water need less gain or they need "input filtering".
- The higher the moment of inertia, the greater the necessary gain.
- The more pitch torque created by the power source, the greater the necessary gain.
- Steep balanced turns will require a high gain to avoid losing height when under high G loads.

The real value of calculating height and gain is in comparing one boat to another. For more on this, go to chapter 15 for "Comparative Analysis of Designs"

This method can be applied to most front foils. The Gain/inch universally covers foils with flaps, foils with variable incidence, and foils with spoilers. All these systems link changes in height to changes in C_L.

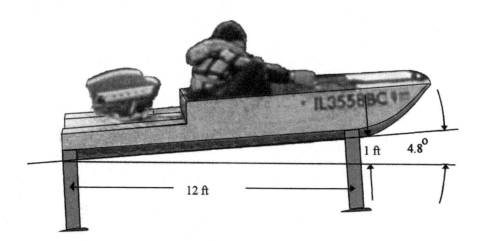

Figure 8-21. Maximum pitch angle is limited by geometry and this limits speed variation. The change in angle can be determined by trigonometry or by simply printing a picture (I print a .jpg image) and applying a protractor.

How does a **high center of gravity** effect pitch control? We will apply this question to the design of a sit-up human powered hydrofoil (HPH). Look at Figures 8-22a and b that are photographs of Dwight Filley's Bandersnatch. They are exaggerated in forward and backward pitch. When an elevated heavy load–such as the pilot on a HPH–pitches forward the center of gravity shifts, the load on the front foil increases, and the load on the rear foil decreases. A pitch backward has the opposite effect. Incidentally, in this simple design, the pilot controls Bandersnatch'es pitch manually by making constant adjustments to the angle of incidence of the front foil.

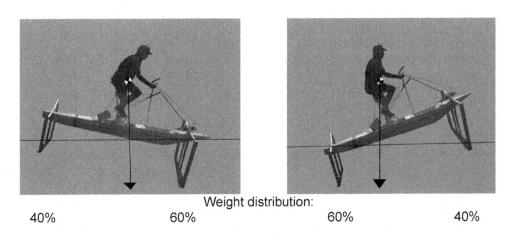

Weight distribution:
40%   60%   60%   40%

Figures 8-22a & b. How pitching moves the center of gravity is shown in this exaggerated change in attitude. This is Dwight Filley's Bandersnatch.

A similar effect on *roll* stability is felt with high center of gravity designs. The big difference is that the angle of attack does not increase on the more weighted foil and the AOA does not decrease on the unloaded foil. It can be concluded that a high center of gravity affects both pitch and roll. See Figure 10-8 for further discussion on recumbent or upright rider's position.

Another condition is worth considering: whether pitching or rolling, there is always a tipping point. When a line drawn vertically downward thought the center of gravity passes outside its support, the structure will have reached its tipping point and the unit will tumble. This is the equivalent of the pea being forced so high up the side of the bowl as to tumble over the side. Stability is lost and is irretrievable. For an illustration, see the Falling Tower of Pisa, Figure 10-13. For more on hull-borne roll stability, go to Figure 10-14 and its text.

Steering and Roll Management: Solutions

o Definitions and locations of roll axes
o Roll around the center of mass
o Roll around the axis of lateral aquadynamic resistance
o Maneuverability vs. stability
o Tools for managing roll:
o Dihedral and anhedral
o Advancing and descending wing effect
o Differential turning radius and roll torque
o Optimum dihedral
o Dihedral rolls into yaw, anhedral rolls away from yaw
o Bananas fly poorly
o Rudder
o Turning force is created by the wings
o Three force vectors in a turn: lift, vertical, and horizontal
o Surface proximity
o Swept wings and wingspan
o Flippers, wing warp, and spoilers

Definitions: *Rolling* is rotation around a line extending from stem to stern, called the *roll axis* or *longitudinal axis*. If viewed head on, the roll axis appears to be a point which is called the "*roll center*". *Roll stability*, otherwise known as *lateral stability*, is the tendency, if flying level or making a flat turn, to return to an upright position after a roll disturbance; or, if one is making a banked turn, to return to a balanced bank following a roll disturbance. *Roll control* or *lateral control*, is exercising command over the rotation around the roll axis. The difference is that *stability* is a characteristic of the machine independent of the pilot's input and *control* is the result of the pilot's input. Control and maneuverability are synonymous for our purposes. The two concepts, stability and control, can be combined and called *roll management*, which rivals pitch management as the most difficult challenge to be resolved.

The location of the roll center varies from boat to boat. For any particular craft, it is important to approximate the location of the roll center before attempting to establish or modify roll stability and control.

An object floating in space, if disturbed asymmetrically, will **roll around its center of mass**, because the source of resistance to movement is the inertia of its mass. In a uniform gravitational field, the center of mass coincides with its center of gravity. Hereafter, consider the terms center of mass and center of gravity (CG) to be interchangeable.

An irregular shape, such as a wing and strut combination, when moving through a fluid will rotate around an axis determined by the aerodynamic-aquadynamic characteristics of the shape.

A hydrofoil boat, when flying, experiences a blend of these types of resistances to rotation. It will have inertial resistance above water at the center of the gravity of the combined hull, crew, motor, etc. The struts and foils are relatively light and will lower the CG only slightly.

Lateral aquadynamic resistance is simply the hydrodynamic resistance that water exerts against the sideways movement of a submerged object. The **axis of lateral aquadynamic resistance** will be located below the surface of the water, and in a hydrofoil boat, it will be near the geometric center of combined wetted foils and struts. Both mass and hydraulic force resist rolling, therefore the center of roll will be located somewhere between the CG and the Axis of Lateral Aquadynamic Resistance, and it will normally be closer to the stronger aquadynamic center. Depending on the forces applied to the vessel and the wetting of the components, the roll axis will migrate.

The horizontal orientation of the roll axis will change as well. If the CG is directly above the axis of lateral aquadynamic resistance, the roll axis will be horizontal extending stem to stern. This is seldom the case. For example, often the front foils are loaded more heavily than the rear foil. In other words, the center of gravity will be ahead of the center of the combined hydrofoil surfaces. This results in a forward slanting of the roll axis. Consequently, forces that stabilize or control roll will also cause yawing moments. For details see Figures 10-7a and b along with their text.

Remember, the location of the roll center changes depending on the type of force acting upon it. If a force is applied laterally to the foils and struts, they will shift to the side and the boat will roll around the CG. Likewise, in a small craft if the pilot shifts his weight causing a shift in load away from the CG, or if a boat turns generating centrifugal force, the boat will tend to roll around the Axis of Lateral Aquadynamic Resistance.

For the remainder of this chapter, when dealing with hydrodynamic forces generated by the submerged foils, we will assume that these forces will cause rotation around the CG. On the other hand, forces of inertia or angular momentum, like centrifugal force, will cause rotation around the axis of lateral aquadynamic resistance. For our purposes, the axis of lateral aquadynamic resistance is assumed to be at the geometric center of all the wetted areas. Unless otherwise noted, when dealing with roll forces, the axis of rotation will be horizontal from stem to stern.

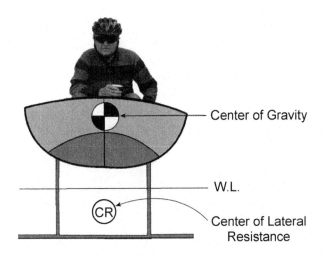

Center of Gravity

W.L.

Center of Lateral
Resistance

Figure 9-1. Shown are the center of gravity and the
center (axis) of lateral aquadynamic resistance.

Early in the planning stage, a designer must make decisions about the handling
characteristics of the proposed flying machine. Remember, **maneuverability and
stability** are at opposite ends of a continuum. Refer back to Figure 3-1. Relatively
speaking, an airliner is stable but has weak pilot controls, while an aerobatic plane is
unstable but has strong pilot controls. It is not a question of which is better, stability or
maneuverability, it is a question of what type of craft the designer hopes to realize.

Too much roll stability can be a disadvantage. To make a boat that banks to the inside of
a turn like an airplane, the designer needs to override the boat's tendency to maintain
level flight. The less stable the design, the less control input will be required to initiate
the bank.

Flying machines may have neutral roll stability. Some private aircraft are like this. They
tend to remain at their present angle of bank. It takes control input from the pilot to level
the wings of such an aircraft, whereas a very stable airplane will be more likely to return
to straight and level flight without pilot input.

There are many **tools for managing roll**: dihedral, anhedral, rudder deflection, surface
proximity, wing sweep, wingspan, wing warp, ailerons, mechanical spoilers, air bleed
spoilers, and autopilots.

Dihedral is where the wing tip is higher than the wing root as shown in the aircraft
photos, Figures 9-2a and b. What makes dihedral work? Consider a wing coming toward
you as in the first photo. If it yaws to its left it will appear something like the second
photo:

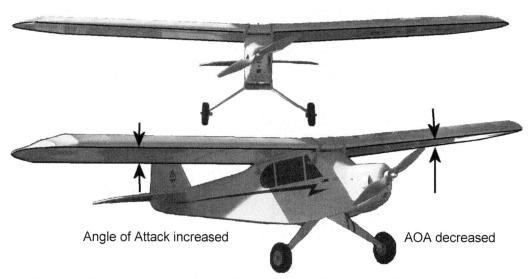

Angle of Attack increased   AOA decreased

Figures 9-2a & b. How yawing or skidding differentially changes the Angle of Attack
in wings that have dihedral. The observer is looking down the slipstream.

Although extreme angles of yaw are not possible with hydrofoils due to strut ventilation problems, the aircraft principles apply, but to a restricted degree. See the graph in Figure 6–1 showing strut ventilation.

The Piper aircraft pictured above shows how yaw affects roll. Notice how the wing on the advanced side increases angle of attack (AOA) while the wing on the retreated side decreases AOA. This will cause an upward roll on the advanced side and a downward roll on the retreated side.

This effect is enhanced by the momentary increase in speed of the advancing wing and the decrease in speed of the retreating wing (more to follow). Furthermore, observe how the fuselage blocks (shadows) the oncoming fluid from some of the retreated wing and the entire downwind horizontal stabilizer (air acts as a fluid). Figure 9-21 shows the shadow effect on a swept wing, similar to the effect on a straight wing. In aircraft with low wings, this shadowing is much more effective because the fuselage partially blocks airflow over the top of the wing where most lift is generated. The struts of a hydrofoil, especially wide struts, will also cast a small shadow on a yawing hydrofoil. Because the strut extends upward from the foil, it will block fluid flow on the upper surface of the foil.

Of course, the pilot can use these effects to control roll by yawing to the right to correct an unwanted roll to the left and vice versa. Thrust-steering enhances these effects.

As you recall hydrofoils, not aircraft, have the special problem of ventilation which can destroy 70% of the foil's lift.

This is a good place to recap, from chapter 6, the things that prevent or reduce ventilation: foils that run deep, foils located ahead of their struts, fences installed on the struts, streamlined pods or fairings at the intersections acting as fences, struts that slant forward from the top down so that the path of ventilation is opposed by the water's flow, and rounded leading edges of foils and struts. Struts and surface piercing foils with knife-like leading edges are more prone to ventilation than those with rounded leading edges.

When flying machines are banking toward the yaw, that is, into a turn, they redirect the vertical forces so that they balance the centrifugal force generated by a turn. This gives the pilot and crew the sensation that the pull of gravity has increased and is still pulling on a line passing from head to toe.

While foil-borne, the keel of the hull will fly above the water and have no effect. The main struts then act as a keel. In order for the dihedral to function, the keel effect must be sufficiently light so that the wing may yaw or skid, producing the cross-flown needed to create asymmetrical lift. Again, the struts must not be yawed past the angle of ventilation.

Dihedral creates another corrective roll response even without yaw. Take a look at Figure 9-3. Imagine flight with wings level. The lift vector would coincide with the vertical force vector, and there would be no side force. The plane would fly straight toward the reader. In level flight the lift vector will equal the weight supported by the wing.

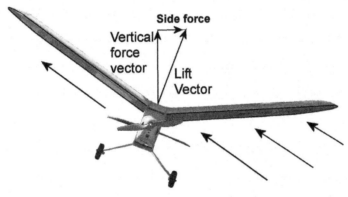

Figure 9-3. How tilting the wings while maintaining a heading creates a sideslip resulting in a roll-correcting dihedral effect.

Observe that when the wings are rolled to the plane's left, the lift vector is likewise tilted to its left. When visualizing the forces of a banked condition it is convenient to divide the lift vector into its components. The vertical vector opposes gravity and the horizontal vector provides the energy for a skid or a balanced turn, depending on orientation of the rudder. If the direction of flight remains the same, the side force will cause a sideslip, and the flying machine will react to it in the same way it does to the rudder-induced sideslip illustrated in Figure 9-2b. The lower wing experiences a higher AOA and greater lift. The higher wing experiences a lower AOA and lower lift. The result is a correctional force that rolls the wings back toward level flight.

Anhedral describes a wing that has its tips lower than its roots. Naturally, anhedral will have an effect opposite that of dihedral, as can be seen in Figures 9-4b and c. Sideslip refers to the sideways movement of the craft:

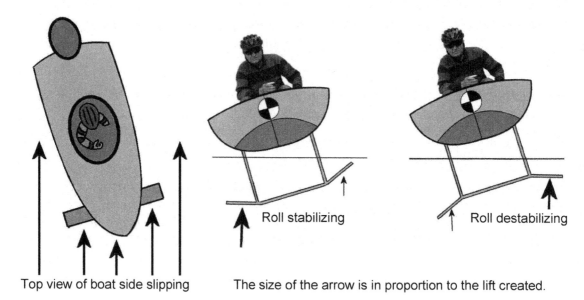

Top view of boat side slipping   The size of the arrow is in proportion to the lift created.

Figures 9-4a, b, & c. Dihedral vs. anhedral for roll stability when side slipping or yawing.

Additionally, a wing will resist rolling because the section near the *descending* wing tip has a higher effective AOA than the section near the *ascending* wing tip. The angle of descent is added to the AOA of the descending wing section and the angle of ascent is subtracted from the ascending wing section. This dampening effect slows the *rate* of roll allowing the pilot time to adjust for the disturbance.

A characteristic that applies to both hydrofoils and aircraft is the **advancing wing effect**. With or without dihedral, as the wing yaws the advancing side will be *momentarily* moving faster than the receding side. The lift vector will increase on the advancing side and decrease on the retreating side. A quick change of direction can be helpful in correcting a roll excursion, provided the pilot doesn't care where he is going for that instant, and this could be the case in a sport hydrofoil. The speed and wingspan of the craft is important. Wide-spanned human powered hydrofoils or high aspect ratio gliding aircraft will be more affected by relative wing speed. High-speed, narrow, motor powered craft will be much less affected. In any case, this lift differential cannot be sustained. As soon as the yawing stops, the lift differential ceases.

There is another similar effect that is *sustainable*, and that is from the **differential turning radius**. When any vehicle turns, the side farthest from the center of the turn circle will travel a greater distance than the closer side. To cover the greater distance the outer side goes faster than the inner side. Very wide, slow hydrofoils turning sharply are most affected. Take a look at Figure 9-5.

At first glance it might seem the speeds of the two wingtips of this hydrofoil would not be significantly different, but in fact they are, and this will make a big difference in lift. The lift formula from chapter 4:

$$L = V^2 * S * C_L$$

The formula shows that lift will increase or decrease with the square of the velocity, V. In our example, there is a 15% difference in the distance traveled. Given equal time in route, the outside wing tip must have a 15% greater velocity than the inside foil, which produces a 32% increase in lift at the outside tips. The result is a strong rolling force to the inside of the curve contributing to a balanced turn.

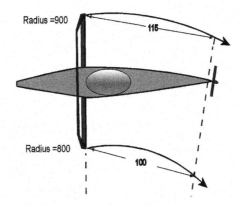

Figure 9-5. During a turn, the outside wing tip travels farther
and faster than the inside. The units are inches.

Let's return for a moment to the dihedral effect and address **roll torque**. Dihedral makes an effective method for stabilizing roll in airplanes with their low CG, but the high CG of the typical hydrofoil complicates dihedral's contribution. Recall that if a foil has dihedral and the boat yaws, the force perpendicular to the foil will increase on one side (the advanced side) and decrease on the other. This is mostly due to a differential change in the angle of attack. Hydrofoil boats have a high center of gravity and therefore a high center of roll. In roll control, it is important that the force vector pass outside the center of gravity, Figure 9-7a.

The shortest distance between the force vector and the CG is called the torque lever, Figure 9-7a. In this case the roll center is approximately at the center of gravity. In English units, the torque lever in feet is multiplied by the force vector in pounds and the result is expressed in foot-pounds (ft-lbs). As the designer increases dihedral, the force vector passes closer to the roll center until the torque lever diminishes to zero. At that point there is no righting force associated with the dihedral effect, and it will contribute nothing to the boat's roll stability as shown in Figures 9-6a and b. Excluding other design features, the boat will have neutral roll stability as illustrated by the ball on a table.

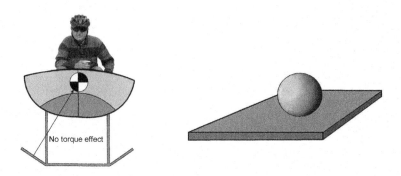

Figures 9-6a & b. Wing tips with too much dihedral creates no corrective roll torque. The examples have neutral static roll stability.

The arrow drawn from the center of the span of the foil is the perpendicular force vector. The force on one side of the foil array will contribute to roll stability only if the vector passes outside the roll center as shown in Figure 9-7a. The ball in a bowl illustrates positive stability, Figure 9-7b.

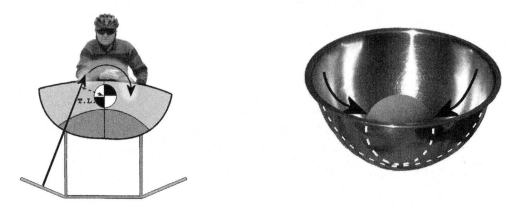

Figures 9-7a & b. The force vector must pass outside the center of roll. The torque lever is the dotted line between the C.G. and the lift vector.

If the force vector passes inside the roll center, the dihedral of the foil will contribute to roll instability as illustrated by the ball on a bowl, Figures 9-8a and b.

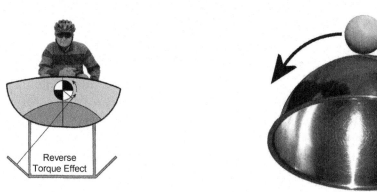

Figures 9-8a & b. The force vector passes inside the center of roll causing the dihedral to be destabilizing.

By design, this balance can be altered when the craft yaws or turns. The effectiveness of the dihedral will be expressed by the increase in ft-lbs of roll torque created because of yaw. During yaw, the greater the dihedral, the greater the imbalance in the force vectors, but the resulting roll torque is dependent on the product of the force vector times the lever arm. In a correctly designed system, this imbalance contributes to roll stability and the ability to make balanced turns.

So what is the **optimum dihedral**? This will take three illustrations to explain. First, assume a "square" foil configuration as shown in Figure 9-9. Herein, a *square plan* is where the average half foil span equals the average strut length measured vertically from the CG. The boat and its measurements are hypothetical; created to illustrate the concept.

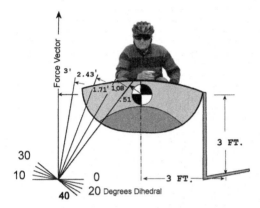

Figure 9-9. Five angles of dihedral are drawn: 0°, 10°, 20°, 30°, and 40°. The angles of dihedral result in force levers of 3.00, 2.43, 1.71, 1.08 and .51 ft. respectively.

Observe, as the dihedral is increased, the length of the lever arm working on the CG is decreased.

Figure 9-10 is a chart that estimates, for various angles of built in dihedral, how yawing (Δ yaw) changes the AOA (Δ AOA). AOA increases on the advancing side and decreases on the receding side. To understand the chart, visualize a foil with 90° dihedral (this hypothetical vertical foil would have the appearance of a strut). Four degrees of yaw would result in 4° change in AOA. This is a 100% correlation (4° x 100% = 4°), and is marked by the circle 1 in the upper right hand corner of the chart. It would seem that if the dihedral is fixed at half of 90°, 45°, the same 4° yaw would cause a change in the AOA about half as much, 50% or 2°. This is almost true, but the relationship between yaw and change in AOA is not linear. You can see on the chart, the line is curved. Look at the circle 2 in the chart. With 10° of dihedral, there is a 20% correlation between Δ yaw and Δ AOA. If you yaw 5°, there will be a 1° change in AOA. (5° * 20% = 1°).

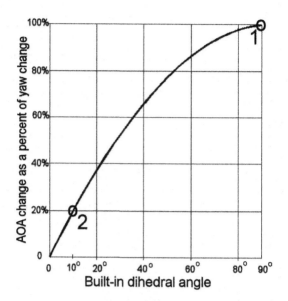

Figure 9-10. The increase in angle of attack caused
by yaw is greater in high dihedral wings.

This chart is helpful in demonstrating the yaw-AOA couple; of course, it goes to impractical extremes for yaw. Deeply submerged foils will be limited by their stall AOA and surface piercing foils and struts will be limited by ventilation which can be a problem starting about 4° (review Figure 6-1). Higher angles of yaw can be achieved by using anti-ventilation devices detailed in chapter 6 including strut fences, junction fairings, slanted struts, foils offset from their struts, etc.

Case closed? Not so fast. Recall the chart in Figure 9-9 that shows each angle of dihedral has a unique lever arm. As more dihedral is built into the design, its effect on AOA increases but its lever arm decreases. Figure 9-11 is a chart showing this relationship.

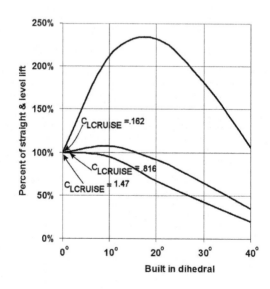

Figure 9-11. This chart shows what happens
to lift when a dihedral wing is yawed 4°.

The chart shows that the most torque effective dihedral to be built into the foil is between $10°$ and $25°$; peaking at $18°$. However, because of the complex relationship between dihedral, yaw, and operating AOA, the dihedral is only effective in controlling roll when the wing is operating in the realm of low lift coefficients. In this example, $C_{LCRUISE}$ = .162, which is minus $4°$ AOA, has the most peaked curve. The other foils cruising at higher coefficients of lift–higher angles of attack and higher wing loading–do not have effective roll control from dihedral.

In this example, yaw = $4°$, and the foil profile is NACA 63-412.

$C_L@$ $-4°$ = .162
$C_L@$ $5°$ = .816
$C_L@$ $11°$ = 1.47

The dihedral effect can be increased if the average foil span is widened or the average strut length is shortened. Either of these changes will increase the torque lever. These wide footprints are seen in catamarans, trimarans, and low center of gravity hydrofoils that operate on the rivers of Russia. Alexander, et.al. in *Hydrofoil Sailing*, used an example of a trimaran with widely spaced outriggers and concluded that a dihedral of $30°$ to $50°$ is the most effective. All the other roll stabilizing and control effects shown in this chapter would also be enhanced by these two changes.

As mentioned, anhedral is very effective, in a bad way, for stability; but it is effective, in a good way, for controllability. If a foil has anhedral, yaw will cause a roll to the outside of the yaw. The imbalance in lift has a strong effect on roll because, up to a certain limit of roughly $45°$, the greater the anhedral the longer the torque lever working against the CG. However, if the anhedral sections have ailerons, or if they are variable angle of incidence winglets (flippers), they will be very effective in controlling roll.

Figures 9-12a & b. Wing tips with the greatest anhedral, up to $45°$, have the longest torque lever. A flat foil will also have long torque lever.

The direction of the moment of roll created by yawing a dihedral or an anhedral foil will not change based on whether they are mounted fore or aft of the CG. See Figures 9-13a and b.

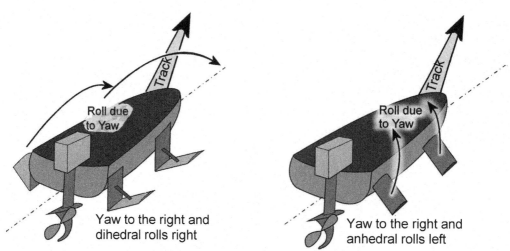

Figures 9-13a & b. **Dihedral rolls into a yaw, anhedral rolls away from a yaw**.
The big arrow represents the boat's track and the dotted line represents the roll axis.

However, if *surface piercing*, both dihedral and anhedral may have a stabilizing effect on roll. In either case, as one foil descends more area is submerged creating an increase in lift proportional to the increases in the area newly submerged. The ascending side experiences decreasing submergence and lift. This is roll stabilizing. If you do some sketches of surface piercing dihedral and anhedral as shown above, but showing various angles of bank, you are likely to conclude that in a bank this type of foil geometry needs to be very wide to avoid having the descending foil become either too vertical or too horizontal to support its side of the boat. The Hydroptère, Figure 10-9, is a good example of wide set dihedral foils that function well. Another solution is the ladder foil, seen in Figures 1-5 and 9-14.

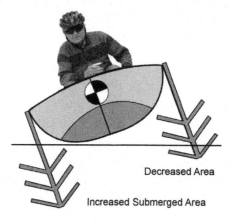

Figure 9-14. These foils combine a
ladder configuration with dihedral.

Incidentally, while banking, the rising wing tips of anhedral foils have the advantage of running deeper than straight or dihedral foils. This also applies to the descending side. This effect is especially important with single track hydrofoils which are designed to make banked turns. On the ascending side, there will be less of a tendency to ventilate at the tips. Figure 9-4c shows a banked anhedral foil and illustrates this effect.

"Time flies like an arrow, fruit flies like a banana", claims Groucho Marx, and I might add that **bananas fly poorly**, as does most fruit. They have an improbable aerodynamic shape. When a wing is curved like a banana with the tips pointing skyward, lift may suffer. When dihedral is required for roll control, it is tempting to design a wing that gracefully rounds up from the center to the tips. If the slipstream could be depended upon to flow straight from the leading to the trailing edge there would be no problem. However, fluid flow always takes the path of least resistance. In this case it will deviate outward and upward. Any transverse flow (toward the tip) along the underside of the curved wing will follow a path that curves like the fluid flow over an inverted airfoil, and this will generate some negative, downward, force in opposition to lift. The same applies to the hull shape as well. See Figure 9-15 and read more on the subject in chapter 12.

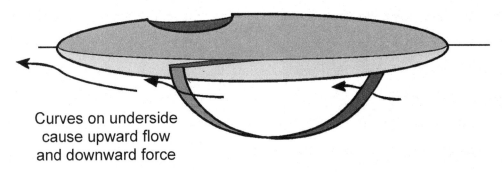

Curves on underside
cause upward flow
and downward force

Figure 9-15. Curves on the bottom side of hulls
or foils can create a downward force.

If the outer sections of the wing have dihedral that differs from the inner sections, the transition should be abrupt to avoid this bottom side curve effect. A good example of such a wing would be the F-4 Phantom. The underside of the Phantom's fuselage is also flat, and that avoids generating a downward force either in straight flight or in a yawed condition. Of course there are well-designed aircraft with rounded bottoms, but given a choice it may be better to keep the bottom flat to avoid unfavorable consequences.

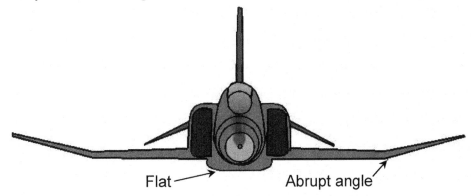

Flat   Abrupt angle

Figure 9-16. The bottom of a wing or a hull should
be flat or have an abrupt transition.

Let's revisit the foil with extreme dihedral or anhedral, say over 45 degrees. At some point of inclination, the foil will generate more side force that lifting force. A foil that is vertical and generates only side force with little or no lifting force is called a **rudder**.

Rudders are used to induce yawing; and, when coupled with a wing that has dihedral, they can be effective in roll control. Also, by exerting a side force well below the center of roll, the rudder alone will create roll torque.

The location of the rudder is important. A stern mounted rudder yaws the stern to the outside of an intended turn, and the keel creates a horizontal force to the inside of the intended turn, thereby initiating and sustaining the turn. A bow-mounted rudder leads the bow into the turn and the keel follows.

Because the rudder's force vector is horizontal and low, it has a relatively long lever arm working against the center of gravity. A stern mounted rudder, when deflected, will induce a rolling moment to the inside of the turn. This is a roll stabilizing effect. Most conventional boats work this way and that is why a typical boat tends to make balanced turns. See Figure 9-17a.

When a stern rudder deflects the stern to the left, the bow moves to the right, and the boat turns to the right. The more the boat turns to the left the more the rudder aligns with the oncoming flow. This is a self-correcting, non-self-augmenting action. It is like an arrow in normal flight.

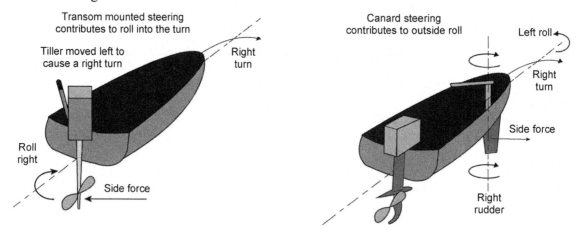

Figures 9-17a & b. Aft steering rolls into a
turn, bow steering rolls away from a turn.

However if a steering system uses a canard or bow-mounted rudder, it will create a rolling moment to the outside of the turn. This is because the boat "trips" over the bow-rudder creating centrifugal force and causing a roll to the outside of the yaw or turn. It is tempting to call this a destabilizing effect. In fact, the typical single-track hydrofoil uses this effect to create a righting moment.

In addition, the bow-mounted rudder has a tendency to *over steer*. The effect is rather like putting the feathers on the leading end of an arrow. The more the arrow yaws, the more the AOA of the forward feathers increases, and the more the destabilizing force increases. This is a self-augmenting feedback loop. Fortunately, in boats the effect is usually controllable, but the pilot should be aware of this tendency and apply front rudder control carefully.

Likewise if a pilot responds to adverse roll by using a bow rudder to yaw away from the roll, the problem will be exacerbated by the resulting centrifugal force. With a bow rudder, the pilot should turn into the roll (also called turning under the fall), and we will revisit this concept in chapter 10. The centrifugal force created will balance against gravity that is trying to pull the boat down to the inside of the roll. A boat designed to rely solely on its rudder for roll control will always be flying a zigzag path, as does a bicycle; but like a bicycle, the corrections might be nearly unperceivable.

Another consideration is the effect of the rudder on dihedral to cause banking in turns. The aft rudder, when initiating a turn, acts on the rear foil tip dihedral to push it sideways increasing the angle of attack on the outside tip and reducing it on the inside tip. This induces a bank to the inside of the turn. A rudder at the bow pushes the bow slightly to the right to create a right turn. The yaw effect on the dihedral of the rear foil is less pronounced.

On the other hand, if the rear-mounted rudder in a canard array is not located far enough behind the main foil and its big struts, there will be too small a lever arm between them (the main foil and its struts act together as a keel). Rather than creating yaw, the side force of the rudder will cause the main foil and strut to skid. The result could be ventilation of the rudder and/or the struts. The solution is to have the rudder sufficiently far behind the main struts, which act as a keel, so that the rudder can do its job of creating yaw. In this case, the front foil should have a strut designed to steer as well, or to easily skid so that it yields to yawing.

A similar example is Scott Smith's hydrofoil runabout manufactured in the 1950s by a prominent aerospace company. Its aft foil is connected to the transom with two parallel struts inclined rearward about 45° positioning the rear foils well aft of the transom. Forward, roughly equidistant between stem and stern, are a pair of large surface piercing front foils mounted at the gunnels. Both are fixed (do not steer). Turns are initiated by deflecting the thrust of the transom-mounted outboard motor. The motor is between the fore and aft sets of foils. The large front foils do not skid and therefore act together as a keel. But the motor's deflected thrust causes the rear foil to skid. As a result, thrust deflection does not create a distinct yawing moment. Scott reports that the boat turns poorly.

With Z drives and outboard motors, the thrust line is redirected from side to side to initiate a turn. If the thrust line (propeller) is lower than the center of lateral resistance, the tendency will be to bank toward the inside of the thrust-induced turn. If the thrust line is higher, the boat will bank toward the outside of the turn.

A design that integrates the characteristics of a rudder with those of a lifting foil would be the steerable inverted V foil. This is an example of extreme *anhedral*. An inverted V foil can create lift, while it controls direction, roll, and height. This combination is a height finding *bow* rudder. Notice in Figure 9-18b that the front foil offsets itself in a turn to balance roll torque forces and cause the rudder to track. We will discuss this geometry in the explanations of Figures 10-1, 10-2, and 10-3.

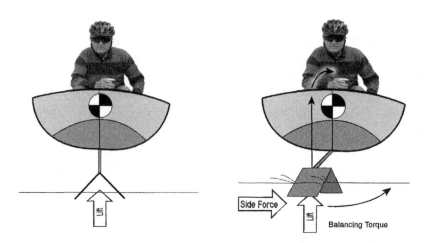

Figures 9-18a & b. A surface-piercing front foil can
be designed to lift, turn and induce banking.

The design shown in Figure 9-18 is not roll stable, but because it is unstable it can be very maneuverable. In the early 1970s the English Hi-Foil (Figure 10-4) used a similar configuration. Although the inverted V is a powerful roll control device, it depends completely on the pilot's quick and accurate input to maintain an even keel. I flew it once and learned the technique quickly—no problem. It was a thrill to fly and I have no idea why it was not a big commercial success.

From experiences with boats, a sailor might incorrectly believe that an aircraft is turned by its rudder, but its rudder is only used to initiate and correct yaw and to balance the turn. **The turning force is actually created by its wings**. To turn, the ailerons on each side are deflected in opposing directions, this creates a bank, and that inclines the lift vector in the same direction as the roll. When banked, the lift vector is a combination of vertical and horizontal forces. It is the horizontal vector that redirects the forward travel into a curved path, and that is how aircraft, as well as banking hydrofoils, make their turns. Figure 9-19 visualizes this concept.

Following the awkward attempts by the French aviation pioneers to make flat turns, aircraft have always been designed to bank toward the inside of a turn. The correct technique is to perform a *balanced* turn so that the perceived path of gravity passes perpendicularly through the plane, pilot, and crew. The pilot does not feel a side force during a balanced turn but he does perceive an increase in *G* force, the apparent gravity. One G is one force of gravity. During a balanced banked turn–or a perfectly executed barrel roll–gravity will combine with the centrifugal force generated by the turn. This is why your drink does not spill when your airliner turns toward its destination. The sum of these forces is expressed by the amount of Gs (gravities) felt by the pilot and crew. A balanced turn that requires a 45 degree angle of bank will experience a pull of 1.4 Gs. See Figure 9-19c. In a hydrofoil these fractional increases in Gs should not cause problems. A balanced turn is comfortable and causes less stress on the struts and crew.

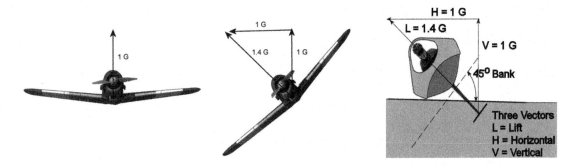

Figures 9-19a, b, & c. The forces in a turn are expressed
as **three vectors: lift, vertical, and horizontal.**

In a turning aircraft the vertical vector remains the same strength despite the inclination of the lift vector, but the lift vector increases. The increased portion of the lift vector is needed to counteract centrifugal force. If unchecked, a slight descent or slowdown will result. Normal pilot technique is to increase power and increase the angle of attack by pulling back slightly on the control stick. This increases the lift sufficiently to compensate for the extra horizontal force required.

This effect is slightly different in hydrofoils because there is little room to descend, so the lift must increase immediately to prevent the hull from settling to the surface. With submerged foils, as the foil sinks, the height sensor of the front foil increases the foil's angle of attack thereby increasing lift which stops the sinking. With surface-piercing foils the wetted area increases to augment the lift. In both cases, the rear foil responds by sinking slightly thereby increasing its AOA until lift and load are balanced. A turning aircraft has the option to recapture energy lost in a turn by descending or increasing power. A turning hydrofoil does not have the option to descend. It must increase power immediately or its speed will be reduced, causing the lift and the vertical force to decrease, and the hull to sink toward the surface.

This increase in power can be slight if the turn is mild. However, in a 45 degree banked turn, like the Yamaha OU32 is capable of making, the power increase will be significant. The additional power required is correlated to the angle of bank and the Gs created, not the speed. Setting aside more subtle effects, when Horiuchi's Yamaha OU32 and the high-speed F4 jet fighter turn with a 45° bank, they will pull the same Gs and will need about the same percent increase in power. The following table is from *Aerodynamics for Naval Aviators*:

Bank Angle	Apparent Gravity	Increase in Induced Drag & Power
0°	1.00 Gs	0%
15°	1.04 Gs	7%
30°	1.15 Gs	33%
45°	1.41 Gs	100%
60°	2.00 Gs	300%

Figure 9-20. Angle of bank determines pull of apparent
gravity (Gs), induced drag, and power required.

In chapter 5 the formula for calculating power, $P = (D * V)$, was introduced. A glance at this formula shows that power (P) is proportional to drag (D). Induced drag and lift drag are direct products of generating lift. Induced drag dominates in the realm of high C_Ls, slow speeds, and high angles of attack. Therefore the effect of increased drag and power required during a turn will be most significant at low speeds. Making sharp turns at low speeds is hazardous and risks increasing the drag until it overwhelms the power available. The result will be a slow-down and a settling to the surface. When this happens with Hifybe, it capsizes to the inside of the turn.

Surface proximity is another effect that can contribute to roll stability. The closer a foil is to the surface, the less its lift. When banking, the distance from the rising wing tip to the water's surface is diminishing and that will reduce the wing tip's lift. Likewise, the descending wing tip will increase its depth, the wing will become more efficient, and it will create greater lift. We have visited surface proximity early in the chapter 8, "Height and Pitch Management".

If the span is wide, the chord long, the water smooth, the speed low and the roll disturbance mild, the surface proximity effect may be adequate to correct most roll excursions. Only a human powered hydrofoil would meet these conditions. Unfortunately, this effect is only significant in depths of about one chord or less. So we may be talking about 3 or 4 inches below the surface for a small or fast hydrofoil.

Swept wings, like those in Figure 9-21, have an effect similar to dihedral. This is due to two conditions. The wing on the side of the direction of yaw will be in the shadow of its strut. The reduced water flow and the increased turbulence will reduce the lift on that side.

In addition, the path of the water over the two sides will be altered. The advancing wing will have a shortened effective chord and the retreating wing will have a longer effective chord. Because the thickness of the wing is constant, the thickness ratio–thickness divided by chord–is increased on the advancing side and reduced on the retreating side. This asymmetrically changes the lift. Lift is increased on the advancing wing and decreased on the receding wing. Max Feil on the web site of the *Universidade de Coimbra* states that "10 degrees of sweep has about the same stabilizing effect as one degree of dihedral".

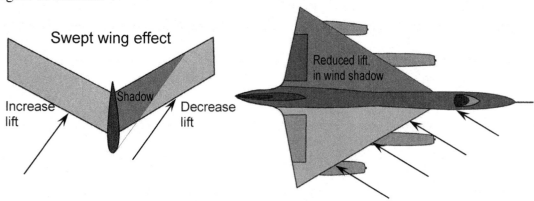

Figure 9-21. Yaw causes a shift of lift in a swept wing and delta wing.

Unfortunately, due to their geometry, all swept-back wings have narrower spans, and delta wings have a small proportion of their area at their wing tips. The wing tips have short lever arms and generate relatively small rolling moments. The handicap is greatest in single-track hydrofoils–those with two single struts, one following the other–where very little roll torque will be created. However, the handicap may have little impact because, as we will see in chapter 10, single track hydrofoils depend mostly on balance and not roll torque. In double track hydrofoils–those with foils mounted at the gunnels– no roll torque will be generated because lift will be lost equally on both outboard sides of the hull.

Longer **wingspans** increase the roll stability and slow down the rate of roll. Added span increases the torque lever and amplifies the effect of any roll control devices near the wing tips.

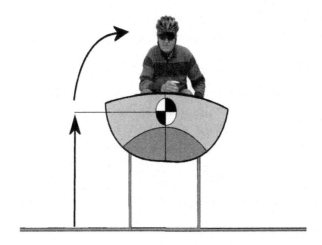

Figure 9-22. A wide, flat wing has a long roll lever arm.

Ailerons are lift altering devices commonly used to control roll.

Figures 9-23a, b, & c. Ailerons change the lift of a wing.

When deflected, the aileron changes the coefficient of lift. Ailerons are the most common device in use to control roll in aircraft. They work as well in hydrofoils.

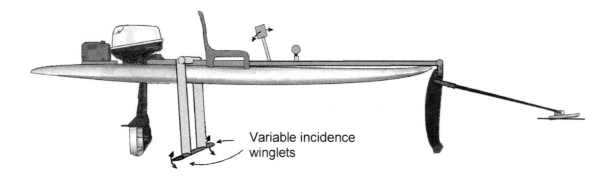

Figure 9-24. Variable incidence horizontal winglets,
or flippers, are mounted on Hifybe.

As mentioned in Figure 8-4 in our discussion about height and pitch management, Variable incidence horizontal winglets, **flippers,** are located at the wing tips and serve the same purpose as ailerons. Hifybe uses flippers for roll control. Although flippers are effective, they are structurally inferior to a wing with an aileron. The extended wing that the aileron is a part of is usually an integral part of the inboard wing, and the two can share the same spars and other structural components. The flipper rotates around an axle nested within the wing section. The diameter of the axle, and therefore its strength, is limited to the space available within the wing section.

Flippers also have the disadvantage of having a low aspect ratio. Because their lines do not smoothly transition with the higher AR center wing section, they operate as low AR separate wing sections. They are, therefore, less efficient than the main wing section.

Downward deflection of the trailing edge of an aileron or a flipper on one side of a wing will increase its coefficient of lift. Upward deflection of the aileron or flipper on the other side of the wing will decrease its coefficient of lift. This will cause the aircraft or hydrofoil to bank and is typically used to begin a turn or to balance roll forces after a turn is started by rudder deflection.

In aircraft, downward deflection of an aileron creates more drag than upward deflection, and so the high wing has more drag than the low wing. The result is *adverse yaw*, or yaw in the direction away from the turn. Pilots are trained to counteract adverse yaw by applying rudder into the turn to maintain balanced flight. Depending on the design, this could be a consideration in hydrofoils as well.

Visual feedback is provided to aircraft pilots by two special instruments collectively called a turn and bank indicator. The turn indicator is a gyroscope linked to a needle that is deflected whenever direction is changed. The bank indicator is a liquid filled tube shaped like the lips of a smiley face. The tube contains a free moving ball that shifts to one side or the other to indicate when a side force such as gravity or centrifugal force affects the ball.

However, an experienced pilot in a turn, slip, or slide can perceive an unbalanced condition. It feels like a shift of gravity to one side or the other. Reacting to these perceptions is called, *flying by the seat of the pants*. Unfortunately, when flying in clouds and out of sight of the horizon, the pants are easily fooled. Since flying in instrument flight conditions would not be expected of the recreational *hydrofoil* pilot, he should not need a turn and bank indicator.

If ailerons are too modern for you, try wing warp. **Wing warp** is just as effective today as it was for the Wright brothers. Their most famous airplane, the Wright Flyer, used this system. Because the wing must be flexible, its load bearing capacity will be limited. As a result, its use will generally be confined to lighter craft with light wing loading. Balancing the requirements for stiffness verses twistability will probably result in engineering compromises.

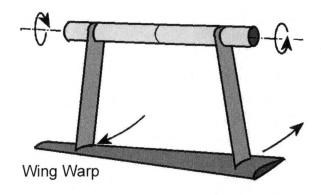

Figure 9-25. Wing warp used as a form of roll control.
This design is by Steve Ball.

Spoilers can be used to control roll. They are usually located on the top of the wing where most of the lift is created. They are deployed on the inside wing of an intended turn to increase lift and drag. Mechanical spoilers are relatively simple devices, as seen in Figure 9-26a.

Another device for spoiling lift involves injecting air through a line of holes along the topside of the hydrofoil wing, as shown in Figure 9-26b. This causes a separation of the fluid flow from the curved upper surface and destroys the orderly flow and/or the partial vacuum. In this way, lift is killed downstream from the air injection site.

Mechanical spoiler   Air spoiler

Figures 9-26a & b. Mechanical and air injection spoilers partially kill lift.

An advantage to spoilers is they do not cause adverse yaw. Unlike ailerons, spoilers are deployed only on one side, the descending side, and there is no corresponding increase in drag on the opposite side. The result is a favorable yaw toward the intended turn. However, because spoilers only kill lift and do not create lift, as ailerons do, there will be a net loss of lift over the entire wing. This is generally not a good thing, and the lost lift has to be replaced. To do this, power is increased along with angle of attack and/or speed.

The effectiveness of roll control utilizing either ailerons, wing warp, or spoilers may be increased by designing anhedral into the outer section of the wing. Anhedral increases the torque lever, so the lift altering devices can create greater roll torque. Remember, anhedral increases control but decreases stability. Dihedral can increase roll stability but decrease control.

The following chapter will cover some of the specialized ways of managing roll in hydrofoils.

Steering and Roll Management: Special Cases

o Single-track hydrofoils
o Turning under the fall
o Moment of inertia and pendulum period
o Caster effect, trail, and head angle
o Inclination of yaw axis
o Recumbent rider vs. an upright rider
o Sailboats are different
o Autopilots
o Surface-piercing foils
o Static roll stability when afloat
o Righting force

The last chapter dealt with the traditional ways of steering and roll management. This chapter will deal with some of the more inventive, advanced, or obscure devices created to deal with the problem. The first half of this chapter will deal with the theory of what keeps a bicycle upright. If your interest is in two or three track hydrofoils, you can skip this difficult concept. If your interest is in *single-track hydrofoils*, i.e., hydrofoils with only two struts that are in line, one fore and one aft, each with a single narrow foil, you may find the bicycle analogy to be helpful in your understanding.

It is easy to see that an array of three or four widely spaced variable lift hydrofoils could be effective in roll management. It is the same idea as the three legged milking stool or the 4-legged chair. But this chapter is mostly about **single-track hydrofoils**. All bicycles and some hydrofoils are single-track. Examples of this configuration are the Moth class hydrofoil sailboat, Dynafoil, Hi-Foil, and OU32. See Figures 10-3, 4, 5, and 6.

With this design, it is easy to initiate roll. The questions are, how is the roll stopped, and how do we return the craft to level flight? To answer this we will forget about airplanes for the moment and consider some other common items: bicycle, broom, and pendulum.

Bicycle riders may recognize the term **turning under the fall,** used to explain bicycle roll stability. When an ordinary bicycle leans to one side, the front wheel automatically repositions itself between the CG of the bicycle and the place where the bike is trying to fall. This is turning under the fall.

Because it is automatic and the bike does the work, the uninitiated can learn to cruise and turn a bike without knowing much about it. Even a child can do it. But there is still some mystery in the details.

Steering and Roll Management: Special Cases

So, adult reader, answer this question, "On a bicycle, to make a right hand turn which way does the rider rotate the handle bars?" Think carefully, my wife just now lost a million dollar bet to me on this very question. That paid off all the bad bets made with her over the last two years.

You get a gold star if you answered, "He turns the bars to the left to initiate a turn to the right". Any reader wagering on my wife's side has not tried this on a bicycle, like I did this morning before risking a million.

Do this: ride hands off. Reach down and gently push the right handlebar forward so that it rotates counterclockwise, to the left. Stop pushing as the bike begins a turn to the right and continues to turn to the right. It turns to the right because by steering to the left you displace the wheel to the left while the momentum of the bike and rider resists going there. The result is a fall to the right. The geometry of the bike then causes the wheel to respond and turn to the right in order to balance the turn. The turn creates centrifugal force and this is balanced against gravity that is trying to pull you down to the inside of the turn. The bike "turns under the fall", and places itself between you and the place where you *were* falling. You are now turning right and the turn was initiated by pushing the right hand bar to the left.

What your body learned on your first bike–and it is said that you never forget how to ride a bike–is that the more natural way to initiate a turn is by leaning into to it. Amazingly most people do not use their brains to learn how to turn a bike. The learning is more reflexive and visceral than it is mental, as if the bike does the thinking.

When the rider leans into the intended turn the bike falls toward the center of the turn, and this triggers the sequence of falling and turning under the fall as described above.

The effect is somewhat like balancing a broom vertically in your hand. The small end of the broom is nested in your upturned palm and as the broom displaces to one side you shift your hand laterally to get under the broom and stop the fall. A bicycle does this too when turning under the fall. It is a form of juggling.

Of course with bicycles, the spinning wheels create a gyroscopic effect but it is weak and does little to slow the rate of roll, so its absence in hydrofoil boats is not important.

This brings up two terms, **moment of inertia and pendulum period.** *Moment of Inertia* has to do with how clustered a body's weight is around its center of gravity. The more concentrated the weight is, the less resistance the body will have to accelerating its rotation. A common illustration used to demonstrate the effect of a changing moment of inertia is the spinning figure skater. The skater begins a slow spin with arms extended. As she raises her arms and brings them closer to the vertical axis of rotation, decreasing her own moment of inertia, the speed of the spin increases dramatically.

The effect of increasing the moment of inertia on a pendulum is to slow its *period*, the time it takes for the pendulum to swing from one extreme to another and then back again.

Those who own a grandfather clock know that adjusting the weight up or down its pendulum shaft changes its speed. The farther the weight is from the pivot the greater will be the pendulum's moment of inertia, and the slower its swing. The same applies to the inverted pendulum. Try balancing a pencil vertically in the palm of your hand–not easy. Now compare this with the balancing act you did with the broom with its heavy end up– easier. This is because the period of the pendulum is increased as the distance between the pivot, your palm; and the mass, the broom head, is increased.

I learned these principles firsthand when in 1981 my wife and I took delivery on a new 41' ketch that was delivered by ship to Rotterdam. The builders in Taiwan had lashed the two heavy masts flat on the cabin roof. We motored the yacht through the canals of Europe to the Mediterranean, and there was no problem while in protected waters. With the masts down we were able to pass under the many bridges along the way. However, during the few rough open water exposures that we had along the way, the ketch would roll quickly and sometimes dangerously.

Upon reaching the Bouch-du-Rhône, the gateway to the Mediterranean Sea, the heavy spruce masts were stepped. One might have speculated that elevating a great weight high above the hull would exacerbate roll and pitch problems. In fact, stepping the heavy masts increased the moment of inertia and that increased the pendulum period enough to make the yacht seaworthy.

This helps explain why sailboats that experience accidental loss of their masts at sea are often abandoned in favor of their life raft. The rolling of the damaged boat becomes too fast and goes too far to be tolerable.

In a hydrofoil the vertical separation between the center of lift and the center of gravity is proportionally high, much greater than in an aircraft, for example. The hydrofoil balances more like a broom than a pencil, whereas a maneuverable aircraft balances more like a pencil than a broom. Both systems take advantage of this difference. Aerobatic aircraft can bank quickly and execute snap rolls. The hydrofoil boat, with its center of gravity high above its supporting wings, exploits this long pendulum arm, because with the longer pendulum period the correctional forces are then quick enough to counteract the disturbing forces.

So we have established that to stay erect, a bike turns under the fall. To keep ahead of the fall, it must have a high moment of inertia resulting in a slow pendulum period, or rate of roll.

But in bikes this is all automatic. How do bikes and some hydrofoils automatically turn right when falling right and turn left when falling left? As comedian Nipsy Russell quipped when puzzling over how a vacuum bottle keeps cold things cold and warm things warm, "How do it know?" The answer is in their steering geometry.

The front wheel of a bicycle is statically and dynamically stable. It is in state of equilibrium when pointed straight ahead. Its tendency to return to the straight ahead position is called the **caster effect**. The caster effect increases with increased trail, see Figure 10-1. **Trail** is the distance between the point where the wheel contacts the road and the point where the head axis intersects the road. Trail is increased by increasing the **head angle**. The *head angle* of a *hydrofoil* is the number of degrees between *vertical* and the axis of the front fork's rotation. The head angle of a *bicycle* is the number of degrees between *horizontal* and the axis of the front fork's rotation. This book is about hydrofoils, so at risk of confusing bicycle engineers, I will use the hydrofoil convention. Most bicycles have a positive head angle of between 18° and 15° (72° and 75° in bike-speak). Curving the forks forward to create the common J-shape also changes trail. The primary purpose for curving the forks is to allow the forks to flex when riding over rough terrain. Increasing the J curve increases the *rake*, and decreases the trail.

Figure 10-1c illustrates why more trail results in a stronger caster effect, i.e., a greater tendency for the front wheel to return to pointing straight ahead after being displaced. If we take the perspective of the bicycle rolling toward us, we can see opposing forces at work. The bike leans to its left, the road supports the wheel at a point to the right of the bike's CG, and the mass of the bike presses down on the wheel ahead and to the left of the point of road contact. The two forces combine to cause the wheel to turn to the left, into the turn. That is how a bike steers toward the lean and thereby creates a turn. But how does this relate to the steerable canard foil of a hydrofoil?

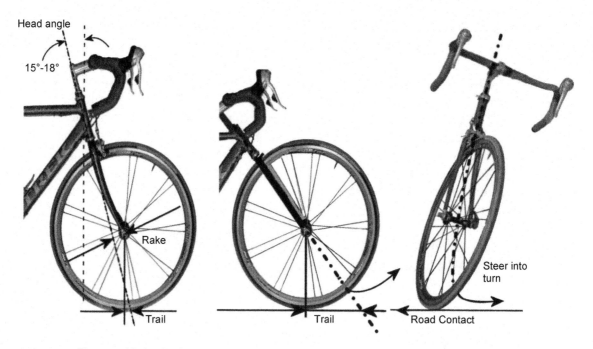

Figures 10-1a, b, & c. The caster effect in bicycles is in proportion to the trail.

Each of our four examples of single-track hydrofoils, Figures 10-3, 4, and 6 have different roll control systems, but they have one thing in common. They all have positive head angles. From measurements taken from available drawings the head angles are as follows: Hifybe = 17°; Horiuchi boats = 17° to 19°; Dynafoil = 23°; Hi-Foil = 18°.

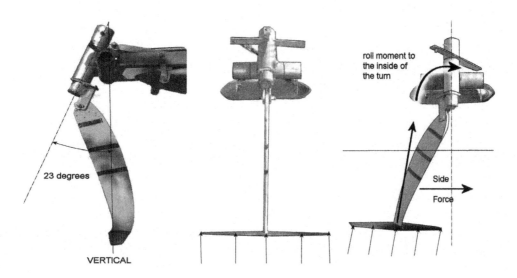

Figures 10-2a, b, & c. Hifybe steering geometry.

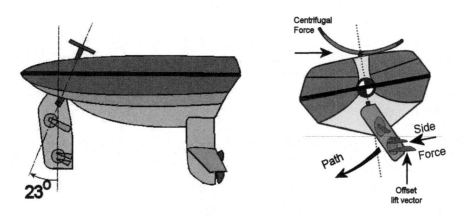

Figures 10-3a & b. Dynafoil steering geometry

Figure 10-4. Hi-Foil, showing an inverted V foil mounted near the bow.

All vehicles that bank when turning, including airplanes, bicycles and single track hydrofoils have something in common: *redirected lift* is the force that powers the vehicle's change in direction. The wings, not rudders or struts create the turning force, and there is little or no side force exerted on the vertical components.

These vehicles bank toward the inside of a turn, and this causes the lift vector to incline. The inclined lift vector can be divided into two component vectors: the vertical vector opposing gravity and a horizontal vector counteracting centrifugal force. The drawings in Figures 9-19b and c shows these vectors. The horizontal vector is the turning force.

Bicycles and single track hydrofoils have up-front steering (Hydrofoil Moths are an exception). Typically the forward steering *tracks,* that is, it automatically points in the direction of travel. To understand how the front foil tracks, see Figure10-3a, and read the following, paraphrased from Cline's Dynafoil patent: The area of the front strut located behind the steering axis is greater than the portion located ahead of it, and since the front strut is free to rotate, the resisting force of the water tends to cause the strut to rotate in the direction of the turn. Some boats, like the Dynafoil, slightly *over-track*, that is, when the boat leans (as in a turn) the boats steers more than enough to track the turn. Over-tracking generates a small surplus of centrifugal force, and the boat tends to right itself.

The corrective force applied is *turning under the fall*. Centrifugal force is the primary righting force pulling away from the lean, and it is opposed by the pull of gravity attempting to increase the lean. To function, the moment of inertial must be large enough and the pendulum period long enough to allow the corrective forces to be quicker than the disturbing forces.

The bicycle, Dynafoil, Hi-Foil, and the OU32 rely on the rider to initiate a turns by momentarily steering away from the intended turn. This causes the foil to shift to the outside thereby initiating a lean into the turn. After the turn is started, powerful centrifugal and gravitational forces are balanced to control roll.

To an aviator, it seems natural that a single track hydrofoil should have ailerons, just like airplanes. Indeed, Hifybe depends on ailerons for roll control. Likewise, when David Cline applied for his Dynafoil patent the drawings showed ailerons on the main foil, but sometime prior to mass production the ailerons went the way of our ancestor's pendulous tails. This could be survival of the fittest, but then again, he may have concluded that if ailerons are not necessary, why suffer the complications.

An airplane has a low CG and to make it bank, powerful ailerons near the wingtips are necessary. A hydrofoil has a high CG and falls to one side or the other naturally and without any control input. The great separation between the CG and the lateral center of effort of the rudder creates a significant lever arm making its side force effective in controlling roll. So, the rudder in a hydrofoil can perform the work done by ailerons in an airplane.

What's it like to fly a Dynafoil? We have the testimony of Scott Smith, who has logged more hours on his than it took Captain Ahab to track down Moby Dick.

Scott says: When foil-borne in a relatively straight line or gentle curve, the Dynafoil handles just like a bicycle, for all the same reasons. You counter-steer to initiate a turn. If you start to lean slightly the front strut (rudder) will caster like a bike, but to carve a turn the lift of the front foil must be increased, and this is part of the job of the height finding front foil. The larger rear foil follows the front in creating more lift. The increased lift, and the horizontal component of the increased lift, powers the turn and counteracts centrifugal force. If the rider could roll without increasing the lift, the boat would not turn. The rudder's side force affects the *leaning* of the Dynafoil but does not create the powerful vector needed to carve a turn.

He continues: To turn sharper you must act more aggressively. You forcefully counter-steer to lean the boat so hard into the turn that the gunnel drags in the water; see the photo below. The maneuver is counter intuitive, if it were a motorcycle it would crash. The Dynafoil has that big rear wing, now nearly perpendicular to the surface, giving it plenty of traction. It is easy and safe; but the first few times you try, it seems really wrong. In a sharp turn, with the hull dragging, the propeller drives a circle around the hull to make the turn. The rear foil prevents the hull from excessive slipping to the outside of the turn. The drag of the hull along the inside of the turn, coupled to the thrust of the prop along the outside of the turn, does most of the work. Notice in the picture (below) I'm turning hard, but the rudder is almost straight.

Figure 10-5. Scott Smith making a sharp turn with his
Dynafoil. Notice the front strut is only slightly turned.

As Scott has observed, propeller driven hydrofoils, like the Dynafoil, have an additional force that creates a strong turning force. The propeller must remain submerged and is therefore always lower than the CG. Particularly in a highly banked turn, the curved thrust line will be outside the curved path of the CG. Furthermore, if the hull contacts the surface, it will act as a fulcrum to the force of thrust. This causes a rotational force around the hull and CG that augments the tendency of the foils to carve a curved path. The OU32 with its highly placed water-jet thrust does not have this advantage. To compensate, the OU32 links the handlebars to the front foil so that the pilot pulls back to increase the AOA of the front foil. The increase in AOA generates more lift and this provides for the horizontal force necessary to counteract centrifugal force and power through the turn.

In delicately balanced machines such as the Horiuchi designed Yamahas OU27 and OU32, Figures 10-6a and b, this inclination of the roll axis requires special design adaptations. The OU27 and OU32 have narrow foils and single struts, one positioned fore and one aft. It has no ailerons and it controls roll like a bicycle by *steering under the fall*. If the boat falls (rolls) to the right, the pilot corrects by displacing the front foil to the right to "scoot" under the fall, thereby creating a corrective centrifugal force to the outside of the turn. By altering the relative wing loading, thereby changing the inclination of the roll axis, Horiuchi was able to create the right mix of yaw and roll control. Figures 10-7a and b illustrate the tilting of the roll axis and its relationship to differential wing loading.

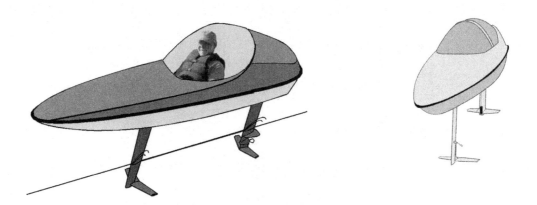

Figures 10-6a & b. Artist's conception of an early Horiuchi-Yamaha boat, OU27, and the two-place, water-jet powered OU32.

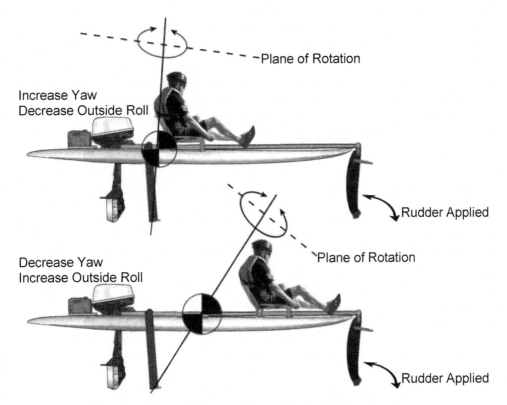

Figures 10-7a & b. Changing the CG location
changes the inclination of the yaw axis.

Horiuchi's two-place Yamaha OU32 evolved from a smaller one-place boat of similar appearance called the OU27. As he explains in his excellent book, *Locus of a Boat Designer*, the OU27 made turns that were coordinated with bank, however the longer, heavier OU32 rolled to the outside of a turn with embarrassing results.

After some sleepless nights, his thoughts focused on weight distribution. The new boat's center of gravity had been moved farther ahead of the rear foil. Remember, the yaw axis passes between the submerged center of resistance and through the much higher center of gravity. If one were above the other, the axis would be vertical. Advancing the CG caused a forward **inclination of the yaw axis** so that by yawing-steering with the front strut, the boat rolled to the outside of the turn. To counteract the excessive outside roll, he coupled the rear and front strut so that to turn right, the rear motor strut rotated left at 25% of the right rotation of the front strut. He states that had the CG not been moved forward, the rear steering could have been avoided.

As you recall from material covered earlier in the text and illustrations of Figure 9-17, when yawing is induced by a bow rudder, the boat "trips" over the it and rolls to the *outside* of the turn. However, a rudder located conventionally aft of the CG creates horizontal vectors that cause a roll to the *inside* of the turn. In the OU32, too much outside roll created by the bow rudder had to be offset by a 25% steering contribution from the aft rudder. It was necessary for him to find the correct proportions of outside and inside rudder induced rolling moments before his boat could perform a *balanced* turn.

In my way of thinking, a path to finding the correct proportional steering in a prototype would be to create a dockside adjustment for altering the fore and aft steering ratio.

It should be apparent from this discussion that single-track vehicles (including hydrofoils) that steer by the stern will not have positive roll control coupled to its steering. Most kids who try to ride a bike backwards will testify that a backward moving bicycle cannot be ridden (stunt bikes excepted).

To illustrate: When the backward moving bike leans to the right the caster effect causes the wheel to steer left toward the outside of the turn and the rear wheel "scoots" to the outside, away from the fall. The rear wheel yields to centrifugal force just when corrective centrifugal force is needed. Without centrifugal force, the bike uncontrollably falls to the inside of the turn. It is the same with a single-track aft steering hydrofoil.

Early on in boat testing, our California human powered boat group had to answer a related question. For roll management, is it better to have the **rider in a low recumbent, or a high upright position?**

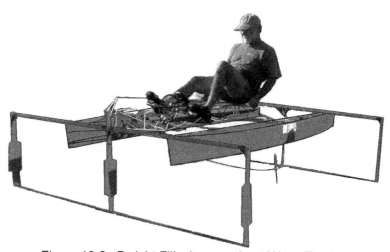

Figure 10-8. Dwight Filley's recumbent Wave Evader.

One might guess that the recumbent is the best, but the advantage of the lower center of gravity is offset by the disadvantage of a lower momentum of inertia. The upright position increases the moment of inertia and it therefore slows down the pendulum period. This gives the pilot more time to correct for roll problems. However, increasing the height of the center of gravity over a base of a fixed width decreases the maximum roll angle before the tipping point is reached. See the falling Tower of Pisa, Figure 10-13. Also the shift in C.G. is greater for a given amount of pitch. See Figure 8-22 for an illustration.

As a result, our group never arrived at a solid conclusion based solely on roll management, but the upright position was chosen because of the comfort and increased pedal endurance. When upright, the weight of the rider could be applied to the pedal. In the recumbent position the rider must wedge himself against the seat back to apply force to the pedals. Also, the upright position is more comfortable (because the rider is using gravity not the seat-back to provide resistance to his intense pedal force), the rider has more mobility allowing better balance, and he can generate power for a longer period. We speculated that this is due to better blood circulation.

Nonetheless, the confusion over how high the CG should be might be best cleared up by dividing the boats into two classes: a *wide class* that depends on a wide footprint to resist tipping, like a catamaran or trimarans or any boat that has hydrofoils on three or four corners. These boats benefit from a low CG. With a low CG the boat must be tipped very far to pass the *tipping point* (recall the falling tower analogy). This is a stationary type of stability that is as effective at rest as it is underway.

Narrow class, would be the other. These boats, and bikes, rely on balance and turning under the fall to stay upright. They benefit from a high CG to increase the moment of inertia and lengthen the pendulum effect to allow a slower reaction time. Any single track hydrofoil would be in the narrow class. Examples are the Dynafoil, Hi-Foil, and OU32. This mobile type of stability is only possible while the vehicle is underway.

If it is determined that the moment of inertia should be increased, it can be done by distributing the other heavy elements of the boat, besides the rider, away from the center of gravity. Of course, increasing the mass would also increase the moment of inertia, but in flying machines it is important to minimize weight.

Correctly recognizing the *proper axis* of the moment of inertial is important. Distributing weight to the outriggers will do nothing to slow the boat's pitch rate, and moving weight fore or aft will do nothing to reduce the rate of roll.

Other ways of slowing down the rate of roll in a hydrofoil are to increase the wingspan and/or redistribute more wing area near the outboard tips.

Mae West observed, "Too much of a good thing can be wonderful", but what did she know about hydrofoils? It is possible to design a boat that banks too much. In this case too much of a good thing is not wonderful. We built a human powered boat that tended to capsize into the inside of a turn. To compensate, prior to turning, the pilot would lean the boat to the outside of the intended turn. The turn had to be completed before the boat rolled uncontrollably to the inside. This particular boat was designed to use the rudder to make flat turns, but when turns were initiated, the widely spaced outer tips accelerated and traveled farther and faster than the inner tips. In addition, its modest dihedral was too effective. The combination resulted in enough roll moment to the inside of the turn to overcome centrifugal force and cause the boat to capsize to the inside. To balance this design, we had to cut back on the "good things" like dihedral, wide span and generous wing tip chord. One could speculate that if Horiuchi's Yamaha OU32 used only aft rudder it would have suffered the opposite problem and rolled excessively to the inside.

Sailboats are different. The wind working on the sails creates an imbalance of the roll forces. The *center of effort* of a sail is that point where the average of all wind forces is balanced. In general, stronger, steadier winds are found when the sails are high above the surface, and high aspect ratio sails are more efficient. That is why tall and narrow sails are favored in fast boats. A high center of effort working against the lower center of resistance creates a long lever arm. The result is a lot of roll torque–especially when sailing either on a reach or a close haul.

Most successful hydrofoil sailboats use the conventional airplane array of foils. To balance against the roll torque, sailboats often have a very wide foil system, and they split the largest foil in two parts with each part attached at the gunnels. The large foil(s) need to be positioned forward of the center of gravity to prevent pitchpoling when sailing downwind. This places the lift at the extremes of a three-point array, the third point being the rudder and inverted "T" foil combination at the transom.

When a wide boat, such as a catamaran or trimaran, has two large front foils mounted wide apart and ahead of the CG, both sides will need independent height finding devices. These devices usually control roll as well as height. When one side is depressed the lift will increase, and the boat will return to a level roll condition. When one side is elevated the lift on that side will decrease and will settle toward an even keel. A unique advantage of widespread submerged hydrofoils on a sailboat is that the rising windward foil can be used to exert a downward force. This downward force would otherwise be provided by ballasting the upwind outrigger. So the foil's down-force permits a reduction in weight. An example of a boat using this system is the Windrider Rave. On the other hand, the record setting French Hydroptère has surface piercing foils and can be seen flying with 5 or more crew members hiking on the windward outrigger acting as ballast to provide the required downward force.

Not all hydrofoil sailboats depend on a wide array for roll stability. One notable exception is the well-established class of Moth sailboats. A fast growing number of these lightweight and narrow racing boats are being fitted with hydrofoils. In the common configuration, the Moth balances on two inverted "T" foils. The forward foil strut is mounted in the centerboard slot and the aft foil strut replaces the rudder at or slightly behind the transom. The front foil has flaps, but no ailerons. A height-finding wand hinged off the bow actuates the forward flap, and the aft foil's AOA is trimmed by turning the tiller extension. Roll control consists of changing the tipping force by pulling or releasing the mainsail sheet, or turning into or off the wind. In addition, the one-man crew scrambles about to adjust the center of gravity. Shifting the center of gravity not only helps control roll, but shifting back will increase the angle of attack of both foils, and make the boat fly higher. You have to see it to believe it, so do a Google or YouTube search on the web for Moth videos. See chapter 18 for details on designing a Moth.

Figure 10-9. The French speed record setting
Hydroptère. Notice the sailors on the ama.

Our final device to manage roll in submerged foils is the **autopilot**. Although it is outside the scope of this book to fully describe how to design and build one, it is possible to briefly suggest how these remarkable devices function. For our example, we will use Harry Larsen's Talaria IV. You may recall this is a 24-foot Bayliner retrofitted with hydrofoils.

On the Talaria IV, the front foil has a mechanical surface follower that senses flying height and responds by changing the angle of attack of the front foil. The rear foil has ailerons– deflected by hydraulic pistons–that control the roll, electronic solenoids respond to signals from the autopilot to control fluid flow to the hydraulic pistons.

Figure 10-10 shows banking and the associated autopilot controls. The illustrations are what the autopilot commands: (a) This is a balanced turn—no correction needed. (b) The boat is level and turning to the left. The ailerons begin to cause a bank to the left to produce a balanced turn. (c) The boat is going straight but some disturbance has caused a roll to the left. The ailerons begin to cause a corrective roll to the right.

Figures 10-10a, b, & c. Three conditions of
turn and bank corrected by the autopilot.

For a visual aid on how the Navy's PHM fleet's dealt with the challenge of stability and control, observe the following diagram:

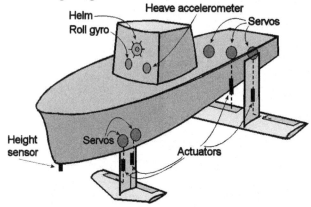

Figure 10-11. This is a schematic for a three-axis autopilot for a military hydrofoil.
It is inspired by a sketch in *Twenty Foilborne Years* by Ellsworth.

For very lightweight hydrofoils, it may be possible to design a simplified system by eliminating the hydraulics. Today, small, inexpensive solid-state gyroscopes and tilt sensors are available. Solid-state amplifiers can provide adequate power to servos and stepper motors that actuate control surfaces. Some work has been done adapting model helicopter control systems to scale model hydrofoils and these systems might be modified to be used in light weight human-carrying hydrofoils. For more ideas go to the bibliography to find: "Control Systems for International Moth on Hydrofoils", by Chris Miller.

Of course, there is not enough information here to start building an autopilot, but the reader can see that it has been done (without the backing of a national budget) and that technology is available to those who dare to adapt it to hydrofoil control.

Most of the principles of roll management shown in this chapter are relevant to the **surface-piercing foil** as well as the submerged foil. Surface piercing foils that are located at the gunnels will increase their wetted area on the descending side and decrease the wetted area on the ascending side. With correct geometry, this can produce a powerful righting moment. See Figures 9-14 and 10-12.

Figures 10-12a & b. Surface piercing dihedral and anhedral.

Notice that the two illustrations in Figures 10-12a and b are drawn with a wide array. Obviously, both these designs are intended to make flat turns. Steeply banked turns are impossible because to turn in such a way would deeply bury the inside foil and un-wet the outside foil. Hydroptère is a good example of a wide array surface-piercing hydrofoil. See Figure 10-9.

A hydrofoil needs to have **static roll stability when afloat** as well as when flying. Hull stability requires a little explanation. We all know that structures having wide bases and narrow tops are stable; consider the pyramids or the Eiffel tower. Generally a structure with low center of gravity and a wide base will have high static roll stability. Tall narrow structures are less stable. When leaning, a tall thin structure will have a greater lever arm that will encourage bending in the direction of the lean. Additionally, a tall thin structure, like the Tower of Pisa in Figures 10-13a and b, will reach its tipping point with fewer degrees of horizontal displacement than will a short fat structure. The tipping point is reached when the vertical line drawn through the center of gravity falls outside the supporting base.

Leaning   Falling

Figures 10-13a & b. The leaning and the falling Tower of Pisa.

Catamarans and other wide beamed boats serve as good examples of vessels with good static roll stability. They demonstrate that hydrofoils set widely apart will generally have more static roll stability than narrow foil systems, under flat water conditions. However, when these boats reach their tipping point, they capsize. Furthermore, because they ride flat on the surface, they are uncomfortable or even dangerous in steep seas. A catamaran sailing on a wave face will conform to the angle of the wave face, and if it tilts past its tipping point it will capsize and cannot recover.

This analogy to land based structures is incomplete when applied to waterborne hulls where there is no inflexible support to define the tipping point. In particular, mono-hulls follow a different set of rules for static roll stability. Narrow sailboats are capable of recovering from heeling angles of 90° or more. Ships operate in a relatively narrow range of inclination, but it is amazing how a cruise ship with a towering superstructure or a cargo ship with a mountain of heavy containers can remain upright in storm ravaged seas.

Calculation of these righting forces is complicated. It took naval architects over 2,000 years to figure out the calculus. According to Wikipedia, "the concept was not introduced formally into naval architecture until about 1970." If naval architects avoided doing the math for so long we can probably avoid it ourselves, but understanding the concept is important.

The force that puts a boat on an even keel is called a **righting force** (GZ), and it is similar in concept to the *torque lever* introduced in Figure 9-7a. When a boat is at rest, the center of buoyancy (CB) and the center of gravity (CG) are in vertical alignment as illustrated in 10-14a. Any heeling of a stable hull will cause a shift in the CB in the direction of the heeling. The CG is fixed, as long as the cargo does not shift. Figure 10-14b shows the creation of the righting force. It is the horizontal distance between the CG and a line drawn vertically through the (shifted) CB. The longer the horizontal line, the greater the righting force.

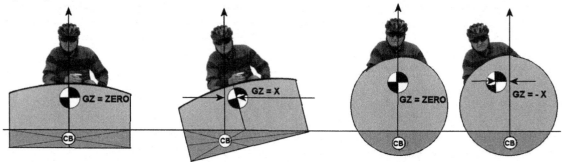

Figures 10-14a, b, c, & d. A shift in the center of buoyancy creates a righting force.

The most stable hulls have hard chines and steep sides, causing the CB to shift significantly as the boat heels. Of course, widening a flat bottom hull will increase the distance the CB shifts with heeling. Ironically, a wide box passes the high tech stability test. The least stable hulls are narrow and rounded on the bottom, like a tube. When heeling, the round bottom does not shift the CB, the CG shifts to the side, and no righting force is created. See Figures 10-14c and d.

Also a lowering the CG will increase static roll stability. Sailboats with rounded hulls compensate by having heavy keels submerged deep below their hulls. Hydrofoil boats have the advantage of carrying the foil's weight well below the hull thereby lowering the CG. This contributes to roll stability afloat.

Today's ship's designers use powerful calculus to determine the CG, center of buoyancy, metacenter, metacentric height, maximum angle of roll, water line location, and so on. This takes a lot of time using powerful computers and is outside the scope of this book. However, when a ship is launched all these things are instantly recalculated–by the water. This is another example of man being dumber than water.

Should the task of roll stability and control be assigned to the front foil, the rear, or to both? The job of managing roll will usually go to the foil with the most *roll authority*, and that would be the widest, largest foil. Usually this foil carries the most weight. For example, in a canard system that has a rear foil designed to support 85% of the total weight, the job of roll management would naturally go to the rear foil. In this example, the rear foil would be about six times bigger and much wider than the front foil. It would be the master of about six times the forces of the small front foil. Only the big foil would have the necessary authority to manage roll.

If the largest foil is forward of the CG, in addition to creating the majority of lift and managing roll, it will be required to manage flying height (the front foil always manages flying height). This rather complicates its design, because the front foil will have three important tasks while the smaller rear foil will manage only pitch. (Remember, pitch is controlled by the rear foil rotating, or weathervaning, around the height set by the front foil).

The large commercial surface piercing hydrofoils such as the Italian Rodriquez, Figure 1-2, the Swiss Supramar and the Russian Meteor (the three resemble each other), carry a high proportion of weight forward. This requires the largest foil to be located forward of the center of gravity. However, each of these three examples use surface piercing foils, which manage both height and roll in a simpler, cheaper fashion than the more sophisticated submerged foils. As previously discussed, sailboats also have a need to locate the big foil in front to prevent pitchpoling. In this case, the large front foils do all the heavy lifting as well as manage roll *and* height.

So what's the problem with using the big foil to manage flying height? To do a proper job, the height finding foil is tuned for height finding and efficiency becomes a secondary consideration. This results in an inefficient main foil and a less efficient boat in general. Refer to the bibliography to find the studies on the development of Canadian Bras d'Or. The Canadians concluded that the canard configuration is preferred.

If the system is balanced with roughly half the weight supported by each foil, fore and aft, it is possible that neither foil will have sufficient authority to do the job alone. In this case, it may be necessary to divide roll management between the two. Boats have been designed with height managing devices on all four corners.

In this chapter we talked about how some hydrofoils make banked, balanced turns by slanting the lift vector toward the inside of the intended turn. We also discussed how some hydrofoils make flat turns. In flat turns the wing generates only a vertical lift vector, and little or no side vector. When these boats turn, the struts, and-or propeller thrust, generate the necessary hydrodynamic sideways force. They act as rudder and keel. When struts are used in this way, they need more lateral strength, and to create horizontal vectors to turn in either direction, the cross section should be that of a symmetrical hydrofoil, like the NACA 0012. While foil-borne, they will need adequate wetted area. The shorter the wetted area, the more likely the struts are to skid and ventilate. In turns, dihedral foils will also develop sideways forces. This side load will be transferred to the struts and adequate lateral strength must be provided.

Hopefully, this detailed examination of dihedral and other ways of managing roll has not become tedious, but often attention to detail can prevent or solve the mystery of unexpected results. Sometimes despite the best efforts of a designer, the correctional forces will be too strong or too feeble. To adjust, it is necessary to know something about all the forces at work. The math and charts provided will help you to quantify and make comparisons about the effectiveness of the indicated changes.

Trouble shooting. Go to the checklist in chapter 19 for a review of steering and roll conditions that can yield unexpected results.

Materials, Stress Calculations, and Fabrication

- o Characteristics of materials
- o Aluminum, TIG, MIG, temper
- o Stainless steel, CRP, FRP, wood
- o Structural analysis
- o Sectional modulus defined and calculated
- o Irregular shape of profile
- o Main foil stress
- o Determine sectional modulus
- o Cantilevered winglet rod stress
- o Safety factor and operational limitation
- o Hollow box factor
- o Construction: wood, CRP, or FRP
- o Female mold, computerized milling machine
- o Ogival profile and leading edge radius

So far we have examined the various types of hydrofoils and the key decisions that go into a design. The next topic is the material and the fabrication methods to be used in building the boat.

For most of our construction we will chose materials that are corrosion resistant, lightweight, strong, rigid, affordable and obtainable. The materials must be workable with the available tools.

We can quickly narrow the list to these common boat materials: carbon fiber reinforced plastic–commonly epoxy (CRP), fiberglass reinforced plastic–typically polyester (FRP), aluminum, stainless steel, and wood.

The characteristics of the selected materials will be examined, and then we can consider where they are appropriately used. All of these materials are somewhat corrosion and electrolysis resistant in fresh and salt water. Some aluminum alloys are more susceptible but others are very resistant. Resistance to salt water corrosion is better controlled by the 5000 series, but of all the aluminum alloys, 6061 is perhaps the most common and best understood by the typical fabricator. Wood can be prone to water absorption, swelling and rotting. The approximate engineering qualities–strength, rigidity and density–can be compared in table form:

Material	Yield strength, psi	Ridigidity, Young's Modulus	Density, lbs / ft^3	YS / density, strength / lb
CRP	117,000	21,800,000	322	364
FRP	90, 000	7,000,000	369	244
Aluminum 6061 T6	39, 000	10,000,000	567	69
Aluminum 6061 T1	7,000	Low	567	12
Stainless steel	75,000	30,000,000	1,610	47
Wood, oak	600	1,600,000	141	4

Figure 11-1. Key mechanical properties of useable materials.

Aluminum, compared to steel, is somewhat corrosion resistant, light, strong, and is commercially available. However, welding this metal requires special skill and equipment. The weld is especially sensitive to any impurities in the melt, including aluminum oxide. Aluminum combines with oxygen slowly at room temperature, but at welding temperatures its surface oxidizes quickly. To weld this metal, the melt must be shielded from oxygen in the air. The most effective technique is to envelop the weld in an inert gas, typically argon. There are two types of welders capable of doing this. They are called Tungsten Inert Gas, *TIG*, and Metal Inert Gas, *MIG*.

Of the two, **TIG** is the most versatile but most expensive. The process is also called Gas Tungsten Arc or Heli-arc welding. I happen to have a TIG welder and enjoy the challenge of using it. Pre-heating is an example of a special technique sometimes required. Because aluminum is such an excellent conductor of heat, the temperature of large pieces must elevated so that the cold mass does not draw heat from the part being welded. For this, my wife has unwittingly contributed the family gas BBQ. Pieces up to 3 feet long are heated quickly at the same setting as used for lamb chops. The material is ready for welding when spit boils on its surface.

MIG welders, sometimes called GMAW (Gas Metal Arc Welding), feed an aluminum wire through a gas nozzle. The wire acts as an electrode and continuously feeds into the work. Because of the continuous feed, these welders are often the fastest. Generally, MIG welders are less expensive than TIG but may have less versatility.

Flux encased aluminum welding rods can be used with non-gas arc welders, but not with just any non-gas arc welder. The rod and the welder must be matched. This is the most limited method, and it will not weld some alloys of aluminum. It is the least expensive.

With aluminum, it is difficult to maintain the desired level of **temper** (hardness and yield-tensile strength) during welding. For example, one of the most commonly available aluminum alloys is 6061 T6. The T6 indicates the temper, with larger numbers indicating the harder, stiffer materials. Bringing this alloy to welding temperature reduces the temper almost to T1. As Figure 11-1 shows, T1 has a tensile strength of only 7,000 psi, compared to 39,000 psi for T6. That is an 80% loss of tensile strength.

There are two ways to correct this problem. Age tempering is best done while your wife is visiting distant relatives. The welded material is heated to 350 degrees and allowed to remain there for 8 to 10 hours to recover about 70% of the original hardness. It is obvious to any man the best place to do this is in the kitchen oven. Unfortunately not all genders see it this way. The second solution is to use another aluminum alloy. The 5,000 series would be more suitable because it is less prone to de-tempering. (See www.engineersedge.com).

Stainless steel is stronger than aluminum, but weighs more for a given size. However, from the table it can be seen that tensile strength *per pound* is only about 1/3 less than 6061 T6 aluminum but is stronger than T1. If the size and thickness of the assembly can be kept down, stainless steel can be used to make strong and lightweight parts. The good news is that it is much easier to weld than aluminum. A simple "buzz box" welder will serve, assuming one uses the appropriate welding rods. Because the material does not conduct heat like aluminum, stainless steel can be welded at lower power settings, perhaps allowing the use of a smaller, cheaper welder. Take care when welding long thin pieces, e.g., sheet metal. These have a tendency to warp when heated in one location. The solution is to tack weld the pieces in several separated places to form a stiff assembly before concentrating the heat to make longer welds.

Another art form involves molding of cold-setting reinforced plastics such as carbon fiber reinforced plastic–epoxy (**CRP**). This high tech product was developed in the 1960s by aerospace gurus. A glance at the table will show why this is the champion of materials for making foils and struts. It is lightweight, extremely strong and stiff. It has more strength per pound than any other material shown. It does not corrode and it can be formed with common hand tools. If you are rocketing to the moon and cost is not a problem, choose CRP. Otherwise, you might be forced to visit its older cousin, fiberglass-reinforced plastic–polyester (**FRP**).

Fiberglass is also a wonder product, but it is not as strong and it is about one third as stiff as carbon fiber. The polyester resin has less bonding strength than epoxy resin. FRP does, however, cost much less than carbon fiber epoxy.

For molded parts, depending on the design, the higher priced CRP may or may not be required. Long and thin foils may require the strength and stiffness of the better material, whatever the cost. Another idea comes from Scott Smith who has experience in constructing supersonic rocket wings milled from G-10/FR-4 fiberglass billets. This *is* rocket science. Doing the stress calculations in this chapter will help guide you to make the proper choice.

The final material is **wood**. This versatile substance can be used for thick foils and struts were the spans are not too great. Wood is readily available and easy to work with. On the other hand, it absorbs water, swells, and rots. It is also more difficult to form joints compared to materials that are molded or welded. Some builders have success hand forming wood and covering it with FRP. The joints are made reasonably strong with screws inside and FRP outside. The joints are bulkier this way, but good streamlining practices dictate fairing at the joints anyway. Of all materials, wood smells the best.

Materials, Stress Calculations, and Fabrication

An obvious way to choose and size the materials for constructing components is to build it, fly it, and see if it breaks. Another way is to use a sample of the sized material, attach it to something fixed and apply a load—until it bends or breaks. Or a builder could duplicate a successful existing design. It is also possible to *calculate* when it will bend or break. This is not easy and may take some time. So why not simply build it and break it? You may find that hours of calculations can be saved by just a few months of building and testing.

Careers are built on the science of **structural analysis**, and to do precise and complete structural calculations is beyond the limits of this book. However, rough figuring can help avoid some gross errors in dimensioning or selecting materials. With a few simplified equations, one can get a working idea about how specific material will perform. Card carrying engineers and mathematicians may choose to skip this part. Obviously a professional stress analysis would be better, if available. Certainly be cautious and don't use these methods on anything that flies high, is really fast, or has paying passengers.

The equations of Figures 11-2 and 11-3 show the maximum stress on the load carrying materials *outer fibers*, of the middle and cantilevered sections of a foil supported by two struts. We are assuming that the struts are stiff enough to provide rigid connecting points for the foils.

Calculating Stress (S_M & S_C) on the main foil and cantilevered winglets:

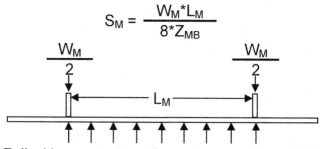

Foil with constant section - stress at the middle

Figure 11-2. Stress on the main foil
(a beam) in between two supports.

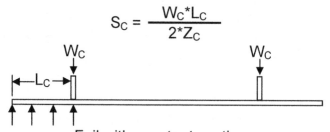

Foil with constant section –
stress on the winglet outboard of the strut

Figure 11-3. Stress on a winglet,
which is a cantilevered beam.

140

Where:

S_M = Stress, Main foil, in psi at its maximum point.
S_C = Stress, Cantilevered winglet, in psi at its maximum point.
W_M = Weight supported by Middle section, pounds (weight equals lift).
W_C = Weight supported by one Cantilevered section, maximum.
L_M = Length (span) of the Middle section of the foil in inches.
L_C = Length (span) of one of two Cantilevered sections of the foil in inches.
Z_{MB} = Sectional modulus of the foil's equivalent Middle Box cross section.
Z_C = Sectional modulus of the cantilevered Circular cross section of the pivot rod .

Now that we have some equations, let's do some practical analysis. Hifybe uses the following rear foil, in inches:

Middle span, between struts, inches:	41	68%
Cantilevered end spans, variable incidence roll control 9.5 * 2 =	19	32%
Span, total	60	100%
Chord, inches	4.75	

The chord's cross section is NACA 63-412, molded in CPR by FastaCraft, Perth, Australia.

Weight supported by the span between struts is: 311 lbs * 68% = 211 lbs.
Weight supported by each cantilevered end sections is: 311 lbs. * (32% / 2) = 50 lbs.

The values for Hifybe are:
S_M = Stress on Main foil, unknown.
S_C = Stress on Cantilevered winglet, unknown.
W_M = 211 lbs. For the 41" center section.
W_C = 59 lbs. For each of the two 9.5" cantilevered winglets.
L_M = 41 in.
L_C = 9.5 in. (for each of two).
Z_{MB} = Sectional modulus of the foil's equivalent Middle Box cross section.
Z_C = Sectional modulus of the foil's pivot rod with a Circular cross section.

In structural engineering, the term modulus refers to stiffness and sectional modulus refers to the stiffness of a section. Having adequate sectional modulus for a foil's middle box cross section (Z_{MB}) ensures the foil will not deform excessively under its expected loads. Having adequate sectional modulus for the foil's pivot rod (Z_C) verifies the rod will be stiff enough to function under its design load.

The *sectional modulus* of a beam (the foil and its pivot rod are both beams) is defined by Wikipedia to be "the ratio of the second moment of area of the beam's cross section to the distance of the extreme compressive fiber from the neutral axis."

Calculating the sectional moduli can be difficult. The methods will be shown below, but there is fortunately an easier way: search the Internet for "sectional modulus" and you will find several on-line calculators. Enter the relevant size and shape and the sectional modulus will appear. But even if you intend to use an online calculator, reading about the calculations below will give you a better understanding of what the calculator is doing. It's good for you, so read on.

Calculate Sectional Modulus (Z_{MB} & Z_C):

If you chose to do the full calculation for Z_{MB} or Z_C, here are the formulas:

$$Z_{MB} = (C * H^3 / 12) / (H / 2)$$
$$Z_C = \pi * D^3 / 32$$

Where:

Z_{MB} = Sectional modulus, Middle Box cross section.
C   = Width or Chord, 3.56 in. for Hifybe (Engineering books use "W").
H   = Height = .53 in for Hifybe.

Z_C = Sectional modulus, Circular cross section.
D   = Diameter = .375 in.

Adjust for irregular shape of the foil section:

Did you notice that the width and height shown for Hifybe are not the same as the chord and thickness of its foil section (4.75 * .625)? No matter if the sectional modulus is looked up on the web or calculated by hand, a common shape will have to be used in place of the complex foil profile. The solution is to substitute a simple single-cell box structure for the foil profile. Besnard, et al., proposed using 85% of the thickness and 75% of the chord, as shown in Figure 11-4. Later in the chapter, we will adjust for the hollowness of the section.

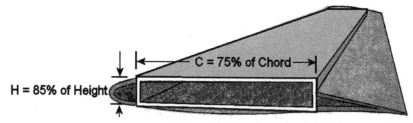

Figure 11-4. A common box section shape is substituted for the uncommon foil profile.

Hifybe's rear foil measures 4.75 in. by .625 in. To calculate the box dimensions:

Box chord = 4.75 * .75 = 3.56 in.
Box height = .625 * .85 = .53 in.

To determine the Z_{MB}, the Middle Box's sectional modulus:

$$Z_{MB} = (W * H^3 / 12) / (H / 2)$$
$$Z_{MB} = (3.56 * .53^3 / 12) / (.53 / 2)$$
$$Z_{MB} = .168$$

Calculate the stress (S_M) on the main foil:

Now we can apply the stress formula of Figure 11-2:

$$S_M = (W_M * L_M) / (8 * Z_B)$$
$$S_M = (211 * 41) / (8 * .168)$$
$$S_M = 8651 / 1.344$$
$$S_M = 6437 \text{ psi}$$

Our calculations show that the stress is far below the yield strength of CRP of 117,000 psi. We can safely use this material or even another of lesser yield strength.

Our next task is to calculate the cantilevered winglet's axis rod. The cantilevered end sections (flippers) are designed to pivot on their long axis in order to change their angle of incidence and angle of attack. When applied asymmetrically, the change in AOA will asymmetrically change the lift and that will induce a rolling moment. They operate like ailerons on an aircraft.

It happens that a 3/8 in. (.375 in.) rod can nest in the hollow part of the Fastacraft foil. If we use a stainless steel rod through the entire 60 in. span, will it permanently distort under operating conditions?

First we determine W_C, the maximum weight to be supported. In this case W_C will be more than half the total weight supported by the two end spans, because when they are deflected, to induce or counteract roll, they will accelerate the weight supported. The maximum they can lift will depend on how much the lift coefficient can be changed by increasing the AOA.

The V_{MAX} AOA has been determined to be $-.1°$. Referring to our C_L table, Figure 13-3, this results in $C_L = .30$. The NACA 63-412 stalls at $C_L = 1.55$

That is a potential momentary lift that is equal to 517% of the normal lift (1.55 / .30) * 100. This is an enormous potential increase in lift, however in reality it is exaggerated because the flippers, with their low aspect ratio, cannot generate that much lift (AR = 9.5 /* 4.75 = 2). Refer to Figure 4-9 and we see an AR = 2 merits an F_{AR} of .50. Multiply 517% * .50 = 258%

Materials, Stress Calculations, and Fabrication

Therefore our momentary maximum lift including the aspect ratio factor is:

W_C = 50 lbs * 258% = 129 lbs.

And our Factor, Momentary Lift is; F_{ML} = 2.58. We will be using this to calculate the stress on the cantilevered winglet.

Determine sectional modulus for the axis rod**:**

Now we determine the sectional characteristics of a .375 in. circular cross-section rod. I am going to *http://www.engineersedge.com/Calulators_Online.shtml.* (Hopefully this excellent web site will be available to you at the time of reading, if not look through existing engineering books on stress calculation or search the Internet for other web sites). Go to "Sectional Properties, Selected Shapes" and under that heading look for "Sectional Properties, Round at Center". Select inches and enter .375 as the diameter. The result is Z_C = Sectional Modulus = .00517 in^3.

If you wish to calculate the sectional modulus yourself, here is the formula for a round rod, or solid circle:

$$Z_C = \pi * d^3 / 32$$
$$Z_C = 3.14 * .375^3 / 32$$
$$Z_C = 3.14 * .05273 / 32$$
$$Z_C = .00517 \text{ in}^3$$

We now have the following inputs:

W_C = 50 lbs.
L_C = 9.5 in.
Z_C = .00517 in^3
F_{ML} = 2.58

Calculate the stress (S_C) in the cantilevered winglet rod:

We apply the stress formula of Figure 11-3:

$$S_C = W_C * L_C / 2 * Z_C$$
$$S_C = 50 * 9.5 / 2 * .00517$$
$$S_C = 475 / .01034$$
$$S_C = 45,938 \text{ psi. This is for straight and level flight.}$$

To provide for the additional stress caused by winglet deflection to induce or control rolling forces we apply the Factor, Momentary Lift (F_{ML}):

$$S_C = 45,938 \times 2.58 = 118,520 \text{ psi.}$$

144

The yield strength of 304 Stainless Steel as shown in table 1 is 75,000 psi. The calculated stress of 118,520 psi exceeds the strength of this material, and could well fail under peak load.

For safety and reliability, a **safety factor** is prudent. Conservative engineers might council that an additional 50 to 100% should be in the stress calculations. In our example, there is obviously no room for a safety factor.

What can we do when, as in this case, the anticipated stress is excessive? The 3/8" rod is the largest size that will nest in this foil section. We need a hard non-corrosive material like stainless steel to act as a pivot and a bearing. Due to the environment, we cannot resort to a material that is sufficiently stronger but is subject to corrosion. Yet our calculations predict that if full winglet deflection is applied at V_{MAX} the stainless steel shaft will bend. But is it necessary to apply full winglet deflection at V_{MAX}?

If the answer is no, we could solve the problem by placing an **operational limitation** on Hifybe: "No maximum deflection of the winglets while operating near V_{MAX}". This is a valid answer to a difficult question, and it has precedence. Military and other operational aircraft often have operating restrictions posted in the cockpit. For example, the venerable T-28 Navy trainer is restricted against snap rolls. In our case, the answer is to restrict Hifybe against full speed, full roll control deflection. Chances are that extreme roll correction at high speed will not be necessary in normal operation, so posting the restriction deals with the problem.

Because the box is hollow, we have an additional complication. Obviously a solid box will be stronger than a hollow box, and a common way of providing for the void is to calculate the strength of the box as if it were solid and then calculate the strength of the inner box (the void). Then subtract the inside from the outside.

A short cut method is to apply a **Hollow box factor:**

To adjust for the missing center material, a factor can be incorporated into the calculated stress results. An approximate strength factor may be taken from Figure 11-5.

% of Box that is Hollow	Weight Bearing Strength as a % of Solid Box
10%	100%
20%	99%
30%	97%
40%	94%
50%	87%
60%	78%
70%	66%
80%	49%
90%	27%
100%	0%

Figure 11-5. Factor for adjusting the relative strength of a hollow box.

Materials, Stress Calculations, and Fabrication

It may be a surprise that the hollow box has much of the strength of the solid box. The reason is that the bending load is carried by the "extreme outer fibers" and the inner fibers contribute little to bending strength. This explains why beams, such as "I" beams, carry their mass at the extreme top and bottom parts that are separated only by a thin web.

Of course in a foil section, just as in an I beam, it is important to have a solid in the central void to prevent the top and the bottom from collapsing onto each other under bending stress. This material need not have a high tensile strength, and it does not have to fill the entire void from side to side. The solid can be most any material that will not collapse under the load. Wood, metal or engineering quality foam are a few of the suitable materials.

A handy way to use this factor is to modify the stress formula from earlier in this chapter:

$$S_M = W_M * L_M / 8 * Z_{MB}$$

and solve for W_M:

$$W_M = 8 * Z_{MB} * S_M / L_M$$

For Hifybe the calculation for a solid box would be:

$$W_M = 8 * .168 * 117,000 / 41 = 3,838 \text{ lbs.}$$

To determine the hollowness of the box, the vertical thickness is the important dimension for vertical loads. Earlier we determined the relevant box thickness to be .53 inches (the vertical dimension). The CRP walls are .05 in. each for a total of .10 in. wall thickness. The percentage of box that is composed of solid material is 20%. 10 / 53 = 20% (rounded). The percentage of hollowness is 80%. 100 – 20 = 80%. Figure 11-5 shows us that a 80% hollow box will have 49% of the bending strength of a 100% solid box. Therefore the uniform weight that can be supported by the foil's center section will be 1,880 lbs. (3,838 x .49 = 1,880 lbs). Using hollow struts and foils reduces weight and cost while providing a place for structural rods, control links, etc.

Remember, the stress calculations used in this chapter have been abbreviated to make them easy to use by a designer who needs only approximate results. These results will be less accurate than those done conventionally by a professional. If the stresses calculated by these methods result in a marginally adequate structure, or if the assembly is critical for safety or dependability, consult with a professional engineer, or increase the size and strength to the point where there is no doubt about the unit's adequacy. Furthermore, for critical parts the safety factor can be set at 150% to 200% to be extra prudent.

Construction:

A simplified method of fabrication is to plane or shave a foil from a plank of **wood**. The wood should be strong, hard and fine grained with no knotholes or other imperfections. It should be a variety that does not swell excessively or become soft with exposure to water. Oak is one choice, but a little experimentation and research will uncover other suitable candidates.

Alexander, et al., reports good results from using *Agba*, a type of mahogany. They suggest reorienting the grain of the plank to increase strength and reduce warping, as demonstrated in Figure 11-6. A 1" x 10" plank, for example, will have the grain running with the width and parallel to the thickness. Rip the plank into ten, rectangular stringers. To save material and reduce planing, the stringers can be ripped to sizes corresponding to the thickness of the profile where they will be placed. Turn each stringer 90 degrees and glue them together side by side. This changes the orientation of the grain from horizontal to vertical. Be sure to use the highest quality marine adhesive and firmly clamp the assembly during curing and before shaping.

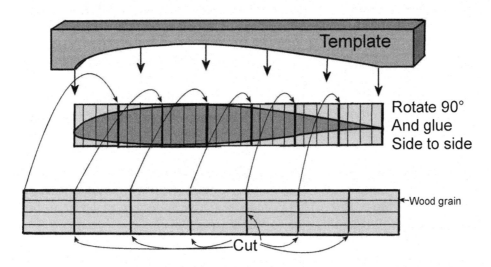

Figure 11-6. Reorienting the grain of a plank to save wood, increase
strength, and reduce warping. A Paper template is glued to
the end of the plank to serve as a planing guide.

To provide for gripping and controlling the plank during shaping, glue a ½" x 1" stringer on edge to the bottom side of it. The stringer will allow the use of a vise or clamps to hold the work without damaging it.

Accuracy in duplicating the foil profile is paramount and requires good techniques and craftsmanship. The chosen foil profile can be downloaded off the Internet or photocopied from such publications as *Theory of Wing Sections* or *Airfoils at Low Speeds*. The chord length of the paper profile can be scaled with a photo copier, or a Photoshop-type computer program. Using scissors, cut the profile from the paper. The central paper part is the *male* profile, and the remaining, outside, paper is called the *female* profile.

To create a template, the female profile is glued to a thin hard piece of suitable material. 1/8" aluminum plate is a good choice because it is stiff, non-corrosive, unbreakable, and easy to shape. The form is roughed out using a jigsaw or a band saw. The finer shaping is done by hand with half-round pattern files. Start with rough-cut and progress to fine cut files as the work progresses.

Materials, Stress Calculations, and Fabrication

It is essential that this template be as accurate as possible. The curved shape must be smooth and without waves. A trick for detecting waviness is to look at the reflection of a florescent light bulb off the inside cut of the template. As the template is rotated in the light, the width of the reflection should change uniformly. If there is waviness, the reflection width will grow and shrink irregularly as it passes from leading to trailing edge.

After securing the laminated plank in the jaws of a bench vise, the template is used to trace the foil profile on the end-grain of the plank. Rough out the foil with a hand or power plane, then use pattern files. As the work progresses use sanding blocks to carefully shape the material. Frequently lay the template on the emerging foil to guide the accurate formation of the shape.

Once the form of the foil is achieved, one of two directions may be taken. Direct application of **CRP or FRP** to the outside of the form will create a usable foil, or the wooden shape can be used as a male pattern to create a **female mold**. The female mold is then used to layup a solid or hollow reinforced plastic hydrofoil.

Of the two methods, the second is preferred. Using the wooden piece as a male pattern preserves the tediously created form for future projects, and the molding process will result in a more accurate profile. This is because the wrapping of material around the accurate male form will distort its exterior dimensions.

There is much more to be learned about creating structures from CRP or FRP, and for this explore the Internet, libraries, and bookstores.

Other possibilities for creating hydrofoils are milling and molding aluminum. Publications such as *Theory of Wing Sections* and *Airfoils at Low Speeds* provide "airfoil coordinates", numbers that describe the shape of various airfoils. These can be supplied to a machine shop, foundry, or extruder and the experts will create an aluminum hydrofoil to your specifications.

One successful builder used extrusions to create a kit that would transform a catamaran into a hydrofoil boat. Unfortunately, the results were mixed. The die used for the extrusions was expensive. This would not be a problem if a large production run is expected, but the need was limited. I bought some of the extrusions and shared the builder's frustrations that the upper surface had enough lengthwise striations to require filing and smoothing. That modified the NACA 4412 profile, so the performance was affected. Furthermore, extrusion required the use of the soft, flexible 6005 alloy causing structural compromises.

On the other hand, Harry Larsen's successful Talaria IV has a main foil that was cut from an aluminum billet by using a CNC, **computer numerical control, milling machine**. These digitally controlled mills take the airfoil coordinates and carve a smooth and accurate shape out of a billet of appropriate material. Complex shapes involving taper and twist are possible. Cutouts for elevators, ailerons, etc. do not cause a problem, because little heat is created in the milling process, and the original temper of the material will not be changed. The drawback to CNC is its high cost, but it seems to be dropping. Considering the savings of time and the increase in accuracy, CNC may pay for itself.

An **ogival foil profile** has a segment of a circle on top and a flat plate on the bottom. If the foil-maker is handy with metal fabrication the ogival foil can be made using an abbreviated technique. For such a craftsman, this might be the easiest foil to construct, however its profile is the worst performer of those shown in this book. Return to Figure 13-3 to make a performance comparison.

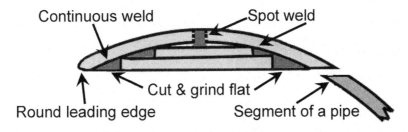

Figure 11-7. Construction of an Ogival Foil from Pipe and Plate.

Start with a large diameter aluminum or stainless steel pipe. By haunting local metal recycling companies, I have acquired some 12" diameter, ¼" wall thickness aluminum pipe. This was probably electrical conduit in a previous life. Today it serves as the upper surface of a built-up ogival foil, or the two sides of a built-up strut. Equally good curved sections can be rolled to shape by a sheet metal company. The bottom surface of the foil assembly is a flat plate of like material. To provide stiffness and prevent collapse, a smaller plate of aluminum, or any material that resists collapse, is encapsulated within the two outer pieces. The assembly is welded at the leading and trailing edges as shown above. Bondo brand, or other similar automotive filler material, maybe used to fill in the surface imperfections.

If like material is used for the center filler, some additional strength and stiffness can be achieved by welding it to the lower plate prior to assembly. After assembly, 3 to 6 holes, ¼ inch in diameter, can be drilled along the upper plate to allow spot welding. This makes a completely integrated unit. The rounded leading and sharp trailing edges are shaped by grinding the joint, and *voilà*, you have an ogival hydrofoil wing.

Aluminum struts can be made in a similar fashion. Two curved sections of a pipe are sandwiched around a solid or hollow bar. The bar is welded to one side before the other side is added and welded along the leading and trailing edges. Drilling small holes mid-span will accommodate spot welds to tie the units together structurally. Five or six spot welds per strut should be sufficient.

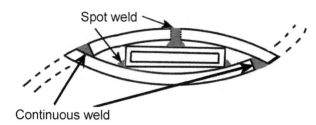

Figure 11-8. Aluminum Strut Fabricated from Pipe and Plate.

The "T" joint between the foil and the strut, when welded and hardened, is nearly as strong as the joined pieces. On the other hand, aluminum has about 1/2 the bending (tensile) strength of FRP, and about 1/3 the strength of CRP. Furthermore, if the fabricator fails to heat age the aluminum after welding there will be a significant reduction in tensile strength. Return to the part of this chapter discussing TIG and MIG welding for ideas on heat aging of aluminum.

Figures 11-7 and 11-8 show sharp leading and trailing edges. Such sections have the unique quality that they can fly equally well advancing or retreating. This could be an essential design feature in, for example, a sailboat with a single leeward ama that is designed to never tack. Instead of tacking, the boat reverses direction always keeping the ama downwind.

Except in special applications, the profile of the ogival foil has improved flying characteristics and is safer when the leading edge is rounded. A **radius on the leading edge** improves stalling, ventilation, and C_{LMAX}. Rounding the leading edge of the strut will likewise improve its performance. This improvement will be most evident while the strut is yawed, i.e., has a measurable angle of attack.

Needless to say, the greater the divergence from the ogival shape, the greater the departure from the published ogival lift and drag curves, but if the change is for the better, why not? However, to create more complex foil profiles and plan forms, aluminum is not the best material. CRP and FRP are much more flexible and stronger, pound for pound, than almost any other commonly available materials.

So now we have a clue as to how much engineers suffer to keep our bridges, skyscrapers, and yes–hydrofoils–from breaking. Possibly you just made a solemn pledge to yourself to never wade through these calculations just to avoid a few broken parts. That may work for you, but "build 'em. fly 'em, break 'em" can be costly and dangerous, and by using these calculations on the most critical parts you can increase the possibilities of early success.

Hull and Motor Selection

- o Displacement hull vs. planing hull
- o Hull speed, explained
- o Hull speed equation
- o Displacement hulls explained
- o Planing hulls have no V_{HULL} limitations
- o Foil configuration: canard, conventional, and balanced
- o Outboard motor
- o Safety
- o Jet pump
- o Hull material
- o Hull buoyancy near motor
- o Power curve
- o Propulsion vs. the drag hump

Simply put, a **displacement hull** is supported by its buoyancy, and rides deep in the water. A **planing hull** relies primarily on aquadynamic forces for support and scoots on the surface.

When a boat reaches **hull speed**, V_{HULL}, it attempts to transition from the displacement mode to the planing mode. Above V_{HULL}, the displacement hull acts badly, but a planing hull mounts the water and slides along its surface. For displacement boats, V_{HULL} represents a practical upper limit on speed, while planing boats can exceed this limitation by riding on top of the water–at the expense of much higher required power.

As briefly stated in chapter 5, the **equation for estimating hull speed**, V_{HULL} is:

$V_{HULL} \cong 1.5 \sqrt{L}$. Where L = Length at the water line.

Here is a table of V_{HULL} calculations, Figure 12-1:

Waterline in feet	Max hull speed in mph (V_{HULL})	Waterline in feet	Max hull speed in mph (V_{HULL})	Waterline in feet	Max hull speed in mph (V_{HULL})
4	3.1	15	6.0	26	7.9
5	3.4	16	6.2	27	8.0
6	3.8	17	6.4	28	8.2
7	4.1	18	6.5	29	8.3
8	4.4	19	6.7	30	8.4
9	4.6	20	6.9	31	8.6
10	4.9	21	7.1	32	8.7
11	5.1	22	7.2	33	8.9
12	5.3	23	7.4	34	9.0
13	5.6	24	7.5	35	9.1
14	5.8	25	7.7	36	9.2

Figure 12-1. Approximate maximum hull speed (V_{HULL})
for displacement hulls based on $V_{HULL} \simeq 1.5\sqrt{L}$

Typically ships, tugboats, and cruising sailboats have **displacement hulls**. The buoyancy of these hulls is exactly equal to the weight of the water they displace, no matter the size of the vessel. The density of seawater is about 64 lbs / cu. ft. According to http://Woodsgood.ca, balsa is 10 lbs / cu. ft., and the lightest ebony is 59 lbs / cu. ft.

Fill a swimming pool to the edge with seawater and float a 64 pound cube of balsa wood (6.4 cubic feet). 64 pounds of water will be displaced and flow over the side of the pool. Now remove the balsa, refill the pool and float 64 pounds of ebony wood (slightly more than 1 cubic foot). Again, 64 pounds of water will be displaced and flow over the side of the pool. When the density of an object is less than water it will float and the weight supported is independent of the object's volume. But when an object is forcefully *submerged*, the weight of the water displaced is determined by the volume and is independent of the weight of the object. Force the ebony below the surface and it will displace 69.4 lbs. ((64/59) x 64 = 69.4). Force the balsa cube below the surface and it will displace 384.4 lbs of water (6.4 cu. ft. x 64 lbs / cu. ft. = 409.6 lbs).

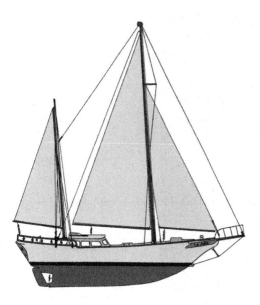

Figure 12-2 This 41' ketch, formerly owned
by the author, has a displacement hull.

At slow speeds, displacement hulls are very efficient. They are designed to pass through water with a minimum of disturbance. Their fine bows and rounded sterns separate and close the water as they pass. This separation is in three dimensions, so the bow and the stern usually have dead rise to move the water vertically as well as horizontally. The dramatic way displacement hulls react when exceeding V_{HULL} is explained in chapter 5.

The hull of a hydrofoil boat must be capable of traveling faster in water than the takeoff speed, $V_{TO,}$ of the foils. There are examples of successful *displacement* boats that use long thin hulls combined with large foils. Some of the California human powered hydrofoils are like that, such as Sid Shutt's Hydro-ped, Figure 17-3. However, because V_{TO} is usually about half of V_{MAX}–see the last two pages of chapter 4–takeoff speeds are often in excess of V_{HULL}. To exceed V_{HULL}, the hull must be designed to plane.

Planing hulls are not subject to the V_{HULL} limitations. A planing hull quickly rises to the top of its bow wave before the wave becomes too large and energy consuming. Flat-bottomed boats present a somewhat constant angle to the oncoming fluid flow, and relatively uniform lift is created along the bottom. This lift causes the hull to rise to the surface. When that lift replaces buoyancy as the primary source of support, the boat is *planing*. The speed when planing is limited by available power rather than the definitive V_{HULL} limitation when in the displacement mode. There is no $V_{MAX\text{-}PLANNING}$ corresponding to the definitive V_{HULL}.

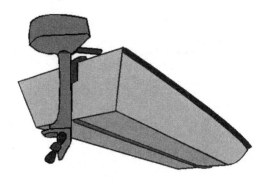

Figure 12-3. This Jon Boat has a typical planing hull.

While it is possible to calculate the power required for a planing hull configuration at a given speed, it is not easy. It may be easier to go with common sense. Local boat dealers, hull manufacturers, or motor providers can give a good idea of how fast the hull and motor will go. If they cannot help, one can always talk to an owner of a similar boat. When figuring maximum planing speed based on limited power, don't forget to make an adjustment for the additional drag and weight of foils and struts. Within size and weight limitations, the power of the motor selected should be more than the expected minimum. The minimum power required will be determined first by the drag "hump" and then by the top speed. The hump was explained in Figure 5-4 and its associated text.

The hump refers to the shape of the drag curve just prior to takeoff when hull, struts, prop shaft, and foils are all creating maximum form drag. The drag at the hump could be as much as twice the drag of the clean hull alone.
For the designer who chooses to create his own planing hull, here are some guidelines. The bottom side of the most efficient planing hull will be very flat. Any deadrise will increase the drag of a planing hull. Imagine the water flow around the hull in three dimensions. The flow of the passing water will conform to the curve of the hull; refer to the Coanda effect in chapter 2. It is not good if the water travels upward after passing part of the hull. Remember Newton's 3rd law? "For every action there is an equal and opposite reaction". If the passing fluid is forced upward, a downward force on the hull will be created. The downward pull is energy wasted (drag).

The sloping, near vertical line of the bow will need to be curved horizontally to blend with the keel line, but aft of the planing surface, lines curving away from the keel should be avoided. Lines running lengthwise along the bottom should be as straight as possible. There should be an abrupt transition from the horizontal planing surface to the vertical transom. This encourages the flow to make a clean break.

In chapter 9 we concluded "bananas fly poorly". A banana hull has a fat middle, a convex curve on the bottom that rises at the stern, and a narrow transom. Even my boat, Hifybe, the High Flying Banana, does not use a banana-shaped hull, because banana-shaped hulls suck.

Our California group of human powered hydrofoil aficionados discovered this the hard way. Dwight Filley, who has experimented with many hull configurations, showed up at our test site with a hull that curved vertically from stem to stern. His hydrofoils were properly configured, but neither Dwight, Steve Ball, nor I could pedal vigorously enough to lift off.

After exhausting everyone, we took some digital action photos and saw what might have been predicted. We observed that the bow is rising while the stern is squatting. The harder we pedal and the faster the movement, and the deeper the hull burrows. When the peddling stops, the hull buoys to the surface. The hull is being sucked into the water. We dubbed the problem as "the damned uncanny banana effect".

Still, it was worth the effort considering all the amusement we had saying, "This hull sucks, earth sucks, *ad nauseam.*" Surfboards and windsurf boards, like the one Hifybe uses, are relatively flat on the bottom with a slight curve up at the bow to prevent submarining into oncoming waves.

The designer is faced with a surprising number of choices concerning the layout of the main components, i.e., the foils, power source, pilot, and passengers. However, the foils themselves are limited to **three configurations: canard, conventional airplane, and balanced,** as you may recall from chapter 7.

In this book we will be using the canard layout for motor and human powered hydrofoils, and conventional layout for sail powered hydrofoils. These choices have to do with the important and unique function of the front foil. How the front foil functions was examined in chapter 8 and the canard configuration was covered in chapter 7.

One logical choice for a canard-style hydrofoil is a light hull with a transom designed to accommodate an **outboard motor**. As with all flying machines, weight control is paramount. Check current specifications, but Mercury and Suzuki outboards used to have some of highest power to weight ratios. The lightest engine available would be a two-stroke type, but in today's ecologically sensitive world, two-stroke engines are becoming an endangered species. Still, foreign made ones may be available in some states. Be aware that some local laws may limit the places where you may operate. For example, a two-stroke engine is not allowed on fresh water reservoirs in my county.

Hifybe uses an ancient 8 hp 2-cycle Suzuki engine weighing 56 lbs. This may sound light, but my old 7.5 hp Montgomery Ward Sea King—now in outboard heaven—weighed 32 lbs. Those were the good old days

Presently, four stroke engines weighing 55 pounds are available, but they produce only 6 hp. The maximum horsepower is less, but the shape of the four stroke power curve is better for hydrofoil's than is the two stroke's. The four stroke engine has more torque at low rpm, and this is where power is needed to overcome the drag hump. Possibly, when used to power a hydrofoil, the 6 hp four stroke engine can match the performance of the 8 hp two cycle engine.

When selecting an outboard motor, be sure to pick the most powerful one within its grouping. For example, in 2006, Mercury produced two different models each 111 pounds. One engine was rated at 15 hp and the other at 9.9 hp. The lower power engine is detuned to conform to 10 hp limitations of some waterways. Where power vs. weight is important, like in a hydrofoil, the choice is obvious.

Depending on your design, a long shaft motor may provide enough penetration into the water to accommodate flight. Three shaft lengths are commonly available. Presently, for example, Tohatsu and Nissan have 6 hp four stroke engines that come in shaft lengths to accommodate 15", 20" and 25" transom height. If the 25" shaft choice is available, it will usually be the best; however, be sure to check the gear ratio of any long shaft engine. An engine that is designed to be an emergency backup for a heavy boat may have lower unit gear ratio suitable for low speed operation. If you somehow acquire a short shaft model, extension kits are available from both the engine's manufacturer and the after-market providers. An extremely high-flying design may require a custom-made shaft extender.

Safety. As with other motor driven boats, the spinning propeller poses a potential danger to the dismounted rider. In Hifybe, several safety features address this problem. The propeller has a ring shaped strike guard surrounding the propeller. The rider is tethered to an ignition kill switch that cuts the power if the rider should leave the boat. The throttle is spring-loaded and shuts down to idle automatically when released. Some racing boats shut their throttle down to zero when released. These last three engine-killing devices may prevent water ingestion, should the boat capsize. One more safety possibility is to make the gearshift spring loaded and connected to the seat so that it shifts to neutral when the rider dismounts. These devices stop the propeller or kill the engine, so to prevent being accidentally stranded in open water, be certain to provide for reengaging or restarting the engine–without returning to the dock.

Eliminating the propeller and switching to a **jet pump** can resolve propeller safety issues. With this in mind, I bought a Yamaha Jet Ski with the good intentions of making it the first one to fly. How neat would that be: having all that water jetting from the transom? It is still on my to-do list. So many boats, so little time.

The downside to the Jet Ski idea is that they are heavy–mine weighs 280 pounds, and at low speeds they are not as efficient as a propeller driven craft. There may be inadequate power to overcome the drag hump, because the water jet is particularly inefficient at low speeds, such as V_{TO} when the hull, struts, and foils are wet and producing drag–especially induced drag–prior to takeoff. Look back at Figure 5-9 for a chart comparing the water jet to a marine propeller.

Incidentally, don't feel guilty about all that water shooting into space. The propulsion is an opposite reaction to the acceleration of the water–Newton's 3rd law–and does not need to "push off" of anything. Backing the nozzle up to the quay to get a quick start is not going to increase the jet's effectiveness.

The **hull's material** should be of lightweight Fiberglass Reinforced Plastic (FRP), aluminum, or a buildup of other lightweight materials such as marine grade plywood with light wood stringers. If too much money is your problem, try carbon fiber reinforced plastic (CRP). Modern foam or honeycomb materials are useful in constructing lightweight laminates when combined with FRP or CRP. When selecting the material for the hull, consider your skill level and what tools are available. Few special tools are needed to work with FRP or plywood, but special equipment is needed to bend and weld aluminum.

The transom should be solid enough to support an outboard motor and possibly the main foils, depending on your design. The hull must be strong and rigid enough to allow it to be supported and take impact loads at the two or three hard points where the foils attach. To support the hull-borne weight of the engine and pilot (if he is positioned near the stern), the transom region must have sufficient volume, or the hull must extend aft of the transom to provide the needed displacement.

The **hull's buoyancy** in the vicinity of the motor, rider and main foil needs to be calculated. Nothing could be more embarrassing on launch day in view of friends and family than to have your sophisticated hydrofoil boat sink transom first. Please don't ask how I know.

To avoid this problem, on paper divide the hull into five sections, equal in length, starting at the bow and working back. Referring to the weight and balance calculations you made in chapter 7, assign total weights to each of the five sections. Then calculate the volume of each section and multiply the volume by the unit weight of water.

Seawater weighs 64 lbs / ft^3, but here, with my American readers (as well as readers from Liberia and Myanmar, the remaining other places where feet and pounds are still in use), I will share a secret held closely between me and 6 billion others. The metric system is easier to use—especially with volume calculations. One yard or three feet, roughly equals one meter. There are 10 decimeters in one meter. 1 liter = 1 cubic dm = 1 dm * 1 dm * 1 dm. One liter of water weights one kilogram. A kilogram equals 2.2 lbs.

I like to use these units for volume because it is easy to do the rough calculations in my head and follow up with a pencil and paper for precise results. For example, I know Hifybe's motor = 56 lbs, rider = 180 lbs, and their total is 236 lbs. Divide this by 2 and round down to 120 kilos.

The displacement of 120 kilos is 120 liters. The dimensions of 120 liters in decimeters (dm) are 120 * 1 * 1, or 10 * 6 * 2. Hifybe is about 1m (10 dm) wide so we know that a section of her hull 6 dm long and 2 dm deep will support the heaviest elements. A dm is about 4 inches, so our hull section in inches is 40 * 24 * 8. The weight of 120 kilos can be supported at the middle of the calculated hull section.

Hull and Motor Selection

These quick buoyancy calculations come in handy during the early stages of design when the shape of the hull and the location of the main elements are being decided. In any buoyancy estimations, be sure to at least double the minimum displacement indicated for safety and stability. Remember that it is the reserve buoyancy above the water line that provides roll and pitch stability when the boat is floating.

What about hull design? The beam should be narrow if you wish to allow banked turns when flying, but not so narrow that there is a danger of capsizing when at rest, or so narrow that planing is not possible. A slight dead-rise from the keel to the chine will provide additional clearance during steep banks, and strengthen and stiffen the hull. Dead rise and some fineness to the bow is desirable to provide for wave encounters and inevitable crashes. Kotaro Horiuchi's OU27 and OU32 hulls are well designed for a banking hydrofoil. See Figure 10-6.

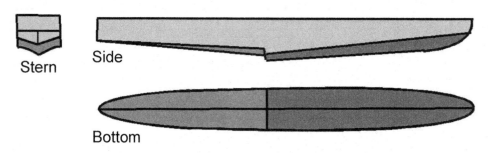

Figure 12-4. Flying boat type hull with step amidships.

Although it is not clear from Figures 10-6, both boats have slight steps in their planing hulls. This allows the planing force to be forward of the stern and in some boats, closer to the CG. Flying boats and their outriggers usually have a step in their hull for this reason. This allows for a flatter, less pitched-up, takeoff. However, the elevated stern also provides for rotation at takeoff attitude (bow high takeoff), if needed.

Of course there are many advantages to multi-hulled boats, but the width of a catamaran or trimaran will preclude making bank turns. Most hydrofoil sailboats, with the exception of the Moth class, are multi-hulled and therefore make flat turns. A compromise is to use outriggers or amas to make the mono-hull roll stable when at rest. In this case, the outriggers are best kept small and close to the hull to allow banking while turning.

Because hydrofoils are more efficient and have less drag than displacement or planing hulls, the designer can hope for higher maximum speeds when foil-borne (within cavitation limitations). Two things besides cavitation, will limit top speed. Power must be equal to or greater than the drag, and the propeller pitch and diameter must be correct to allow the power to be efficiently converted to thrust, see Overall Propulsion Coefficient in chapter 5. In that chapter we showed that the drag will increase with the square of the speed and the power required will increase with the cube of the speed.

To review, even with adequate power, the proper propeller must be selected to allow the engine to reach its peak-power rpm. If the propeller diameter is too small or its pitch too low, the motor will obtain its peak rpm before the potential top speed of the foils is reached. On the other hand, a propeller that is too large or has too high of a pitch may not provide enough low speed thrust to overcome the hump drag or enough high-speed thrust to push a boat to its V_{MAX}.

Of course, power and rpm are linked in engines. Horsepower vs. rpm is plotted as a **power curve**. Here is a typical gas engine. The data is from the website, http://continuouswave.com/whaler/reference/propellerPowerCurve.html.

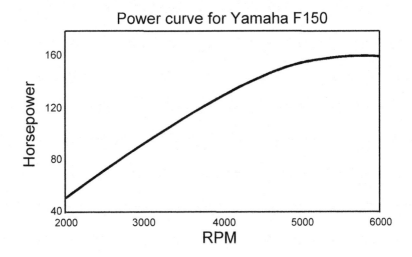

Figure 12-5. This is a typical power curve.

Propulsion vs. the drag hump. As indicated, maximum power rpm should roughly coincide with V_{MAX}, provided that at the drag hump speed the rpm is high enough to generate propulsion to exceed the drag hump. Figure 12-6 shows a small propeller (S = small diameter and/or small pitch) that creates adequate thrust at the drag hump. Its V_{MAX} may be limited by the maximum design rpm of the engine. The big propeller (B = big diameter and/or big pitch) cannot power past the drag hump. It cannot takeoff. However, if it *could* takeoff, it would have a slightly higher V_{MAX}, while still operating well within its maximum rpm limits.

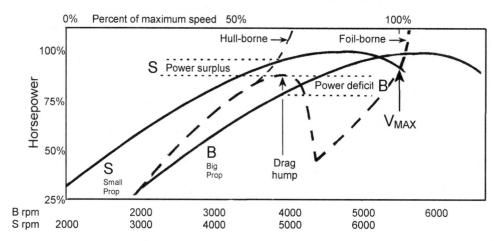

Figure12-6. Two propulsion curves superimposed on a drag curve with hump.

This chapter has covered some general ideas about hull and motor selection. In chapters 16, 17, and18 we will deal with the selection of specific power sources: engine, human, or sail.

Selecting Wing Section, Planform, and Aspect Ratio

o Wing section explained
o Guidelines for selection
o Subcavitating foils
o C_L Slope
o Supercavitating sections
o Thick or thin sections
o Ailerons and flippers
o Center of pressure
o Symmetrical vs. asymmetrical, cambered profiles
o Laminar or turbulent flow
o Boundary layer
o Drag bucket, dimples on golf balls, and turbulators
o Reynolds numbers, calculations
o NACA 63-412, NACA 4412 (Clark Y),and Ogival wing sections
o Leading edges should be rounded
o Strut thickness
o Wing loading, aspect ratio, induced drag, wing tip vortices
o Wing tip fences, winglets, high aspect ratio, low aspect ratio, and washout
o Planform: rectangular, tapered, swept back

To an outside observer, it seems just about any long skinny board with a curved upper surface could pass for a wing. Of course that is not something a peace-loving man would blurt out in a bar filled with aerodynamicists. In order to defend yourself in this unlikely situation, or if you choose to design a hydrofoil wing, you need to know something about what makes a wing a wing.

"A **wing section** is the cross-section of an airfoil that determines its aerodynamic characteristics, in particular the lift and drag coefficients and the lift/drag ratio", from the "Glossary of Flying", *Aeroplane Monthly, UK*. A typical wing section, or *profile*, will resemble a streamlined shape. If the top and the bottom sides have the same curve, the wing section is said to be symmetrical. Struts, braces and aerobatic wings are typically symmetrical. Most load bearing wings are *cambered*, having a curved upper surface and a flat or less-curved bottom surface. Some of the names of sections are descriptive, such as the NACA 2415. According to Abbott and Von Doenhoff, "The NACA 2415 wing section has 2 percent camber at 0.4 of the chord from the leading edge and is 15 percent thick." There is a lot more to know about wings and their many descriptive name systems. See *Theory of Wing Sections* for most answers on this subject.

Selecting Wing Section, Planform, and Aspect Ratio

There are many textbooks and technical papers dedicated to choosing wing sections. This subject is deep and complicated enough to sustain a career. Computer programs, free and for sale, are available for additional amusement. However, for most common hydrofoil applications fundamental knowledge about wing sections will be sufficient.

Here are some **guidelines** for selecting a hydrofoil wing section.

> Unless planning to fly very fast–over 40 or 50 mph–consider subcavitating sections only.
> Use a type that others are having success with and choose sections that can be constructed using available skills and tools.
> Do not choose a profile that has not had real testing in a wind or water tunnel. Computer generated profiles are tempting, but nothing beats the real world.
> Because of strength limitations, chose a thickness no less than 10% of the chord.
> To limit form drag chose a thickness no more than 14%.
> Utilize flaps, ailerons, variable incidence controls, etc. to regulate lift.
> Chose a rounded leading edge for milder stall and cavitation characteristics.
> Try using fences to control ventilation along struts and on surface piercing foils.
> A wing section should be chosen by comparing C_L, C_D, and L/D curves from published wind tunnel tests.
> Unless planning to do inverted flight (joke), avoid symmetrical sections for the main lifting foil.
> Symmetrical sections may be appropriate for the smaller height finding front foil.
> Symmetrical sections would also be appropriate for outboard winglets used for roll control, where negative lift could be needed. In particular, foils mounted on the windward amas of sailing boats provide downward force to resist capsizing.
> Symmetrical sections may be chosen for the aft foil of any sailboat that may need to produce a down force to counteract pitchpoling.
> Laminar flow wings will not show superior performance unless they are very carefully formed and used under ideal conditions. Except for special purpose hydrofoils, such as subcavitating speed record breakers, you may choose to go with the more consistent results that come with non-laminar flow sections.
> Whether a wing section is chosen from those of successful flying machines or from those of wind tunnel tests, determine its operational Reynolds number. Comparison between wings is more accurate when both operate in the realm of similar Reynolds numbers.
> In publications like *Theory of Wing Sections*, several curves may be shown, each representing a Reynolds number. Be certain to use the appropriate curve.
> The remaining elements to consider for an effective wing are: wing section, wing loading, planform, and aspect ratio.

To expand on these guidelines: **Subcavitating** foils are roughly limited to speeds of below 40 or 50 mph. A subcavitating foil section will generally have the appearance of a typical sub-sonic aircraft wing.

Clark Y   NACA 63-412

Figures 13-1a & b. These profiles are typical
of aircraft wings or subcavitating hydrofoils.

There are some exceptions such as the Ogival shape that is not a typical aircraft wing section shape.

Ogival

Figure 13-2. This simple profile is suitable only for non-critical uses such as hydrofoils on scale-models or on bi-directional amas.

NACA 63-412 profile
R_N = 3,000,000
C_L slope = 0.1090 / degree

AOA	Coefficient of lift	Coefficient of drag	L/D ratio
-8	-0.600	0.0102	-59
-7	-0.491	0.0094	-53
-6	-0.382	0.0085	-45
-5	-0.273	0.0079	-35
-4	-0.164	0.0072	-23
-3	-0.055	0.0065	-8
-2	0.054	0.0058	9
-1	0.163	0.0056	29
0	0.272	0.0054	50
1	0.381	0.0056	69
2	0.490	0.0057	86
3	0.599	0.0064	94
4	0.708	0.0070	101
5	0.817	0.0090	91
6	0.926	0.0107	87
7	1.035	0.0120	87
8	1.144	0.0132	87
9	1.253	0.0147	86
10	1.362	0.0161	85
11	1.460	0.0176	83
12	1.520	0.0191	80
13	1.560		
14	1.580		
15	1.550		
16	1.450		
17	1.270		

NACA 4412 profile
R_N = 3,000,000
C_L slope = 0.1000 / degree

AOA	Coefficient of lift	Coefficient of drag	L/D ratio
-8	-0.45	0.0090	-50
-7	-0.34	0.0085	-40
-6	-0.23	0.0077	-30
-5	-0.12	0.0073	-16
-4	-0.01	0.0070	-1
-3	0.10	0.0070	14
-2	0.20	0.0070	29
-1	0.30	0.0070	43
0	0.40	0.0070	57
1	0.50	0.0070	71
2	0.60	0.0070	86
3	0.70	0.0070	100
4	0.80	0.0070	114
5	0.90	0.0073	123
6	1.00	0.0080	125
7	1.10	0.0100	110
8	1.20	0.0130	92
9	1.30	0.0155	84
10	1.40	0.0190	74
11	1.48	0.0240	62
12	1.53		
13	1.55		
14	1.51		
15	1.45		
16	1.40		
17	1.35		

Ogival profile
R_N= 750,00
C_L slope Average = 0.079 / degree

AOA	Coefficient of lift	Coefficient of drag	L/D ratio
-4	0.007	0.0309	0
-3	0.100	0.0223	4
-2	0.192	0.0164	12
-1	0.278	0.0136	20
0	0.375	0.0129	29
1	0.445	0.0140	32
2	0.525	0.0164	32
3	0.590	0.0190	31
4	0.675	0.0245	28
5	0.770	0.0338	23
6	0.835	0.0447	19
7	0.900	0.0600	15
8	0.987	0.0750	13
9	1.050	0.0950	11
10	1.085	0.1182	9
11	1.090	0.1550	7
12	1.080	0.1850	6
13	1.040	0.2150	5
14	0.950	0.2450	4
		0.0309	0
		0.0223	4
		0.0164	12

Figure 13-3. This table shows the coefficients of lift and drag for three foil profiles. The maximum C_L (shaded) is at the angle of attack where the wing begins stalling. The maximum L/D (shaded) is also indicated.

The NACA profiles in Figure 13-3 are 12% thickness and the ogival thickness is 7%. The three foils are of infinite span. The NACA foil data comes from *Theory of Wing Sections*, and the ogival data comes from *Water Tunnel Observations on the Flow Past a Plano-Convex Hydrofoil*.

Following the Reynolds number, R_N, is a value labeled **C_L slope** which is short for *coefficient of lift curve slope*. Because the C_L curves are linear (straight line) in the realm of normal operating angles of attack, the slope of the line can be expressed as a single value. The *slope* is the difference between one C_L and the next one following a one degree change in AOA. Let's use the NACA 4412 for an example. At 1° AOA the $C_L = .50$, at 2° AOA the $C_L = .60$. The difference, or slope, is .10. Knowing this number can simplify the some calculations, like those used to determine *gain*.

Supercavitating sections are designed to operate best in the higher speed ranges and are not efficient at lower speeds. Interestingly, they are not efficient at high (cavitating) speed either. As you recall, from the Chapter 4, the lift chapter, 2/3s of lift comes from the topside of the foil. If the flow over the topside is disturbed, the majority of the lift will be lost. So it is with operations under cavitating conditions. To avoid a radical lift transition, the supercavitating foil section spoils the lower-speed topside lift that would otherwise be created. Of course this reduces the C_L of the wing during all modes of operation. It might be expected that the takeoff speed would be excessively high, but the super-cavitation foils are sized larger because, as mentioned, about 2/3 of the available lift is eliminated at high speeds as well.

The principles that apply to supercavitating wings also apply to similarly functioning propellers. One difference is a propeller designed to cavitate may also be designed to ventilate. By operating partially submerged, these propellers suck air in from above the surface. These are called super-ventilating propellers and have a due role as one of the three points of lift common to three-point hydroplanes, such as Miss Budweiser. These machines have big motors and enjoy a surplus of power at low speeds. They are able to sacrifice some efficiency in propulsion and still reach V_{TO}. Of course, ventilation continues through the entire speed range.

There is another important reason for the blunt trailing edge of a supercavitating propeller or wing. The cavity formed is filled with water vapor that exists only so long as there is a near vacuum. This cavity will collapse on itself a short distance downstream from where it was formed. The cavity collapse is remarkably violent and is notorious for its destructive power. If the trailing edge is blunted, the cavity collapse occurs downstream of the foil or wing and no damage will occur.

Figure 13-4. Supercavitating foil profiles.

It would seem that a sharp leading edge would smoothly slice through the water. This may be so at low angles of attack, but as the AOA increases the sharp edge contributes to upper surface flow separation, and to stalling, ventilation, and early cavitation at comparatively low angles of attack.

Thick or thin sections? Given the same material, thicker wing sections can be built stronger and stiffer than can the thinner sections. The wing acts as a beam in resisting bending, and the strength of a beam is in its "outer fibers". In a monocoque wing section the skin of the upper side and skin of the underside are the outer fibers. The outer fibers are more effective in resisting bending if they are widely separated; in this case, if there is more space separating the upper and lower skin. Obviously, thicker sections can pack in more material as well, but the material in the center of the cross section of a beam contributes very little strength compared to the outer fibers. As a rule of thumb, 10% thickness ratio is a practical minimum for ordinary hydrofoils. Struts may have a lower thickness ration because some struts, functioning as rudders, will have very long chords. *Thickness ratio* is thickness / chord. For a more detailed explanation on strength and bending, see chapter 11, "Materials, Stress Calculations, and Fabrication".

Form drag, the drag that dominates at high speeds, increases in proportion to the frontal area. Naturally, the smaller the frontal area the less drag there will be. Keep all wetted frontal areas as thin as practical. For a rule of thumb applicable to foils and struts, consider a 14% thickness ratio to be the maximum.

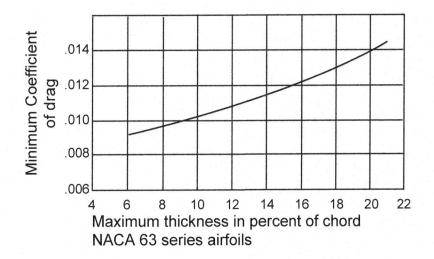

Figure 13-5. The minimum drag of a foil increases with thickness. From NACA TN 391.

The lift created by the foils must be variable to manage pitch, roll, and yaw. Since the introduction of **ailerons** in the early 1900s, the tendency has been to hinge to the trailing edge of a wing to create ailerons or flaps, or hinge to a strut to create a rudder. Rudders can also be one-piece, variable incidence, symmetrical foil shapes cantilevered vertically from the hull.

Hifybe uses variable incidence outboard winglets, or **flippers**, for roll control. An adjustment to the angle of attack changes the coefficient of lift. Similarly, hinged ailerons increase or decrease the coefficient of lift by altering the camber of the foil. Flippers are simple and sometimes easier to link to than the smaller ailerons, but the control pressures might be higher with flippers. Hifybe's flippers rotate around a single cantilevered 3/8-inch stainless steel rod projecting perpendicularly from the lower end of the main struts. A conventional fixed wing with hinged ailerons would be much stronger. Inside the hollow wing, a beam of steel 3/8 inch high and 3 times the width could have been embedded to provide a strong unit to which the ailerons would be attached. This would more than triple the unit's strength.

All else being equal, deploying an aileron, comprising 30% of the chord, can generate about 45% more lift than can be generated by rotating a flipper. According to Beaver and Zseleczky, "a 2.2 degree change in flap angle is required to obtain the same result as a 1 degree foil change". Low aspect ratio flippers and ailerons will have reduced efficiency, and I speculate that flippers are penalized the most.

The **center of pressure** of a foil section is the point on a chord line where pitching forces balance. A wing has a span-wise *line* joining these points where the pitching forces balance. This line moves as the wing's angle of attack changes but in normal operation it is about 25% of the chord aft of the leading edge. In some foil shapes the center of pressure moves more than in others. Generally a *symmetrical foil*, a foil where the top and underside of a foil mirror one another, will have a less mobile center of pressure. A *reflex camber*, a shape with a slight turn-up of the trailing edge, will also have a less mobile center of pressure. Balancing these moments can be important. For example, a symmetrical profile where the foil pivots on its long axis to operate as a flipper will have relatively consistent pressure on the hinge and controls. Asymmetrical foil shapes will have more variation in hinge and control pressure

Symmetrical shapes at zero degrees AOA create zero lift. **Asymmetrical, cambered profiles** create lift at zero degrees or at a modest negative AOA. Flaps and slats, in effect, increase the camber of the foil.

Dreese states that most wing profiles have a slope of about .11 per degree AOA change, and stall comes at about 15 degrees above zero lift AOA. That would be an increase in C_L of 1.65 (.11 * 15 = 1.65).

Hifybe's rear foil serves as an example. The NACA 63-412 profile slope for R_N = 3,000,000 is a follows: at AOA = -3°, its C_L = zero. Its lift curve is fairly straight for about 15 degrees (to 12°). From -3° to 12° the C_L changes 1.525 (from .055 to 1.58). This is a .102 change (Δ) in C_L for each degree change in AOA, substantively agreeing with Dreese.

Actually if we examine the 63-412 foil between -3° and 10°, where the curve is the straightest, the ΔC_L / degree = .11. If we include a small portion of the curve as the lift approaches the stalling point, the ΔC_L / degree = .109. It is .109 that we have chosen to represent the slope of this particular lift curve

The primary difference between the Dreese example and the NACA 63-412 is that his wing section is a symmetrical, whereas Hifybe's wing section is cambered, or asymmetrical. His wing has zero lift at AOA = 0° and ours, AOA = -3°.

Dreese further states that changing the profile moves the slope around but the .11° change per degree AOA is fairly consistent until the 3 dimension effects are modified: aspect ratio, wing tips, etc.

The take away message is, don't get obsessed with finding the perfect foil profile. Most common wings will work OK. Still, some gains in performance can be realized with rational profile selection, and the larger main lifting foil in particular should have its profile selected for superior L/D characteristics. The best lifting profiles have positive camber. It is important to have a rounded leading edge and a sharp trailing edge. Generally, the larger the radius of the leading edge is, the more docile will be its stall, the higher its AOA_{MAX}, and the higher will be its C_{LMAX}.

If a foil section is to be selected based on efficiency, it must first be decided if the section will be one classified as **laminar or turbulent**. To make this decision, we need to understand boundary layers. We briefly visited this concept in Figure 5-1 and its text. The **boundary layer** is an area of velocity transition. The foil is traveling at a given velocity through a fluid that we will assume is stationary. Due to skin friction, the fluid touching the foil will be moving with the foil. As we move away from the foil, the fluid flow will approach the velocity of the free stream. This area of velocity transition is called the *boundary layer*. The speeds of the layers within the boundary area are represented by the length of the arrows in Detail A of Figure 13-6.

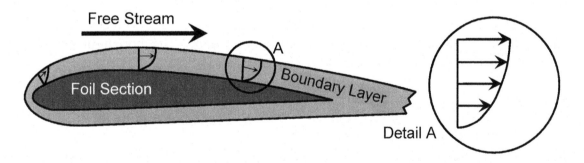

Figure 13-6, Boundary Layer, exaggerated in thickness, with detail.

In an ideal world, all flow around a wing would be laminar. That is, it would pass by the foil in lineal, orderly manner; and change velocity smoothly in the layers closest to the foil's surface. Visualize taking 500 sheets of fresh copy paper out of their wrapper and tossing them diagonally onto the rug. The bottom pages are stopped from sliding because of the friction of the rug, but the top sheets continue to move ahead to form a leaning stack. Each sheet has its own velocity with the top ones moving fastest and the bottom ones touching the rug not moving at all. All the pages remain flat and orderly. This is laminar flow. If a handful of loose papers were thrown to the wind they would tumble and separate in a chaotic fashion. This is turbulent flow.

Laminar flow is orderly flow and turbulent flow is tumbling, chaotic flow. Typical airfoils have laminar flow beginning at the leading edge and continuing on to some point along the chord until the flow separates from the surface and becomes turbulent. A laminar wing section is one that has a high proportion of laminar flow along its chord. Some aerodynamicists state that a wing with 60% laminar flow can be considered a laminar wing.

Conventional wing sections have the thickest part of their cross section near the leading edge. Laminar sections are thickest midway between the leading and trailing edges.

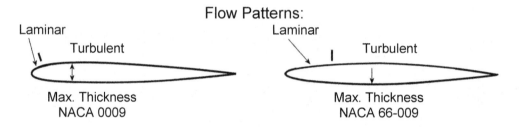

Figure 13-7. Conventional and laminar wing sections with the point
of separation being indicated by the 'I'. Note, these happen to be
symmetrical foils, but cambered foils would serve equally well in
this illustration. Source: *Aerodynamics for Naval Aviators.*

It is in this boundary layer that skin friction, a form of parasite drag, is created. The thicker the boundary layer the greater the skin friction will be. The more turbulent the flow, the thicker will be the boundary layer.

It can be seen from Figures 5-1 and 13-8 that the laminar boundary layer is much thinner than the turbulent layer. Laminar boundary layers accelerate less near the foil's surface and have a more gradual velocity change.

The Turbulent boundary layers close to the wing's surface stick to it and accelerate quicker than do laminar layers. The acceleration up to the velocity of the wing occurs in less space, but the area of change is thicker and involves more fluid. The rapid acceleration as well as the larger mass of disturbed layers consumes more energy than does the laminar flow.

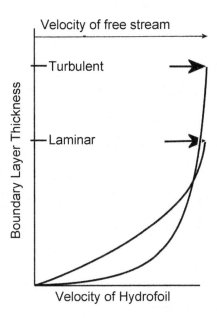

Figure 13-8. Relative velocities
within the boundary layer.

A laminar wing has a significantly improved lift / drag but only while operating within a
narrow range of angles of attack in asymmetrical wings. The best L /D is usually
experienced around 4 to 6 degrees. When coefficient of drag is plotted against the
coefficient of lift, a depression is created at the bottom of the curve. This depression is
named the **drag bucket**, and this is the realm of laminar flow. See Figure 13-9.

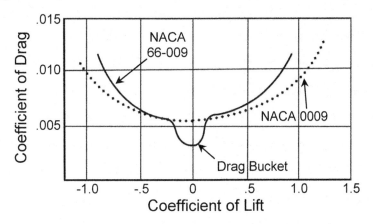

Figure 13-9. Drag Bucket of a Laminar Flow Wing Section. Notice
that the X-axis is C_L, not AOA. Reynolds Number = 6,000,000.
Source: *Aerodynamics for Naval Aviators.*

Laminar flow wings were made a part of operational military aircraft during WWII in the
B-24 Liberator bomber, and the P51 Mustang fighter. It was quickly learned, however,
that a real wing with rivets, seams, and bug guts cannot maintain laminar flow like the
perfect wings used in laboratory wind tunnel tests. As a result, the benefits of the drag
bucket were not fully realized in these two military designs.

Furthermore, because the boundary layer of laminar flow has such low energy, like a smart yet lazy student, there is a tendency for it to lose interest and drift off somewhere. This is boundary layer separation and it results in a lift / drag penalty. The P-51 pilot could compensate by slightly advancing the throttle on his 1,220 hp Allison.

Some collateral benefits were realized in the P-51 when its dive speed approached the speed of sound. All wing sections encounter high drag and flow separation problems as they approach the sonic barrier. The laminar wing was found able to fly closer to Mach 1 before encountering such problems. This characteristic does not benefit hydrofoils.

Since WWII we have developed fiberglass and carbon reinforced plastics that permit the construction of the near perfect wing. Whether or not it is worth facing the difficulty is a judgment call. For example, our Human Powered Group attempted to create a laminar profile hydrofoil. Despite our best fabrication efforts and carefully controlled test conditions, we were unable, on the first try, to create a wing that could operate in the elusive drag bucket. The failed attempt was in a significant setback.

Our experience and skills have increased and interest is shifting toward pushing the speed limits of human powered hydrofoils. To mount a serious challenge, it will be necessary to again risk the necessary time and money to capture the gains promised by laminar flow.

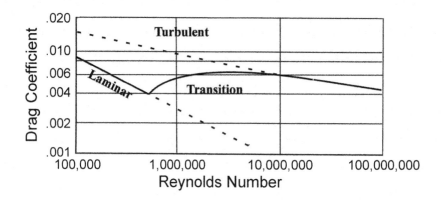

Figure 13-10. Friction drag on a smooth plate for various Reynolds numbers. Source: *Aerodynamics for Naval Aviators*. The logarithmic graph indicates that there is a low coefficient of drag for these shapes around R_N = 600,000.

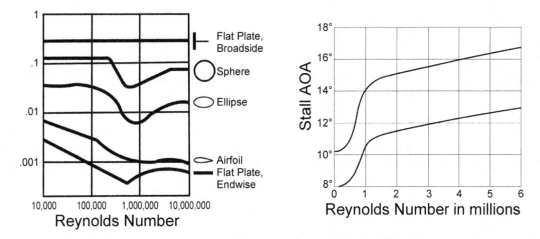

Figures 13-11a & b. (a) How Reynolds Number affects the C_D for various shapes. The stream is flowing from left to right past these shapes. Again, observe the dip in the logarithmic drag curves around R_N = 600,000. From *Fundamentals of Fluid Mechanics.* (b) The stall angle decreases rapidly when R_N = < 1,500,000. A NACA 0015 profile was used to construct this chart. From *Low-Speed Wing Tunnel Testing.*

Wouldn't one conclude from the discussion on laminar vs. turbulent flow that a golf ball, tennis ball, baseball, and jet wing should be perfectly smooth to encourage laminar flow and thereby reduce skin friction?

Then why are there **dimples on golf balls**, hairs on tennis balls, or stitches on baseballs? Why do some jet planes have little blades mounted in rows on their edges along the top of their wings? This brings us to what is called, "d'Alembert's paradox".

The paradox is: these balls go farther and faster when they have rough surfaces. The reason is: laminar flow has less drag, but is inclined to separate abruptly from the curved backside and thereby create a large energy-consuming wake. Remember boundary layer separation?

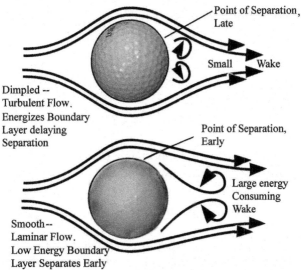

Figure 13-12. Dimpled vs. Smooth balls.

The dimples energize the boundary layer. The turbulent flow has a little more skin drag initially, but the energized flow has greater adhesion to the surface. This allows the boundary layer to follow the curve around the backside of the ball and therefore create a smaller wake than if the flow had an earlier separation from the backside surface. The smaller wake translates into reduced form drag.

The dimples, fuzz and stitches on balls are called **Turbulators**. The little blades on the top of some wings are also turbulators. They cause more friction drag, but by energizing the boundary layer they increase adhesion and therefore increase the lift on the downwind parts of the wing. This is especially needed for the flow over high lift devices such as flaps.

You are probably wondering, why are there no dimples on cannon balls?
Because cannonballs have an R_N of 2,800,000. Golf balls have an R_N of 193,000.

The golf ball is small and slow– by aircraft standards. Therefore, it is in the realm of low Reynolds numbers and the flow will be predominantly laminar. It profits from boundary layer energizing.

The cannonball is larger and faster; even faster than a subsonic aircraft. The boundary layer at the widest point of the ball will be energized and quickly become turbulent as it curves around the backside of the ball. There is no need to increase boundary layer energy. Skin friction will cause much of the drag and is best minimized. Turbulators would slow the ball.

How else does R_N affect us? The smaller and slower hydrofoils shown in this book operate with R_N less than 1,500,000. Unfortunately at this low R_N the maximum AOA, and the stall AOA, drops quickly. See Figure 13-11b.

Calculating Reynolds numbers, using this simplified formula first visited in Figures 4-3a and b, and the text that follows it:

For water flight:
$$V_{mph} \times C_{ft} \times 121,000 = R_N \qquad \text{Or} \qquad V_{ft/sec} \times C_{ft} \times 83,000 = R_N$$

For air flight:
$$V_{mph} \times C_{ft} \times 9,300 = R_N \qquad \text{Or} \qquad V_{ft/sec} \times C_{ft} \times 6,300 = R_N$$

For example, Hifybe cruises at 16 mph and has a rear foil chord, measured from leading edge to trailing edge, of .4 feet. Apply the formula:

$R_N = 16 \times .4 \times 121,000 = 774,400$. Round to 800,000.

Incidentally, the factors in the above equations are used in a ratio to represent the change in R_N when a shape is taken from the air and operated in water and there are no other changes. From air to water there is an increase in R_N by a multiple of 13. (121 / 9.3 = 13).

Back to cannonballs vs. golf balls. A pro golfer can tee off at 150 mph and the ball is .14 feet in diameter (substitute for chord). 150 x .14 x 9,300 = 195,300 R_N.

Cannons used in the Middle Ages had muzzle velocities calculated to be up to 600 mph. Assume an ordinary cannonball with diameter of 6 inches, or .5 feet. 600 x .5 x 9300 = 2,790,000 R_N.

Now that we have examined the characteristics common to all wings, let's narrow down the search by choosing three possible wing sections each with its own distinctive advantages and disadvantages. The three are the NACA 63-412, NACA 4412 and ogival introduced in chapter 4. Here are the important curves for the two highest performing:

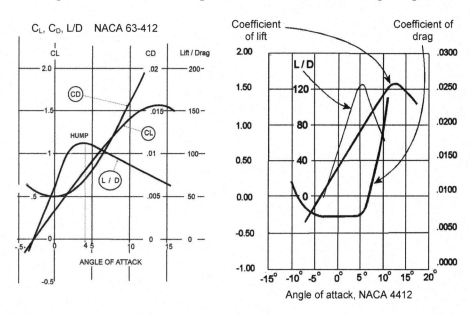

Figures 13-13a & b. NACA 63-412 and NACA 4412 airfoil performance curves, from *Airfoils at Low Speeds* and *Theory of Wing Sections*. R_N = 3,000,000.

Notice that the C_D curves look different than in the chart used to illustrate the drag bucket, Figure 13-9. The drag bucket curve was C_D vs. *coefficient of lift*. The curve in Figure 13-13 is C_D plotted against *angle of attack*. Of course, the NACA 4412 is not a laminar flow wing so there would not be a drag bucket anyway, but the NACA 63-412, when plotted against C_L, will have a drag bucket when in the realm of lower R_Ns.

The **NACA 63-412** shape is the most sophisticated of the three. It has a complex convex curve on top, the bottom-side is convex near the leading edge, and it has a slightly concave underside near the trailing edge. Its performance figures are better than the others. This type of foil has been used in the race winning Moth class sail boats as well as in the main foil of Hifybe. It is presently available in epoxy and carbon fiber composite from several companies including two in Australia, Fastacraft and Full Force.

The **NACA 4412** is chosen because it is most like the traditional **Clark Y.** The Clark Y was created 1922 by Professor Virginius Clark. Certainly the airfoil's most celebrated performance was as the wing section for the Spirit of St. Louis, the Ryan NYP used by Charles Lindbergh to make his famous transatlantic crossing in 1927. The Clark Y, NACA 4412, and the Göttengen Gö 398 are nearly duplicates of one another.

The NACA 4412 is a modern adaptation with plenty of performance data available in the public domain. The shape is relatively easy to accurately construct because of its simplicity: flat on nearly 70% of its bottom side with a smoothly changing convex upper surface. The leading edge is a straightforward segment of a circle. There are no convex segments in the profile.

The NACA 4412 and the Clark Y are not the best performing airfoils and that may be an advantage. Better performing shapes, like the laminar flow shapes, rely on high fabrication standards and must be operated in nearly optimal conditions. No seaweed, barnacles, or surface scratches can be tolerated. The real life performance of the NACA 4412 may more closely match its predicted performance.

The **ogival** shape is used as an example because it is the easiest to accurately fabricate by a boat builder armed with a welder and a grinder. The upper surface is an uncomplicated segment of a circle. It has a constant radius and can be cut from a large diameter pipe. The bottom surface is simply a flat plate. The profile is symmetrical in the sense that the leading 50% of the profile is the mirror image of the trailing 50% of the profile–not symmetrical in the conventional sense of having no camber. Both leading and trailing edges are sharp or nearly sharp. The lift created by flying forward is the same as the lift flying backward–provided that the angle of attack is the same in both directions. On the other hand, it has a lower C_L curve than the other two shapes, its L/D ratio is lower and it has an abrupt stall. I have used this profile to build simple hydrofoil test and display models where performance was not an issue. If performance is important, avoid using this short cut.

Any of these foil shapes can be fabricated by creating a male plug of a hard, smooth, and rigid material, applying mold release to its surface, casting around it a two piece female mold of FRP, applying mold release to the newly created mold and then filling the it with FRP or CRP.

Recall that on foils and struts **the leading edge should be rounded** to reduce ventilation and flow separation. The ogival profile follows this general rule and will be improved by rounding its leading edge. Review chapter 6 for more on this.

Strut thickness should be 10 to 15 % of its chord. Slender struts have less form drag and thicker struts have more strength. The trailing edge on struts and foils should be as sharp as safety allows. The most used strut profiles are NACA 0012 and 0014.

To summarize, of the three the profiles, NACA 63-412 is the best performer with the most complex shape. It is the most difficult to accurately construct. The NACA 4412 has a simpler form, yet is a good performer and has a long history of successes as the *Clark Y.* The ogival is the simplest form of all and the easiest to fabricate. But, its performance is the weakest of the three. Here are the three coefficients of lift curves:

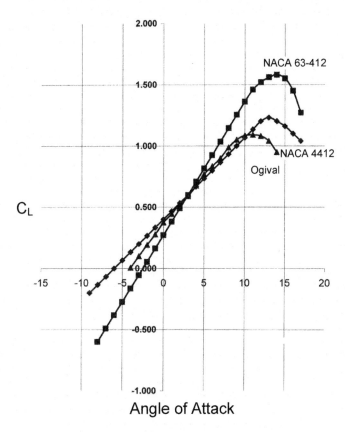

Figure 13-14. Lift coefficients vs.
AOA for three wing sections.

See Figure 13-3. For a table to compare coefficients of lift, drag, and L/D between the three foil profiles.

Wing loading describes how much weight a wing supports for a given area. In English units it is expressed as pounds per square foot, psf, or pounds per square inch, psi, for scale models and other very small wings. Wing loading is useful for comparing one hydrofoil wing to another.

Aspect ratio affects lift and induced drag, especially induced drag. Aspect ratio is a measure of fineness of the wing. In constant chord wings it is the ratio of *span / chord.* In tapered wings, it is the *span squared* divided by the wing *area.* A high aspect ratio wing–a wide fine wing–has less wing tip influence due to the tip's small size relative to the wide span. Therefore it creates less induced drag. Return to Figures 4-8 and 4-9 and their associated text for an expanded explanation.

Induced drag is created at the wing tips where high pressure fluid at the bottom of a wing attempts to flow into the low-pressure area on the upper side of the wing. This move to equalize pressures reduces lift as well. Because the wing is moving forward, the laterally moving flow is deflected rearward. This creates spiral patterns called **wing tip vortices**. This movement of fluid consumes energy and the loss of energy is called *induced drag*. The effect is greatest at conditions of high angles of attack, high coefficients of lift, and low flying speeds. Under these conditions, the pressure differential is greatest.

Using wing tip fences or winglets may reduce wing tip vortices. The winglets may be up-turned and oriented vertically. Winglets, as the name implies, are little wings. Vertical winglets function by blocking the flow of fluid around the wing tip. In doing so they decrease induced drag and allow the outboard portions of the wing to generate a C_L close to that generated by the inboard portions of the wing, so the finite span wing performs more like an infinite span wing

Interestingly, extending the winglet horizontally can create the same effect. The wing and winglet combination can be seen from above as a high aspect ratio tapered wing—see the next paragraph. Still, vertical winglets can be found on some of our favorite airliners. Vertical winglets are trendy, sexy, and can seduce aircraft buyers. Also, the narrower wings make it easier to find a parking space. In Figure 9-24 and its text we looked at a different type of winglet, one with variable angles of incidence. This type, also called a *flipper*, serves in place of ailerons by controlling rolling moments.

The good news for some hydrofoils is that struts attached to the extreme ends of the foils may serve a dual purpose. They connect the foils to the hull while doubling as vertical winglets or wing tip fences. As in aircraft, this allows a narrow wing to operate more efficiently. This reduces the importance of using a high aspect ratio. Of course two wing tip struts create more form drag than the one center strut seen on the inverted "T" foil. The designer must balance the differences in induced drag, form drag and structural strength when choosing between a "U" shape or an inverted "T" shape foil and strut combination.

The **high aspect ratio wing** has the additional advantage of being more roll stable. This is because the arc of movement of the wing tips around the roll center is proportional to the wing's half span, and the wider the wing the faster the wing tips move for a given degree of roll. The geometry is such that the descending wing tip has a greater angle of attack than the ascending wing tip. The result is a differential change in lift that has a damping effect on roll, and the wider the wing, the greater the dampening.

Taken to extremes, the long wing, when rolling, may experience *wing tip stalling* on the descending wing. This, of course, is destabilizing.

Mother Nature and aircraft designers know all this and it is reflected in birds and airplanes. Those that cruise, soar, and conserve energy have long thin wings, the fighters and the acrobats with ample power have short stubby wings.

For some hydrofoil boats, **low aspect ratio wings** may be necessary. Narrow hydrofoils allow for banking. During a turn they are less likely to touch the seabed or breach the surface. Narrow foils are better for coming next to a dock or avoiding object strikes while underway. These stubby wings have greater strength and are more resistant to torsion and tip deflection.

Washout is a term describing a changing lift pattern along the span of a wing. It can be in the form of wing twist or varying sectional profiles alone the span. In aircraft, the goal is to allow the outboard parts of the wing to stall following the inboard sections. Roll control is maintained in a partial stall and a full stall is more benign.

In aircraft and hydrofoils there is a reduction of wing tip vortices and induced drag when a lesser proportion of lift is generated near the wing tips. This can be achieved by lower wing tip AOA or making the profile near the tips more symmetrical or otherwise altered. Sophisticated wings will have modified profiles in the wing sections where flaps or ailerons are accommodated.

Planform, the shape when looking vertically down on the wing, is important. A long chord at the wing tips will create stronger wing tip vortices and higher induced drag. Again, this is especially so at low speeds and high angles of attack where induced drag dominates. Generally speaking, the elliptical planform is the most efficient. Tapered wings and wings with rounded wingtips are better than rectangles. Wings with vertical winglets, wing tip fences, or wing tip struts interfere with the creation of wingtip vortices and are more efficient. However, hydrofoil wings often have a rectangular planform, and this is not an efficient shape, but most hydrofoils do not operate in the realm of high-induced drag. Unlike aircraft, they are limited in how much they may pitch up.

A **rectangular planform** has reduced efficiency, but nonetheless this form has some natural advantages. It is easier and cheaper to fabricate. In a short, low aspect ratio, wing, it is especially important to have a high proportion of lift created near the tips where the lever arm for roll control is greatest.

Wing taper increases the efficiency of a hydrofoil in the same way that high aspect ratios do. With this wing planform, the wide inboard sections, away from the tips, generate much of the lift. Tapered wings can be structurally lighter, because less lift is generated at the ends of the cantilever. On the other hand, tapered wings are more complex and harder to build. They are less roll stable because there is less lift area at the tips where roll control and roll dampening have the greatest lever arm.

Sweeping back the leading edge of a hydrofoil wing may be useful for reasons not shared with their airborne cousins. Few planes have problems with seaweed, but hydrofoils do. A sweptback leading edge allows snagged debris to work its way back and, assuming no fences, shed itself. It's tempting to think about a sharp leading edge to cut through weeds but seaweed is surprisingly tough and resists cutting. It can rest on a fast moving knife-edge indefinitely. It is better to have a smooth, round leading edge to allow the seaweed to slide backward and outward until it falls off the wingtips. The sweptback wing also has a more gradual lift curve. However, it is more complex to build.

In this chapter, we have examined the characteristics of hydrofoil wings. The wing is the most distinctive feature of a hydrofoil. Without a wing there will not be flight. So it is essential to unravel the mysteries of what makes a good hydrofoil wing.

Up to this point, we have discussed the principles of what makes a hydrofoil fly and how to design one. The next chapter will touch briefly on how to scale down, or scale up, in the implementation these principles.

Scale Modeling

- o Scaling up and scaling down
- o Dynamic similitude
- o Bras d'Or scaled to Pouce d'Or
- o Model scaling factors
- o Hifybe, Scaled down

Scale modeling is not just for kids; sometimes the most practical solution to a problem is to change its scale. Scaling can reduce costs, make a development project progress faster, increase safety, and be lots of fun.

Scaling up and scaling down. Prior to building a full-sized prototype, many designers will prudently choose to scale down to and test a relatively small, cheap, and easy-to-build model. Likewise, a successful small-scale prototype can be reproduced in a larger scale.

Small boats are easier to build than large ones. Scaling up from a successful model can give better results than building full-scale as a first attempt. This is common practice for the government and large companies. For example, Boeing built Sealegs and Fresh-1, Figures 1-6 and 1-7, before attempting to build its 400 passenger Jetfoil, and its line of military hydrofoils. The Canadians first built the RX test craft, a quarter-scale hydrofoil model not illustrated herein, before tackling the 151 ft., 200 ton Bras d'Or, Figure 1-4. Harry Larsen put foils on a 14 ft. outboard-powered open boat prior to creating his 24 ft. flying Bayliner, Figure 8-11. Once these smaller vehicles were tested, modified and proven, they were scaled up to their famous counter-parts.

In the opposite direction, it is a well-established pastime to take a passenger-carrying, load-carrying, or military vessel and reduce it to a working miniature. This can be done strictly for the pleasure of completing a complex task. Others are pleased to own a miniature of something that could otherwise only be owned by taxpayers or shareholders.

I propose a third idea. Why not take an existing large-scale working hydrofoil, one that has completed all the designing, modeling, testing and tuning, and reduce it to a one or two man fun machine. Wouldn't it be cute to tool around the bay in a little hydrofoil like the one illustrated in Figure 1-13? The idea is to change the magnificent Canadian warship, Bras d'Or (Golden Arm) into a personal watercraft, Pouce d'Or (Golden Thumb). This would be an excellent application of the principles of modeling to create an original PWC.

The Bras d'Or was chosen for the following reasons: The design combines the best of simplicity and sophistication. The simple surface piercing front foil is easy to understand and to duplicate. It is rugged and practical. The job of this front foil is to control flying height and provide steering. When accelerating to takeoff speed, the surface piercing foil has 100% of its area wetted and providing lift. As speed increases, the foil rises and the wetted area is reduced until the correct flying height is obtained. Any disturbance from this state of equilibrium will result in a change in wetted area and the foil will automatically find its correct flying height for the speed at which it is travelling and the weight it is supporting. Its angle of attack is trimmed by pivoting the foil on its lateral axis at the point of attachment at the base of the bow. It steers simply by rotating on its vertical axis.

The rear foil is also surface piercing. Because the span is wide, the outboard portions of the foil exerts powerful roll control. The rear foil is designed to carry 80% of the load, so these foils are sufficiently large to have the necessary roll authority. The outboard winglets have anhedral angle and therefore their outward pointing lift vectors have a long lever arm, as measured from the craft's center of gravity, with which they apply roll correction forces. The winglets are also lineal extensions of the main outboard struts. It would be an easy thing to run a straight shaft inside the outboard struts to the winglets. From the cockpit the pilot would rotate this shaft to control the angle of incidence of the winglets and thereby control roll.

It happens that the weight and foil area distribution are also favorable. With the main foil designed to carry 80% of the weight, it would be natural to cluster the motor and the pilot around it.

Because the original project was publicly funded, there is a wealth of information available. For example, the book, *Fastest in the World...*, by John boileau; and the excellent 28 page report, *HMCS Bras d'Or–An Open Ocean Hydrofoil Ship*, by Eames & Jones (see bibliography).

Before you head out to the garage to start hammering and gluing, take some time to think about **dynamic similitude**. This has to do with the similarities between a full-scale device and a scaled down or scaled up version. Perhaps this is best explained by example.

Suppose you decide to scale down **Bras d'Or** to a 1/8th scale model, **Pouce d'Or.** This means you would reduce the original 151-foot length to 1/8th or 18.9ft. Can you simply divide the other dimensions and specifications by 8?

It is more complicated than that. The rules dictate that the model and the original will be proportional and in scale, but not always the same scale. To illustrate, let's scale down a cubic foot of seawater. 1ft * 1ft * 1ft = 1ft^3 = 64 lbs (100% or 1/1). If we scale down the measurement linearly to 50% it does not follow that the volume and weight will be reduced by 50%, because .5ft * .5ft * .5ft = .125ft^3 = 8 lbs. The resulting volume and weight have been reduced to 12.5% or 1/8th of the full-scale cube. Furthermore, the area of one side of the cube is 25% of the area of the full-scale side. That is, .5 * .5 = .25ft^2 (25% or 1/4).

It can be seen that scale modeling is not a simple thing, and in depth coverage is beyond the scope of this book. However, to give the basic idea of the calculations needed, the following table, Figure 14-1, can serve as an introduction to relative scaling ratios needed to achieve dynamic similitude. This table is developed based on what is called *Froude Scaling,* so it does not account for the fact that viscous resistance becomes relatively greater at a smaller scale. As such, the required horsepower might be somewhat under-estimated when scaling down using the relationship shown below.

Model Size:	1/2 Scale	1/4 Scale	1/8 Scale	1/16 Scale
Linear Dimensions	1/2	1/4	1/8	1/16
Area	1/4	1/16	1/64	1/256
Volume and Weight	1/8	1/64	1/512	1/4096
Moments	1/16	1/256	1/4096	1/65536
Moments of Inertial	1/32	1/1024	1/32768	1/1048576
Wing Loading	1/2	1/4	1/8	1/16
Linear Velocity	1/1.14	1/2	1/2.83	1/4
Linear Acceleration	1	1	1	1
Angular Velocity	1.14	2	2.83	4
Angular Acceleration	2	4	8	16
R P M	1.14	2	2.83	4
Horsepower	1/11.3	1/128	1/1448	1/16384
Reynolds Number	1/2.83	1/8	1/22.6	1/64
Time	1/1.14	1/2	1/2.83	1/4

Figure 14-1. **Model scaling factors**. Data from Consolidated Aircraft Corp and edited by Martin Grimm, International Hydrofoil Society.

Let's apply some of these ratios to the Bras d'Or measurements to scale down to the Pouce d'Or:

	Bras d'Or	Scaling factor	Pouce d'Or
Scale of model		1/8	
Linear dimensions, ft	151	1/8	19
Weight, lbs	475,000	1/512	928
Linear velocity, mph	72	1/2.83	25
Horsepower	20,000	1/1446	14

Figure 14-2. Model scaling applied to Bras d'Or hydrofoil.

OK, maybe for a first project it is too ambitious to scale down a warship into a personal watercraft, so let's first scale down our ambitions. Say you have some ideas for a height finding device that could be tried out on **Hifybe, scaled down**. It may be worth the effort to build a ¼-scale radio controlled model as a test bed. This could reduce building time, material costs, and be an enjoyable project. In this case the model's length would be 1/4th of 146 inches or 37 inches. The other adjustments would be as follows in Figure 14-2:

	Hifybe	Scaling factor	Mini-Hifybe
Scale of Model		1/4	
Length, in	146	1/4	37
Weight, lbs	329	1/64	5
Velocity-max, mph	16	1/2	8
Wing loading lbs/ft3	1	1/4	.25
Horsepower	8	1/128	.06
Reynolds Number	75,000	1/8	93,750

Figure 14-3. Scaling down Hifybe into a radio controlled model.

Unfortunately, Hifybe is not roll stable, so in a model of it there must be one important design change. The full-sized Hifybe needs continuous control inputs to keep its wings level. This is acceptable because in this fun machine, it makes for an interesting flying experience. However, in a scaled-down version, there will be no pilot on board to make the necessary corrections.

The simplest solution would be to make the rear foil surface piercing near the wing tips, similar to the system used in Shutt's Hydro-ped, described in chapter 17. Follow the rules of roll control after reviewing chapters 9 and 10.

These scaling factors are useful for quick calculations; however, they are like rules of thumb. They should not be totally relied upon. More dependable results will be achieved by using the calculations in the previous chapters for weight and balance, lift, drag, surface areas, power etc. Again, a lot depends on where the designer-builder wishes to spend his time–behind the computer or in the workshop. With a model, there really is a choice, because the small projects take less time, material and money. The mistakes are not so serious, so why not sketch it, build it and see if it flies?

Comparative Analysis of Designs

o Overview
o Flying height range
o Gain and Gain / inch
o Wing loading
o Roll stiffness
o Power to weight ratio
o Lift to drag ratio
o Turn authority

Overview. It is not always necessary to calculate and predict performance results. This is especially true when working with relatively small, inexpensive, and easy to build small boats or models.

However, if you choose to do the calculations, the results will have more meaning if they are compared to other successful designs. From the previous chapters, we know about the principles of aquadynamics. In this short chapter, we will look at some useful ratios that can be used to compare one boat to another. This is comparative analysis.

Naturally, these comparisons are best done between boats of similar size, speed, purpose, Reynolds number, etc. Following are 8 points of comparison, or benchmarks. Calculating and comparing these benchmarks will help the designer predict performance, and isolate problems should they arise.

Following each benchmark's explanation will be an example calculation using values from Hifybe.

Flying height range: The three heights of interest are, from Figure 8-18, height at rest, H_R; height at takeoff, H_{TO}; and maximum height, H_{MAX}. It is the role of the *front* foil to establish the flying height. Flying begins at takeoff from a hull-borne condition. So the *minimum* flying height is zero inches. The *maximum* flying height can be determined logically, and this will be the height where the source of propulsion is no longer efficient, or the foil no longer provides sufficient lift. For a long-shafted outdrive or outboard engine where the propeller is above the foil, this will be the height at which the propeller begins to ventilate, or where the cooling water inlet rises above the surface—whichever is the lesser.

However, a boat may be designed with the propeller below the foil because, in the event of a bottom strike, the outboard is more robust than the delicate wing, and the lower thrust line may function more effectively in cutting turns. Recall how the sharply banked Dynafoil uses thrust to make sharp turns by pivoting around its water-skimming gunnel. Also, if thrust is used for directional control, the lower thrust line will create a powerful rolling force toward the inside of the turn. Once the maximum flying height is established, it's measurement will be applied to the front foil, the height finding foil.

V_{MAX} and V_{CRUISE} will be close to equal in uncomplicated designs, as will the front foil's H_{MAX} and H_{CRUISE}. But the rear foil will be more sensitive to speed as it rotates around the height finding front foil. A typical rear foil might have a H_{CRUISE} of two thirds of the H_{MAX}. Occasionally exceeding the maximum height of the rear foil can be momentarily tolerated without interrupting flight, but if a foil breaches it will carry a bubble of air with itself as it reenters the water and the hull may briefly contact the surface. Obviously, when the flying height falls below zero the boat will slow and it may be necessary to repeat the takeoff procedure.

Hifybe's motor cavitation plate is 15 inches below the hull. Three inches of flow above this plate is needed, so the maximum flying height is 12 in. The cruising height is two thirds of the maximum, or 8 in. $12 * .67 = 8$ in. This becomes the target height for the front foil. Markings visible to the outside observer are made on the front foil, the height finding foil. These markings serve as performance benchmarks to tune the front foil, and will indicate the inches of flying height.

Gain is a measure of height finding stiffness.

Gain / inch (gain per inch) is a sample of height finding stiffness. It is the percent difference in lift (or C_L) of the front foil caused by decreasing its flying height from H_{MAX} to one inch below H_{MAX}. Here is the equation:

$$\frac{\Delta C_L / in}{C_L @ H_{MAX}} = \text{gain / inch (gain per inch)}$$

$\Delta C_L / in$ is the C_L change that occurs when the height is reduced 1 inch from max height. It stands for: "the difference in coefficient of lift per inch of height change".

Go to the text between Figures 18-8 and 8-19 for an explanation and a sample calculation.

If the front foil has been built, calculations of Gain/inch can be abbreviated. Hifybe uses a Shutt Strut. It is easy to find the two AOAs by using a ruler, level, protractor, string and stick (some may prefer to use trigonometry). While the craft is supported on sawhorses, the surface follower is raised to V_{MAX} height and the AOA of the front foil is measured. Raise the surface follower one inch and measure the change in the front foils AOA. Go to Figure 13-3 and find the two C_Ls corresponding to the two AOAs. Apply the equation, *Gain / inch* = ΔC_L / in / C_L @ H_{MAX}, and the result will be the comparative number, Gain / inch.

One caveat, the reference measurement, zero degrees AOA, is determined by comparing a horizontal line to a line passing through the foil's *leading edge* and the *trailing edge*. With most foil profiles, the bottom side of the foil is not parallel to the zero degree line. To facilitate easy AOA measurements, it is worth the time to make a little fixture of balsa wood and Bondo-type body putty to cup over the top surface of the foil. Be sure to cover the foil with something like plastic wrap before applying the Bondo to ensure easy separation. Make the top of the fixture parallel to the zero degree line, and place it on top of the foil whenever making AOA measurements.

	Wand length, in	Δ AOA / in	ΔC_L / degree (Slope) NACA 4412	ΔC_L / in	C_L @ H_{MAX}	Gain / in
Hydro-ped	24	2.3	0.1	0.23	0.3	77%
Dragonfly	35	1.6	0.1	0.16	0.3	55%
Mach .03	35	1.6	0.1	0.16	0.3	55%
Hifybe	40	1.4	0.1	0.14	0.3	47%
Talaria IV	36*	0.5	0.1	0.05	0.3	17%
Moth**	40*			0.04	0.3	13%

* The typical Moth and Talaria IV have a linkage system that modifies the Δ AOA / in
** The typical Moth has flaps, so we take a different approach:
The height changes 22 inches and the C_L changes .9, so the C_L change / in = .9 / 22 = .04
The "Delta" (Δ) means "difference"

Figure 15-1. A few examples of front foil gain. The faster boats have lower Gain / in.

Wing loading. Wing loading is the ratio of lift *divided by area*. The units used are pounds per square foot. Hifybe, including the pilot and gas, weighs 365 lbs. The area of its two foils equals 2.29 ft². Its total wing loading is 365 / 2.29 = 159 lbs / ft². The wing loading of one boat can be compared to another.

It is also useful to compare the fore and aft foils of any particular boat. The forward foil normally has a higher wing loading than the aft for pitch stability. Go back to chapter 8 for more on relative wing loading for pitch stability.

Aircraft, main wing only:	Wing loading, lbs / ft^2
Sailplane	6
Single engine, light	17
Twin engine, light	26
Jet fighter	70
Jet aircraft	120

Hydrofoils:	Main	Bow
Human powered, Hydro-ped. V_{MAX}	203	165
Personal engine powered, Hifybe	145	145
Motor cruiser, Talaria IV	462	541
Military, High Point	1260	1035

Figure 15-2. Wing loading comparison table.

Roll stiffness is expressed as the total weight divided by the maximum roll torque. Hifybe weighs 450 lbs. and at top speed, with maximum deflection of its joystick, it generates a roll moment of 129 lbs. The average lever arm is 1.5 ft, so the maximum roll torque is 193 ft. lbs. The roll stiffness ratio is therefore: 450 / 193 = 2.25.

Power to weight ratio, P/W. This is the horsepower divided by total pounds including rider, fuel, etc. Multiply the product by 100 to eliminate fractional numbers. The result will be horsepower per 100 lbs. The calculation for Hifybe would be 8hp / 365 lbs = .022.
.022 * 100 = 2.2hp / 100 lbs.

Lift to drag ratio, L/D. This ratio is an important measure of efficiency. The L/D of any particular hydrofoil boat should be in the same range as the L/D of similar boats. If the measured L/D is significantly low, there is too little lift or excessive drag. Some examples of L/D are in Figure 5-12. Return to chapter 5 for deeper coverage on P/W and L/D. These ratios were used in engine selection.

Turn authority is the least useful calculation, and so is saved for the last. It is the total weight divided by the maximum turning torque. This would not be routinely calculated, but in the event of problems, these calculations could serve as a useful comparison tool. It is calculated similarly to roll stiffness. Maximum turning torque cannot be a definitive number, because the turning device, the rudder, is often surface piercing and therefore subject to ventilation at even modest angles of attack. Therefore, calculated maximum turning forces cannot be relied upon. Also, as the rudder is turned, the direction of the hull changes and that reduces the AOA of an aft rudder or increases the AOA of a forward rudder. To standardize this measurement, two degrees of rudder deflection is the number we would be using. Fortunately, of all the flight components, the physical rudder is probably the easiest to add to or subtract from. Why worry? Build a rudder that looks adequate and change it if needed.

Design Hifybe Systematic Approach

- o State the goal
- o Select power, foils, and materials
- o Available components
- o Weight and balance
- o Determine surface area
- o Power analysis
- o Structure
- o Safety
- o Pilot technique

OK, enough theory, let's get our feet wet. What you previously knew about aerodynamics, airplanes, boats and fabrication, combined with the material in this book, should add up to enough know-how to be able to design, build and fly a hydrofoil. All we need is to ask ourselves the appropriate questions and then generate the correct answers. This chapter will establish a pattern of questions and answers as we go through the design process using a specific example. In this case, Hifybe will serve. Hifybe is an appropriate subject because it is maneuverable on three axes, it can be built inexpensively in a garage with common tools, it is constructed of ordinary materials, and it is docile enough that a prudent operator can fly it safely.

We will start by stating our design goal, selecting power, foils, and materials. Based on these decisions we will do the necessary calculations: determining weight and balance; calculating foil area, drag, and power. We will make provisions to raise safety to the highest level possible.

In the following chapters, we will apply the design process to other specific examples: human powered and sail-powered hydrofoil boats.

Goal:

In this chapter, we will design a lightweight, canard configured, one-person hydrofoil boat using the hull of a commercial windsurf board that is powered by a lightweight, low horsepower outboard motor. For safety, power is kept low to limit speed. Takeoff speed will be about 8 mph and top speed to be about 16 mph. Other safety measures will be implemented. Fabrication challenges will be reduced by using commercially available components whenever possible.

Design Hifybe Systematic Approach

Select power, foils, and materials:

Motor: A small lightweight outboard. Hull: Assume a 12 ft commercially made windsurf board. For more information, see chapter 12, "Hull and Motor Selection".

Materials: Carbon fiber reinforced resin is preferred for foils and struts. Welded, extruded aluminum is to be used to create the motor attachment point and other hard-points and hull stiffening members. For more information see chapter 11, "Materials, Stress Calculations, and Fabrication".

Commercially available components:

Front Foil

> ➤ Type and source: "Shutt Strut" from Jake Free, FreeEnterprises.com.
> ➤ Profile: Clark Y which is like the NACA 4412.
> ➤ Span = 20.25 in.
> ➤ Tip Chord = 1.5 in.
> ➤ Root Chord = 3.25 in.
> ➤ Mean Average Chord (MAC), tapered = 2.375 in.
> ➤ Area = 48.1 in^2 = .33 ft^2.
> ➤ Aspect Ratio = 20.25 / 2.375 = 8.5
> ➤ F_{AR} = .84. The calculations are in Figure 16-2.
> ➤ Wand length = 40 in.
> ➤ Gain/inch = 48% change in C_L per 1 inch change from cruise height (Figure 8-20).
> ➤ Wing loading = 164 Lbs/ft^2.

Rear Foil

> ➤ Type and Source: Moth rear foil made by John Illett, Fastacraft.com. Trimmed in span.
> ➤ Profile: NACA 63-412.
> ➤ Roll control: Manually controlled ailerons or variable incidence outboard winglets.
> ➤ Span = 59 in. Center semi-span, 20" + winglet, 9.5" = semi span, 29.5".
> ➤ Chord = 4.75 in.
> ➤ Area = 280 in^2 = 1.94 ft^2.
> ➤ Aspect Ratio = 59 / 4.75 = 12.5.
> ➤ F_{AR} = .75 Note: The calculations are in Figure 16-2.
> ➤ Wing loading = 159 Lbs/ ft^2.

Height sensing mechanism (front foil only)

The so-called Shutt Strut, Figure 8-6, is an integrated unit consisting of a foil, strut, wand, and a surface follower.

Hull

Almost any commercially fabricated windsurf board should be suitable; provided its skin is of a material that epoxy resin will adhere to. The length should be about 12 feet and the approximate maximum displacement (buoyancy) should be 600 pounds or more. The thickness should be fairly uniform so that the aft portion displaces enough to support the concentrated weight of the motor and pilot.

Outboard motor

> The motor to be used is a Suzuki 8 hp, two-stroke, long-shaft outboard, weighing 56 lbs., or a suitable substitute.

Design parameters:

> Takeoff velocity, (V_{TO}): no more than 8 mph, 11.76 ft/sec., due to safety and power restrictions.
> The primary roll control device will be counter rotating variable incidence winglets (flippers). They will be linked to a single axis joystick.
> Turning control will be through a pivoting foot bar linked to the bow mounted front rudder.
> The bow rudder will also serve as a strut connecting the front foil to the hull—this is the Shutt Strut combination.

Control principles

> The method for initiating a turn will be to use the joystick to start and control roll when entering the turn. Rudder will be applied simultaneously to initiate yawing. The boat's forward momentum and centrifugal force created by the application of the rudder will be manifest as a rolling moment to the outside of the turn, and this will counteract the tendency to fall to the inside of the turn. In other words, the pilot will turn under the fall to correct for excessive inside roll. See chapters 9 and 10 for more on roll control.
> The rear foil angle of incidence may be decreased while transitioning from V_{TO} to V_{MAX}. This will trim the pitch of the hull from a stern high attitude to a level attitude.
> The front foil gain will be calculated.
> Determine V_{TO} and V_{MAX}, front foil.
> Determine V_{TO} and V_{MAX}, rear foil.

Design Hifybe Systematic Approach

Provide for adequate management of flight components:

- Flying height.
- Pitch.
- Roll.
- Yaw and steering.
- Hull-borne static stability.
- Crash stability.
- Crew containment.
- Consider the possibility of making the foils and motor retractable for ease of trailering, launching and hull-borne maneuvering.
- Consider providing for damage control from debris strike or high speed grounding.

Based on these assumptions, make the necessary calculations:

Determine weight and balance:

- Total weight with foils (essential).
- Weight and lift distribution (essential).
- Drag calculations and power required starting at 8 mph.
- Foil areas.
- Front foil C_L gain resulting from height change.
- Maximum roll torque in ft-lbs.
- Stress calculations, foil (rear only).
- Stress calculations, struts.
- Stress calculations, top bar, the horizontal tube connecting the struts to the hull.

Determine lift, drag, and speed.

Drawings:

- Weight and Balance: overall side view.
- Depth of rear foil.
- Rear foil showing ailerons and lever arm acting on the center of roll.
- Pitch angle of hull.

After setting our goals, we examine what resources and material are available. In my case, I acquired each piece by searching and adapting that which was available.

It is not necessary to buy a new hull to be cut up and reconfigured. Unless the designer has special ideas about how a hull should look, it may be sensible to buy an existing hull. I found a suitable windsurf board at a local surfboard shop. It is an appropriate length and the buoyancy is adequate to support a rider, a small motor, foils, and mounting hardware. Incidentally, a surfboard would lack the required strength and buoyancy.

California, and some other states, require that all new motors be four-cycle. Because oil is not added to the gas of four-cycle engines, they run cleaner, but they are significantly heavier than two cycle. Flying machines must be kept as light as possible. Therefore my search in California was restricted to used motors. My requirements are: Long shaft (20 inch transom), 6 to 10hp, weighing about 50 lbs., 2-cycle and easy starting. I discovered a used 2-cycle 8 hp Suzuki 2-cylinder outboard motor at a motor dealership.

FastaCraft.com/, Bladerider.com.au/, and others fabricate rear foils primarily for the Moth class sailboat. The chords available are approximately correct, based on calculations. To be precise, the area is adjusted by cutting off the ends of the foil to change the span. The carbon fiber reinforced epoxy resin construction is very strong and light. The profile is accurate and the surface is smooth.

Several front foils were built and tested, but the most satisfactory one was a Shutt Strut fabricated by FreeEnterprises.com in Elkhart, Indiana. This foil, like the Fastacraft foil, is strong, smooth and has an accurate profile.

After assuring the availability of the main parts the next step is to **determine the weight and balance**. This is necessary to calculate the precise size of the hydrofoils.

Using Corel Paint Shop Pro X, I print a .jpg photo of the proposed boat on inkjet paper to create an image like in Figure 16-1.

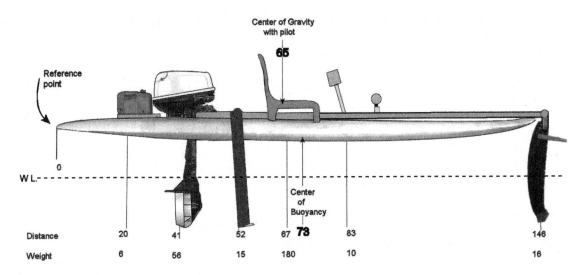

Figure 16-1. Hifybe component weights and locations.

On this image I sketch the components in their logical positions. Using a bathroom scale, each component is weighed. The components are then, on paper, placed in their logical location. Using an Excel spreadsheet the following calculation is done, and after some trial and error the correct location of each component is determined. Here they are as measured in inch pounds of torque applied to the reference point. The reference point can be at either extreme end.

If a component's weight is changeable it must be located as close to the CG as is practical to avoid shifting the CG and trim. Alterations in crew size or number will upset the balance of the boat unless the seat(s) are located at the CG. Gas consumption or replenishment also needs to be provided for. In the case of Hifybe, the seat is near the CG and the gas tank holds only 6 lbs of fuel–not enough to significantly alter the weight and balance.

Component	Weight W	Distance from Stern D	Torque W * D =
Gas tank ½ gallon	7	20	140
Motor	56	41	2,296
Rear foil	15	52	780
Seat & pilot	180	67	12,060
Hull centers, gravity and buoyancy	46	73	3,358
Aluminum frame	35	73	2,555
Control stick	10	83	640
Front foil	16	146	2,336
Bow	0	146	0
Totals	365 lbs.		24,165 in lbs.

In this calculation, torque is the hypothetical force in in-lbs. exerted around the reference point chosen to be at the extreme bow or stern. We will use the stern. With torque information we can determine the center of gravity (CG) and the load carried by each of the two foils. For clarity, all numbers are rounded off and so will vary slightly from computer-generated numbers.

To determine the center of gravity divide the total torque by the total weight: 24,165 /365 = 66 inches from the stern. This is the average distance from the stern where all the weight exerts its force. This is the location of the CG.

Because the hull is nearly symmetrical fore and aft, we can assume that the center of buoyancy coincides with the geometric center. 146 / 2 = 73 inches from the stern.

The center of gravity is 7 inches behind the center of buoyancy (CB). 73 – 66 = 7 inches. The CG must be behind CB, because when at rest the bow must buoy higher than the stern. This allows a takeoff with the bow up and a small additional positive angle of attack on the foils. Don't position the CG behind the CB by anymore than about 10% of the total length. If the CG is too far back, the stern will submerge giving the appearance of the Titanic in its last fitful moments. Ha! If you bought into that image, you didn't see the movie were the Titanic went down with its stern high.

Every surfer dude loves his board, but each board has its shortcomings. Surfboards and windsurf boards are marginally roll stable when a rider is mounted. Adding a motor and rigging raises the CG and makes the board even more unstable.

To correct this problem, Hifybe has port and starboard outriggers made from 4" diameter PVC tubes sealed at the ends and attached to the hull by aluminum thin-walled pipe. Each tube is 20" long and displaces 20 lbs. The tubes are not shown in Figure 16-1, but can be seen on the cover photo.

The foils are tentatively located where they fit best based on structure, appearance, etc. Naturally, the front foil goes well forward to lighten its load, and to maximize the foil base. Generally, lengthening the foil-base increases pitch stability. Review Figure 8-21 to understand how foil-base and pitch stability are related.

The rear foil is placed behind and near the CG so that it will carry most of the weight. Attaching the main foil assembly to the strong aluminum framework that the motor is attached to will reduce structural problems.

Using these preliminary foil locations, we determine the lift required of each foil:

Measure the distance of each foil from the CG. The CG is 66" from the reference point.
Front foil is 146 – 66 = 80" from the CG
Rear foil is 66 – 52 = 14"
Distance between foils is 80 + 14 = 94"

To find the *percent of lever arm* attributed to each foil divide the distance from CG for each foil by the total distance between foils:
Front 80 / 94 = .85. Move the decimal two places to convert to a percentage = 85%.
Rear 14 / 94 = .15. Convert to a percentage = 15% leverage.

To find the percent of *weight* supported by each foil divide the distance from CG for the *opposite* foil by the total distance between foils:
Front 14 / 94 = .15. Move the decimal two places to convert to a percentage = 15%.
Rear 80 / 94 = .85. Convert to percent = 85% weight supported.

Of course there is no need to do the calculations twice as I have done, because the percentage of *distance* of the foil base that it is away from the CG will equal 100% minus the percentage *weight* supported by the foil. For example, the front foil is forward of the CG by 85% of the length of the foil-base. 100% - 85% = 15%. This equation indicates that the front foil will be supporting 15% of the total weight. The rear foil, is aft of the CG by 15% of the distance between foils and it will be supporting the remaining weight, 85%. As a proof of your calculations the sum of the two weight percentages will equal 100%, and the sum of the two distance percentages will equal 100%

Usually for pitch stability the front foil is assigned a higher wing loading than the rear. This rule applies when both of the front and rear foils have a fixed AOI so that when the hull pitches the AOA of both foils changes equally. The Shutt strut is hinged at the bow and it determines its AOA independently of the pitch of the hull. In this case, the wing loading rule does not apply.

We know the total weight, 365 lbs. So predicting the weight to be supported by each foil is easy. In the second column are the weights measured after construction, flying and tuning: Tuning includes all the little changes that are made in response to observations made while testing a new design. In this case, the pilot was moved to increase the loading of the front foil.

Now we can **determine the surface area of the hydrofoils**. To do this we use the lift formula solved for area. An explanation of the lift formula can be seen in chapter 4 "Lift, Area, and Speed Calculations".

$$S = L / (V^2 * C_L * F_{AR})$$

Where:

S   = Surface area in square feet.
L   = Lift in pounds (Lift = Weight, when in straight and level flight).
F_{AR} = Factor, correction for aspect ratio. See the next paragraph.
V   = Velocity in feet per second. 1 mph = 1.47 ft / sec.
C_L = Coefficient of lift from column 2, table in Figure 4-2.

To find F_{AR} refer to Figures 4-9a and b. The application of the equation at the top of column 1 in Figure 4-9b shows the F_{AR} for Hifybe's front and aft foils:

Calculate the Factor-aspect ratio (for Hifybe)

Main, aft foil	Aspect ratio	Percent of total span	F_{AR} = AR / (2+AR)
Aft center	9.00	80%	85%
Aft flipper	1.25	20%	35%
Aft weighted average			75%
Front foil	8.5	100%	84%

Figure 16-2. Factor for Aspect Ratio (F_{AR}) Hifybe.

At this point we know all the values of the variables except the coefficient of lift (C_L). To find this we consult the C_L charts or tables, Figure 4-2 or 13-3. In the table, we use the NACA 63-412 wing profile, column 2. This is the profile used in the main wing of Hifybe. The C_L comparison can be seen in Figures 4-2 and 13-13. If a different section were used, we would change to the appropriate chart.

We see from the table, Figure 13-3, that the highest lift over drag ratio of 114 occurs, for the wing section alone, when the angle of attack equals 4°. This is the most efficient operating realm of this particular foil section. Wouldn't it make sense to be at this AOA at cruise speed for a cruising boat, or at top speed for a fast boat?

A flying windsurf board is just for fun, not for setting speed records, so we will be designing it as a cruising boat. The target for the main foil will be to have the highest lift over drag ratio at cruise speed, but in this simple design, cruising speed and top speed will be pretty much the same. So at cruise-top speed the AOA will be 1°, slightly below the optimum 4°. At 1° the C_L = .381, the C_D = .0056, and the L/D = 69.

Calculate the surface area of Hifybe's foils

	AOA	$S = L / (V^2 * C_L * F_{AR})$	Calculated area	Actual area
Forward foil is	15° V_{TO}	S = 54 / (11.76 * 11.76 * 1.45 * .84) = .015	0.15	0.33
NACA 4412	-1° V_{MAX}	S = 54 / (23.52 * 23.52 * 0.30 * .84) = .039	0.39	0.33
Aft foil is	9° V_{TO}	S = 311 / (11.76 * 11.76 * 1.25 * .75) = 2.39	2.39	1.94
NACA 63-412	1° V_{MAX}	S = 311 / (23.52 * 23.52 * 0.38 * .75) = 1.97	1.97	1.94

Figure 16-3. Determining the surface area of Hifybe's foils. The profile for the forward foil is NACA 4412 and the aft is NACA 63-412. Notice the aft foil has slightly insufficient area to takeoff at V_{TO}, therefore the rear foil will take off at a slightly higher velocity than the front foil will.

The next task is to do a **power analysis**. For this design the outboard motor will provide the most functional power source. Outboards are available in appropriate power sizes, they are readily obtainable, and they are compact units easily maintained or replaced.

We are going to go through the power calculations to determine the feasibility of using the proposed 8 hp outboard in the anticipated vessel design. We chose an 8 hp 2cycle because in the next higher power range the weight of the available outboards almost doubles and their attachment hardware greatly increases in thickness, width and weight.

A stroll along the dingy dock will create the impression that 6 to 8 hp is about the minimum power required to go the speeds we have chosen. Any less power and we risk not being able to overcome the drag hump and the boat will not takeoff. Our calculations will prove or disprove these estimations.

Of course we have the option to redefine our goals and create a boat unlike Hifybe. Steve Ball set a good example of pushing the limits when he replaced his pedal power with a fractional horsepower weed wacker gas engine. The boat flies well at about 6 mph after taking off at 4 mph. He has created a much different machine than Hifybe. The hull is a FRP kayak shell: long, slender and extremely lightweight. The foil configuration is similar to Hifybe's with a very big wing under the rider and a Shutt Strut at the bow supporting 10% of total weight. To keep drag to a minimum the struts and wings have very high aspect ratios, fairings are used at the wetted junctions, all components are very smooth, the foil profiles are skillfully crafted and weight is kept to an absolute minimum. More details are provided in chapter 17.

Back to Hifybe: There are at least three ways to determine drag. Perhaps the easiest is to approximate the L/D of Hifybe by comparing it to other flying machines; Figure 5-12 shows some examples. Among the most efficient are the sailplanes that can exceed L/D = 40. The Cessna 150 with L/D = 7 is an example of a less efficient aircraft. The Dynafoil L/D = 3.5. Of course, in isolation, the wings of any of these machines would have a much higher L/D ratio, see Figure 13-13; but the non-lifting components such as the fuselage, vertical stabilizer, horizontal stabilizer, struts, etc. increase the drag and do not contribute to lift. Therefore, they increase the D without increasing the L.

By comparison, Hifybe has no wetted fuselage when flying so would be spared some drag; however, it has 3 support struts, motor strut, propeller nacelle, and propeller. The upper motor strut in particular is poorly streamlined. When these components are fully wetted, as they are prior to takeoff, the ratio would be low, perhaps L/D = 2.5, which is lower than any of the flying examples. Flying at maximum height, the wetted area is much less and the maximum L/D would increase, to perhaps match the Dynafoil, L/D = 3.5 For now, let's assume those two estimations:

$L/D_{TO} = 2.5$
$L/D_{VMAX} = 7$

To approximate the drag we can use the formula:

$D = L / R$

Where:

D = Drag (drag = thrust)
D_{VMAX} = Drag at max velocity
D_{VTO} = Drag at takeoff velocity
L = Lift (lift = weight)
R = Ratio of Lift over Drag

For Hifybe,

$D_{VTO} = 365 / 2.5 = 146$ lbs.
$D_{VMAX} = 365 / 7 = 52$ lbs.

The second method for calculating overall drag, the accounting method, is not so easy.

Drag accounting calculates the drag of each of the individual components and adds them together to arrive at overall drag. The individual components are calculated by multiplying estimated drag coefficients times the square of the velocity times the frontal areas of all wetted components: foils, struts etc. The foils will be operating at a positive AOA and will have a foil profile suitable for the creation of lift. On the other hand, the struts will have close to zero AOA and the profile will be designed to not create lift.

Because of these differences, drag calculations for the lifting foils and their supporting components should be calculated separately. The formula for both is:

$$D = V^2 * S * C_D$$

For these calculations we would be using the coefficient for total drag, C_D. As you will recall from chapter 4 on lift and drag, total drag is the sum of induced drag and parasite drag. Parasite drag is primarily a function of *frontal* area and increases with speed. Induced drag is a function of *planform* area product of lift and dominates when there are high angles of attack and a high C_L such as occurs at low speeds. Induced drag is directly influenced by aspect ratio. A wing with a long span, and a narrow chord creates less induced drag than a wing with a short span and a wide chord. At the speeds and angles of attack we will be examining now, induced drag will be a minor contributor and parasite drag will be the major contributor to total drag, except for takeoff where a high AOA will create high-induced drag. The relationship, in a high aspect ratio wing, between induced, parasite, and total drags is illustrated in Figures 5-3 and 16-4.

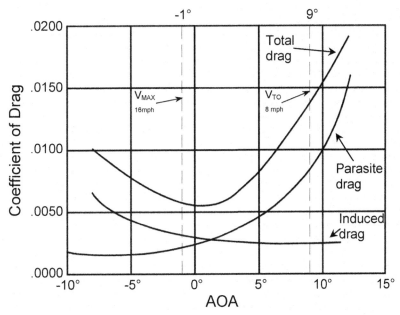

Figure 16-4. Parasite, Induced, and Total drags. C_{DTOTAL} from data smoothed from Figure 13-3. C_{DI} and C_{DP} estimated.

The chart in Figure 16-4 enumerates the coefficient of total drag for our aft foil profile, NACA 63-412. To calculate $D = V^2 * S * C_D$ for the wing alone use this table to look up the C_D for the corresponding AOA.

However, the coefficients of drag for struts may be quite different than those of wings. Remember Figure 5-6 that contrasted the drag of a circular flat plate against a NACA 0033 streamlined shape? The NACA shape has 33 times the frontal area compared to the plate and they have equal drag. Likewise a carefully streamlined strut will have a $C_D \approx$ .04 whereas an oval shape, like in Figure 5-8, will have a $C_D \approx .70$. The more the strut resembles a plate forced sideways through the fluid, the closer it will approach $C_D \approx 1.2$ like the circular flat plate. In particular, the upper portion of the outboard motor's shaft often will have a very high drag profile and will be difficult to estimate.

Likewise, interference drag will be hard to estimate accurately (see Figure 5.3), and any protruding nuts or bolts or rough spots will raise havoc with C_D estimations.

Because the overall drag sum depends so much on the assumptions made in choosing the correct C_D, this method can create wildly variable results. Therefore, we are going to skip this method, and leave its utilization to the adults at Boeing and elsewhere. For those who wish to pursue this dark art, start by reading *Aerodynamic Drag*, Sighard Hoerner.

The third and most direct method for measuring the drag of an existing boat is **towing** it behind another powerboat and measure the strain on the tow rope using an expanding spring scale. Return to Figure 5-10 and its text for towing techniques.

To continue on, we will use the results of the first method, L / D. We can now determine the horsepower needed by using the formula from chapter 5, "Drag and Power Calculations":

$P = D * V / 375$

Where:

P	=	Power in horsepower.
P_{TO}	=	Power at takeoff velocity.
P_{MAX}	=	Power at maximum velocity.
D_{VTO}	=	365 / 2.5 = 146 lbs.
D_{VMAX}	=	365 / 7 = 52 lbs.
V	=	Velocity in ft / sec.
V_{TO}	=	11.74 ft / sec. (8 mph).
V_{MAX}	=	23.5ft /sec. (16 mph).

We enter the known values:

$P_{TO} = 147 * 11.74 / 375.$

$P_{VTO} = 4.6$ hp.

and

$P_{MAX} = 52 * 23.5 / 375.$

$P_{VMAX} = 1.6$ hp.

As we noted in chapter 5, by reading the power formula one can see that the required *power* increases with the *cube* of the velocity. This is because *drag* increases with the *square* of velocity, and power is determined by multiplying drag times velocity. So if speed is doubled, drag is increased 4 times and power required is increased 8 times. This is why strapping on a bigger, heavier motor may not result in significant speed gains. It also makes $P_{VMAX} = 1.6$ hp an appropriate result, because any increase in V_{MAX} will quickly consume the excess power available.

Structure: Now that we know the size of the foils and motor, their location, etc. it is time to think about how these components will attach to the FRP hull, and what structural provisions will be necessary.

The motor mount will be 41 inches forward of stern, on the centerline, and penetrating vertically through the hull. To accommodate the shaft, a rectangular hole 14 inches long by 7 inches wide will be cut. A box of FRP will be fabricated inside the hole, and the box and the surrounding hull will be reinforced with 5 layers of FRP.

Into this box goes a two-piece, top and bottom, aluminum flanged framework. The two pieces are connected with 10 evenly spaced vertical ¼ inch stainless steel bolts or threaded rod sections. Inside the top frame is welded a 1-inch thick traverse inclined flat member that will serve as a transom to receive the motor mount clamps. The bulk of this thick piece can be wood or other light material.

An unmodified windsurf board may not have sufficient strength to carry a 365 pound load supported by two foil mounting points. To support the load forward of the motor, primarily the pilot, we will create a truss that uses the hull to carry the tension loads and an aluminum frame above the hull to carry the compression loans. The hull will be reinforced on the bottom with three layers of bias weave FRP that extend from the motor box to the bow. The two systems will be attached to each at the bow, the motor box, and one or two points in between. Figure 16-5 illustrates this design.

The motor box will be solidly welded to the aluminum frame of the truss. This welded combination will be made strong enough in these ways:

> To serve as an attachment point for the motor.
> To carry all the load of the motor forward to the truss, without placing an excessive load on the penetrated section of the hull.
> To reinforce the hull at this otherwise weakened location.
> To anchor the aft end of the truss so that along with the bow attachment, and one or two attachment points in between, the hull and the aluminum frame will become a strongly integrated truss. Each of the two foils will be attached to the aluminum truss frame at their predetermined locations.

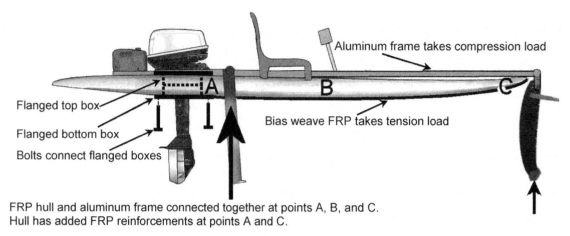

Aluminum frame takes compression load

Flanged top box
Flanged bottom box
Bolts connect flanged boxes

Bias weave FRP takes tension load

FRP hull and aluminum frame connected together at points A, B, and C.
Hull has added FRP reinforcements at points A and C.

Figure 16-5. The Structural Components of Hifybe.

The next step is to determine that the foils and struts are structurally adequate.

To perform abbreviated calculations on Hifybe's foils and struts, return to chapter 11, "Materials, Stress Calculations, and Fabrication", but in many cases stress analysis can be avoided through the simple application of common sense. For example, the Fastacraft carbon fiber foil sections are fabricated to be used on the Moth class sailboat as a main foil connected to the hull by a single central strut. The assembly forms an inverted "T". The Moth consists of foils, struts, hull, sail, mast, and helmsman. It has the same components as Hifybe, except 62 lbs. of motor and fuel. The main foil of Hifybe uses *two* struts and the span between struts is only 41 inches, forming a "U". It would be reasonable to assume that there is adequate strength to function as Hifybe's main foil.

Safety. Although Hifybe, an embellished windsurf board with a top speed of 16 mph, might seem harmless, accidents do happen. Like WWI ace Capt. Eddie Rickenbacker once quipped, "Anything that moves is dangerous". Hifybe shares characteristics with watercraft and flying machines, both of which are no strangers to accidents. So it is important to be aware of and follow good safety practices.

One danger is coming to rapid stop and crashing to the surface. This could be caused by mechanical failure, grounding, debris strike, or a sudden loss of lift. Coming down at steep angle could cause an ungraceful dismount. To avoid cuts and bruises, keep the decks free of pointed or sharp things. Blunt any protrusion, such as the joystick. Allow the joystick to fold forward if force is applied. Wear Levi's and a long sleeve shirt or a thin wet suit, especially if operating in cold water. A light buoyant helmet, like a bicycle helmet, will protect from head injuries and actually help support the head if the pilot enters the water.

If possible, aft foils and struts should provide for retracting in case of an impact. Struts that rotate backward after an obstacle strike may not be suitable for high speed operation because upon retraction the flat topside of the foil will present itself to the free stream putting on the brakes. The rapid deceleration may result in damage to the boat and crew.

Another way to limit strike damage is to use breakaway foils held in place with a sheer pin and tethered by a stainless steel wire cable attached between the foil and the hull.

When the pilot enters the water, his lower body becomes vulnerable to cuts from the foils and the propeller. These submerged components should not have sharp or pointed edges. As with Hifybe, the propeller is less dangerous if it has a circular guard surrounding it. Light shoes will help to keep the feet out of the circular guard and the prop.

Obviously the propeller poses a much greater danger if it is spinning. Hifybe stops the prop by having a kill-switch rigged to a lanyard attached to the pilot. The throttle is also spring-loaded and shuts down the motor if the hand is removed from it. Another possibility is to rig a pressure sensitive kill-switch under its seat. The motor will only run when the pilot is seated. The seat can also be rigged to the gearshift. If the rider is dismounted, the spring loaded gearshift lever will disengage. Some jet skis go to idle speed and are rigged to turn in a circle if the pilot dismounts, but in the worst scenario, this invites being run over by one's own boat

Consider other persons and other things when flying. Do not operate in an area where there is any possibility of being near a swimmer. Be especially aware of divers in the area. Learn to recognize the red flag with the white diagonal stripe indicating a diver is nearby. Beware of large animals, like Florida's Manatees, that could pose a collision hazard. Review charts and listen to the locals about submerged hazards like pilings, boulders, dead-head logs, etc.

Follow the recommendations of the US Coast Guard for small boats. Always wear an approved personal floatation device with a whistle or horn attached. Carry a few flares and don't get any farther away from shore than your rational comfort zone permits. I always have a small pair of swim fins on board to extend my personal swimming range, if needed. Before leaving the dock, make certain the boat's design allows a dismounted rider to remount the boat unassisted without capsizing it, and be sure to create a technique for restarting the engine while in open water.

As with any flying machine, **pilot technique** is necessary. Takeoff, landing, turning, and cruising are the primary conditions of flying. The transition from one flight condition to another must be done properly. Once a condition is established; speed, pitch, roll, etc., it must be maintained or controlled.

A pilot can remain upright on Hifybe while it is stationary, Hifybe can be taxied (proceed slowly) and it can fly. Proper transition goes like this: The boat is at rest, the pilot advances the throttle slowly and the speed increases, but no faster than maximum hull-borne speed. This is a good time to wiggle the stick and pedals to confirm that ailerons and rudder are moving freely and are having the anticipated effect. If everything seems in order, the pilot "levels the wings" and quickly advances the throttle to high power. Avoid increasing the power so quickly that the bow is forced upward and the stern squats into the surface.

This nose up attitude results in extremely high drag and may prevent reaching takeoff speed. While keeping the bow down, rapidly accelerate to takeoff speed. The transition to flight that can be tricky, and with an unskilled pilot it is possible to roll uncontrollably while attempting the takeoff.

An uncontrolled roll can occur during this transition because after the hull rises above the surface it can no longer contribute to keeping the boat on an even keel. At this same time, the velocity is too low for the ailerons or flippers to have enough lift to be effective in stopping or reversing an unwanted rolling moment. It is the pilot's challenge to rapidly transit this unstable condition and get the boat flying a quickly as possible. When accelerating, roll control will develop quickly because lift increases with the square of the velocity.

The same dilemma occurs when transitioning from the flying to the hull-borne condition. First level the wings and then smoothly, but smartly, remove power to allow the boat to rapidly descend to the surface. Slow reduction of power avoids crashing to the surface, while a rapid reduction allows the hull to smartly make surface contact so that the hull again contributes to roll control. The wings are leveled before starting this transition to avoid falling off to one side or the other while having insufficient flying speed for aileron or other roll correction.

Properly executing a turn requires some technique as well. To enter a turn, the pilot first introduces a little aileron induced roll to the inside of the intended turn. Rudder and more power, if available, are then applied simultaneously. Power is kept high throughout the turn. The bank is continuously adjusted with the ailerons or flippers to keep the turn balanced. To exit the turn, ailerons are used to reduce the bank and rudder deflection is used to stop the turn. Here are the reasons why these techniques are important:

Roll needs to be introduced before the turn to prevent the start of an uncontrolled roll to the outside of the turn–a potentially awkward event. Once a roll to the outside has started, it may be necessary to apply strong corrective aileron forces. If overdone, the result could be control surface stalling or ventilation followed by a dramatic loss of lift on the side where it is needed the most. A capsize is then likely.

Power is needed while entering the turn and during the turn because, in counteracting centrifugal force, turns consume more power. If there is no additional power available the boat will slow, limiting the maximum rate of turn. Reducing power in a turn is usually *not acceptable*. Doing so will slow the boat and reduce aileron control while it is banked to the inside of the turn. The result will be "a falling off" to the inside, and the boat may crash and may capsize. The refreshing swim that follows may serve to remind the pilot, *do not reduce power during a turn*.

"If flying were half as easy it would be half the fun", Anon.

Design a Human Powered Hydrofoil

- o Human powered hydrofoils
- o Hydro-ped
- o Power, hull, drive, propeller
- o Front foil
- o Rear foil
- o Flight characteristics
- o Lift calculations
- o Alternative ideas

Human powered hydrofoils (HPH) may not seem like the logical starting place to try one's hand at designing. A HPH must be the most efficient and carefully designed of all classes: human, motor and sail. Power is limited so drag must be minimized and lift must be maximized. Weight is critical. To be strong and reliable the lightweight assembly must be carefully constructed.

On the other hand, we know what power is available–the power of a human, and we can easily calculate the weight: man + foils + hull. Recent history is rich with examples of HPHs, and precisely because of their design limitations most existing HPHs conform to a few proven patterns. They are small, so material costs are small. Because there is no motor or sails, those major expense are eliminated. Finally, these little boats are easier to get down to the beach and into the water.

These boats are not only an interesting challenge to build, but they offer an excellent opportunity for low impact aerobic exercise in an aquatic environment. HPHs are an attractive alternative to runners and bicycle riders.

Sid Shutt created the **Hydro-ped**. On August 18, 1991 the Hydro-ped, piloted by Gary Allen, flew at 17.78 mph for 100 meters setting the world International Human Powered Vehicle Association world water speed record.

Shutt is a California registered mechanical engineer, retired, with additional qualifications in electrical and control systems engineering. He designed the first Hydro-ped in 1980 prior to anyone proving that HPH flight was possible. He first became foil-borne in 1983, but by then the Flying Fish by Allan Abbott and Alex Brooks had established itself as the first HPH to fly.

Lucky for us, Sid has generously provided details on Hydro-ped. The assumptions, and known qualities are as follows:

Power: The assumed energy source for Hydro-ped is a 45-year-old male in good bicycling condition and of average height and weight. He can generate about 1/3 horsepower (hp) for about 20 minutes, 1/2 hp for one minute, and 1 hp for 30 seconds. See the lower curve of Figure 17-1b. The rider is assumed to weigh 175 lbs. The hull and mechanism weigh 40 lbs and the foils are 10 lbs, making a total of 225 lbs. Refer back to Figure 5-11 for a graph of Power Available vs. Drag on the Hydro-ped.

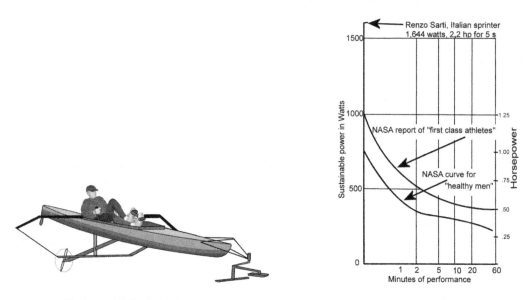

Figures 17-1a & b. (a) The Shutt Hydro-ped. Drawing based on a Shutt illustration. (b) Graph showing that the sustainable power of a human declines over the duration of performance. The Data is from *Human-Powered Vehicles*.

Hull: The Hydro-ped's hull is constructed of wood, FRP, and foam. It weighs only 35 pounds. The foils are shaped wooden forms encased in CRP. The foil profile is NACA 4412. The struts have double ogival sections with a blunted leading edges, and the materials match the foils.

A single hull is used with the rider reclining on a recumbent seat with a backrest. It has a 100" foil span and a 18'6" length overall including foils and forward surface follower. With some versions, small outriggers, 12" x 4" x 4", are mounted at the outboard ends of the main struts for roll stability in the displacement mode. The foil-base is 120" and the CG is 13" forward of the main foil.

Drive: Power input is through bicycle pedals. Following successful stability tests, loose toe straps or quick release clips can be fitted. Shutt uses aluminum crank-arms and drive-sprocket. The overall sprocket ratio is 2:1 to reduce the propeller speed. The crank rate should be between 60 and 80 rpm for the most efficient pedaling. A short chain goes between the drive sprocket and a driven sprocket mounted on 90 degree bevel gear box. The box has a one to one ratio. From the gear box comes a ¼ inch steel shaft connected to a compact U-joint slightly ahead of the horizontal propeller bearing. The bearing and shaft are encased in compact fairings that streamline and provide strength to the shaft and propeller. The bend in the drive shaft fairing that contains the U-joint can be seen in Figure 17-3c.

Propeller: The propeller is formed of CRP and cast in a handmade mold. An important part of Shutt's efforts have gone into limiting the inefficiencies, or *slip*, around the propeller blade. The early handmade propellers of the Hydro-ped have measured efficiencies of 80%, near top speed. His later propellers achieved 90% efficiency, according to Shutt. Theodore Schmidt wrote in "Propeller Designs" published in *Human-Powered Vehicles,* and there he claims that efficiencies of 98% have been achieved. By comparison, power boat propellers are efficient in the range of 85% and the oars of an Olympic type rowing shell have a propulsion efficiency of only 66%.

Fortunately, it is not necessary to design and fabricate a "one off" propeller such as Sid Shutt has done. Acceptable efficiency can be achieved by using carbon fiber propeller blades adapted from engine powered model airplanes. These are inexpensive items off the shelves of model aircraft stores, and HPHs operate at about the same Reynolds number as do radio controlled model airplanes. A good propeller to start testing with would have a pitch of 16 inches and a diameter of 12 or 14 inches. Their pitch to diameter ratios are 1.3 and 1.14 respectively. Schmidt, claims that pitch-to-diameter ratios of between 1 and 1.5 is appropriate for "good all-around practical propellers", while "high speed racing propellers" might have ratios up to 2. My associates who specialize in HPH consider the writing of the late E. Eugene Larrabee, MIT professor, to be the authority on HPH propeller theory.

The **front foil** is a "Shutt Strut," as drawn in Figure 17-3. Its dimensions are 17 by 1.75 inches. Its sectional profile is NACA 4412. The NACA number indicates that the section has a 4% camber, peaking 40% of the chord aft of the leading edge. The foil is 12% (of the chord) in thickness. The area equals .207 ft^2. Go to Figures 8-6a and b to see a beefed-up version. Hydro-ped II used a single strut to connect the front foil to its height finding surface follower, but modified versions use two struts, doubling as wing tip fences.

Prior to takeoff, when the wetted area of the rear foil is 2.51 ft^2, the area of the front foil equals 8% of the total. Following takeoff, when the wetted area of the surface piercing rear foil is reduced to .94 ft^2, the front foil is 18% of the wetted area. The load on the front foil is 15% of the total weight.

The front foil controls the flying height of the bow. It is mounted on a vertical pivot that provides for steering control, and there is a traverse horizontal pivot that allows for a constantly changing angle of incidence. The foil assembly consists of a 7" x 3" buoyant surface follower that is connected to the pivot block by a 24 inch long forward pointing sensor arm. As with all Shutt and Meacham style front foils (review Figures 8-5 and 8-6), if the bow height is too low the surface follower is raised by the water's surface and the foil rotates to increase its AOA. This increases the C_L, and therefore increases the lift. If the bow is high, the surface follower drops, and the front foil rotates to decrease its AOA. This reduces the C_L and therefore the foil's lift. The bow descends until equilibrium is achieved. At takeoff, zero inches, the AOA = 11.7° and its C_L = .97. At cruise height, 9", the AOA = 4.1° and its C_L = .34 (Sid Shutt adjusted his coefficients for aspect ratio, surface proximity, etc. and will vary from the raw data of Figure 13-3). Takeoff is at 11 ft/sec and cruise is 17 ft/sec.

Design a Human Powered Hydrofoil

The canard foil array is more efficient than other configurations. This is because the main lifting foil can be tuned to operate at its highest efficiency, while the tiny front foil sacrifices efficiency to accommodate its function as the height finding foil. The eponymous front foil, refined by Shutt, is used by many lightweight hydrofoil boats.

The surface piercing **rear foil** is also a NACA 4412. Its form as viewed from the bow is flat in the center 50% of span, with dihedral outboard sections. The dihedral sections are reverse-tapered, i.e., they are wider at the tip than the root. This provides automatic roll control. In addition, the foil reduces its own area as velocity increases, and this allows it to operate faster than the $V_{MAX} \approx 2*V_{TO}$ limitation introduced in chapter 4. However, the surface piercing feature has the disadvantage of possible ventilation at the point where the foil pierces the water. Chapter 6 addresses ventilation problems and solutions.

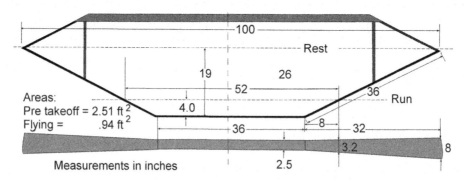

Figures 17-2a & b. Two views of the Hydro-ped rear foil.

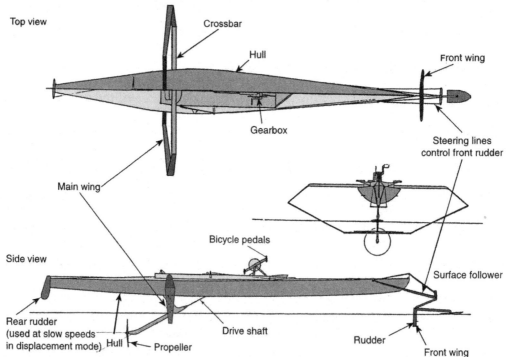

Figures 17-3a, b, & c. The Hydro-ped. This and the preceding drawings were created by Sid Shutt, and reproduced with his permission.

Flight characteristics: Hydro-ped's record speed is 26.1 ft/sec = 17.78 mph = 15.45 knots. Cruise height is 9 inches. Maximum wave height is 2 inches. Endurance at V_{CRUISE} will be about ten minutes, depending on the rider. Refer to the chart in Figure 5-11. It was there that we explained the unusual loop in the "power required" plot. Shutt used a drop-down, variable submergence front foil on the Hydro-ped. It is kept dry during the brief run-up to V_{TO}. When V_{TO} is reached the pilot pulls a line that is rigged to force the front foil to its running depth and the newly generated lift elevates the bow. Momentum pushes the boat past the drag hump. The hinged bow-foil rigging can be seen in the drawing in Figure 17-3. Our group in San Diego built a detuned version (bigger main foil) of this speedster and found in testing that the drop-down front foil could be eliminated and replaced by a conventional always-submerged type.

The **Lift calculations** will be done differently for this example. Because we already know the lift required, the area of the foils, and the velocities, there is no need to use $L = V^2 * S * C_L$ in its traditional form. However, we do need to know what angle of attack to set the foils so that we maximize our chances of success in the early attempts to fly. The angle of attack is taken from our lift table, Figure 13-3, after we determine the required C_L. We use the same formula from chapter 4, but in the form that calculates C_L:

$$C_L = L / (V^2 * S)$$

To determine the rear foil's AOA for takeoff of the Hydro-ped, we look up the formula values in the first two columns of the table in Figure 17-5. We arrive at this calculation:

$$C_L = 183 / (11*11 * 2.51)$$

$$C_L = 183 / 303.71$$

$$C_L = .6025$$

The C_L of the NACA 4412 profile is found looking down the 2nd column, center section of the table of Figure 13-3 until we come to C_L = .600. We see the corresponding AOA is 2°. Two degrees is our takeoff AOA for the rear foil. We can do the same calculation to determine the AOA for the front foil at takeoff and for both foils at V_{MAX}.

Alternative ideas: Our California HPH Group has successfully built and flown submerged rear foils in place of Shutt's surface piercing ones. For example, Steve Ball claims to have remained flying for 45 minutes on his Dragonfly. The biggest foil provides roll control; so the outboard span employs wing warp, ailerons, or flippers. This system is more complicated, harder to build, and increases the pilot's workload; however, the ventilation problems are reduced or eliminated and the boat is more fun to fly.

Figures 17-4a & b. (a) Steve Ball pulls out his Dragonfly and Dwight Filley checks his Foilplay. (b) Laura Ball flies her father's Dragonfly with a modified wing.

In designing any hydrofoil, the foils should be tailored to the flight objectives. In general, for greater endurance larger foils are chosen and, to conserve energy, slower speeds are flown. Smaller foils will have less parasite drag for a given speed, but require higher speeds to create the needed lift, and the power required increases with the cube of the velocity. Hydro-ped and the other HPHs depend on rider strength and boat efficiency to determine endurance and to a lesser extent, speed. To make a rational design decision, one should set a goal and then do the math.

As a guideline, the following table shows dimensions and specifications of some operational HPHs:

	Sid Shutt's Hydro-ped		Steve Ball's Dragonfly		Dwight Filley's Foilplay	
Velocity (ft/sec x .68 = mph)	**mph**	**ft / sec**	**mph**	**ft / sec**	**mph**	**ft / sec**
Takeoff	7.5	11	4	5.9	5	7.4
Cruise, endurance	11.6	17	4.5	6.6	6	8.8
Cruise, normal	11.6	17	5.5	8.1	6	8.8
V_{MAX}	12.1	17.78	9.0	13.2	8.5	12.5
Power (1 watt / 746 = hp)	**Watts**	**Hp**	**Watts**	**Hp**	**Watts**	**Hp**
Takeoff	200	0.27	140	0.19	130	0.17
Cruise	125	0.17	120	0.16	120	0.16
V_{MAX}, 5 seconds endurance	500	0.67	450	0.60	450	0.60
Weight						
Hull & Foils, lbs	40		50		50	
Pilot, lbs	<u>175</u>		<u>160</u>		<u>180</u>	
Total, lbs	215		210		230	
Small wing forward	V_{TO}	V_{MAX}	V_{TO}	V_{MAX}	V_{TO}	V_{MAX}
Chord, in	1.75	1.75	1.75	1.75	4.5	4.5
Span, in	17	17	18	18	40	40
Area sq ft	0.21	0.21	0.22	0.22	1.25	1.25
Percent of Area	8%	18%	5%	5%	20%	20%
Percent Weight Supported	15%	15%	15%	15%	20%	20%
Weight Supported, lbs	32	32	31.5	31.5	46	46
Wing Loading Lbs/sq ft	155	155	144	144	37	37
Aspect Ratio	9.7	9.7	10.3	10.3	8.9	8.9
Gain, % lift / in	(24" wand)	77%	(35" wand)	55%	Manual	
Main wing aft						
Chord, average, in	3.61	2.60	4.75	4.75	4.5	4.5
Span, average, in	100	52	138.5	138.5	160	160
Area sq ft	2.51	0.94	4.57	4.57	5.00	5.00
Percent of Area	92%	82%	95%	95%	80%	80%
Percent Weight Supported	85%	85%	85%	85%	80%	80%
Weight Supported, lbs	183	183	179	179	184	184
Wing Loading lbs/sq ft	73	194	39	39	37	37
Aspect Ratio	28	20	29	29	36	36
Total Wing Area. Sq ft	2.72	1.15	4.79	4.79	6.25	6.25
Running depth, in	19	4	18	9	26	20
Flying Height, resting wl to foil-borne wl	15		11		6	
Roll Control	27° dihedral		3° differential wing warp		3° differential wing warp	
Endurance, V_{CRUISE}, min.	20		45		15	

Figure 17-5. Compare human powered hydrofoils

If two struts are better than three, why not use a single strut? I would envision something like this:

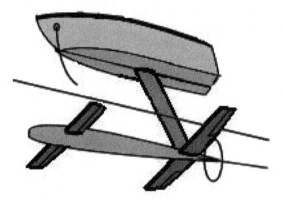

Figure 17-6. A single strut hydrofoil.

Certainly the most efficient design currently in use is the single track hydrofoil. Struts create drag and no lift. Two struts in line obviously have an advantage over three or more struts scattered around the keel. Human powered single-track hydrofoils are not new, and as the stronger, lighter CRP materials increase in use, surely we will be seeing more of them. Some examples can be seen on the Human Powered Boats web site (referenced in the Bibliography). Some names to look for are the Cogito, Flying Fish, Iron Butterfly, New Fisics, Super Phoenix. etc.

HPHs are fun, exciting, and provide a better workout than some gyms. Dwight Filley and Steve Ball have created versions powered by Weed Wacker brand type of engines. Some designers in Japan have built flying solar powered boats similar to the HPH. Here are some other ideas, mostly untried:

> Deploy a kite to catch winds from abeam and abaft.
> Mount a fixed aircraft-type wing on a hydrofoil.
> Make an unpowered hydrofoil boat to be towed behind a ski boat.
> Create a battery powered hydrofoil, or follow the Japanese lead and build a solar powered hydrofoil.
> Make a rugged hydrofoil capable of surfing an ocean wave.

The possibilities are limited only by one's imagination. In the following chapter, we will design a sail-powered hydrofoil.

Design a Sail Powered Hydrofoil

- o Hydrofoil Moth's history
- o Special characteristics
- o Defining the concept
- o Commercially available components
- o Class rules
- o Calculation of weight and balance
- o Determine the main foil's surface area
- o Rudder foil and front foil
- o Height finding system
- o Ideas

The subject of this chapter is the designing and building of a hydrofoil sailboat. The boat will be patterned after the exciting and successful Moth class catboat with a single-track array of foils.

My experience in wind power comes from local California sailing since the 1960s, and from having owned and sailed a 41ft Taiwan ketch in the Mediterranean Sea for 19 years. You can read about it in my wife's book, *Sailing There: Cruising across Europe and the Mediterranean.* It can be found by searching for the author, Patricia Vellinga, at Amazon.com, or Barnes and Noble.com.

Unfortunately the Rave is the only hydrofoil sailboat I have experienced. The Rave is the tamed version of the record breaking 43.55 knot Long Shot. This type of boat played an important role in the history of hydrofoil development. In chapter 1 we briefly reviewed the sailing history of the Rave, Long Shot, Avocet, Hobie TriFoiler, the Neither Fish Nor Fowl, and the 61.7 mph French Hydroptère.

The art and science of hydrofoil sailing has evolved to a high level, and the easy way out is to buy a new or used Moth, Rave, or TriFoiler and sail it away, but this is a book about designing and building. Besides, you might have more fun building one and perhaps save money in doing so. Benjamin Franklin was guilty of small thinking when he said, "A penny saved is a penny earned." He never considered the $14,000 price tag on a new *Bladerider* brand Moth.

The Moth uses cutting edge technology, and its popularity is gaining momentum in the USA, Denmark, Italy, France, Holland, Belgium, Japan, United Arab Emirates, and other nations. But it is Australia, New Zealand, and the United Kingdom where it has its greatest popularity. The **history of the hydrofoil Moth** is as colorful and varied as the boat itself.

Design a Sail Powered Hydrofoil

In 1928 near Melbourne, Australia, Len Morris created the first hull-borne Moth. A year later, Joel Van Sant built the second Moth in Elizabeth, New Jersey. Since then, the hulls have been built as hollow boxes, skiffs, prams, scows, tubes, and dinghies. This variety is inspired by the International Sailing Federation's Moth rules that invite improvising: "the intention of these class rules is to give the designer and builder the fullest liberty …to develop and produce faster boats."

During the 1990s Andy Paterson on the Isle of Wight fitted a Moth with surface piercing foils set in a conventional airplane array to create the first hydrofoil-Moth. In 1997 Rich Miller, California, created the first single track sailing hydrofoil when he mounted hydrofoils on his non-Moth sailboard. It all came together in 1999 when Dr. Ian Ward, an Australian metallurgist, created the first single track hydrofoil Moth. It had its main T foil mounted on the foot of the centerboard and its smaller trailing T foil mounted on the rudder. The design lacked a height finding system and so was unstable in pitch. The single-track array had no roll stability, so one can imagine what a handful this first flying Moth must have been.

In 2000 the Australian Illett brothers, John and Garth, introduced a bow-mounted height-finding wand that stabilizes the bow's height, and allows the pitch of the boat to be controlled. In 2004 their design, in the hands of their fellow countryman, Rohan Veal, won 1st place in the International Moth competitions. Doubts about the new boat were removed when Veal won 8 consecutive races. In the 40 minute long 2006-world championship, Rohan Veal beat the 2nd place *low rider* (hull-borne) Moth by 9 minutes. Moth supporters are working to make hydrofoil-Moth racing an event in the 2012 Olympics.

Before designing a Moth based on class-winning designs, let's review the **special characteristics** of hydrofoil sailboats, Moths and non-Moths:

> Wind power is variable in intensity and direction.
> Takeoff power may be limited.
> The heeling forces may be very strong at slow start-up speeds when the hydrodynamic forces are weakest. Gusting winds exacerbate this problem.
> The center of force of propulsion will be applied high on the mast and forward of the CG.
> The side forces will be strongest when sailing a reach or close haul.
> There may be a hazard of pitchpoling when sailing on a broad reach or a run.
> Tacking some non-Moth hydrofoils is a challenge. Like any flying machine, a hydrofoil is lightweight and has little momentum to carry it through an un-powered turn into the wind. Catamarans and trimarans are broad beamed to resist tipping. These boats, whether hydrofoil or conventional, are notorious for being difficult to turn quickly, as required when turning into and through the wind.
> Moths, in skilled hands, tack well. When flying they have modest drag and, despite their low weight, generally have sufficient momentum to carry them through the eye of the wind.

➢ Moths beat to windward in an unusual way. Conventional sailboats heel leeward. Moths heel windward. By inclining the foils, the Moth's lift is used to counteract leeway. In a conventional sailboat, the nearly-vertical keel creates a side force opposing leeway.

➢ Because of the wide range of flying speeds, there will be marginal lift at V_{TO} and excessive lift at V_{MAX}. At V_{MAX} we will need to control a tendency to breach either foil, which will cause ventilation and will often be followed by a crash. The crash destroys momentum. Speed will not be regained until the ventilation bubble is shed and lift is restored.

We will start with a complete Moth-style, mono-hull hydrofoil, similar to the hulls shown in Figures 18-1 and 18-2:

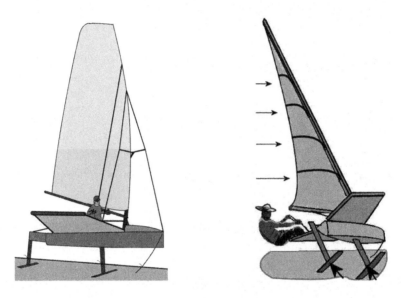

Figures 18-1a & b. Moth class hydrofoil sailboats.

The first step is **defining the concept**: We will be designing a Moth class single-track sailboat to match the state of the art boats similar to those in Figures 18-1a and b. These featherweights fly in light winds, as low as 7 to 9 mph, depending on the weight of the boat and rider. They takeoff slow, 6 mph, go fast, over 32 mph. Because they have a submerged foil system, the hull can fly over choppy water. When the boat is built strictly within the class specifications, it can be raced against other Moths. Because it is a single-track design, flying it involves a high degree of skill, and that makes for some real adventure. Our boat will be designed to be "tame", that is, not especially difficult to takeoff and control. To make a "hot" boat the foils would be reduced in area to match the other fast boats.

Design a Sail Powered Hydrofoil

One the advantage of the Moths is professional support for the class. There are **commercially available components.** Current suppliers, subject to change, can be found on the internet. Presently foils, struts, hulls, sails, rigging, and even complete units are available from:

> ➢ Fastacraft, Australia
> ➢ Full Force, U.K.
> ➢ Bladerider, produced in China, marketed in Australia.
> ➢ Aardvark Technologies, UK.

Today, Fastacraft and Full Force account for an estimated 70% of the new Moths coming under sail.

According to International Moth, USA, the **class rules** are as follows (metrics are exact, inches and feet are rounded):

> ➢ Max length: 3.355m = 132in
> ➢ Max beam: 2.250m = 88.6in
> ➢ Sail area: 8m^2 = 86 ft^2
> ➢ Luff length: 5.585m = 219.8in
> ➢ Mast Length: 6.250m = 246in
> ➢ Weight: unrestricted (so boat weights around 30kg or 66lbs are common)
> ➢ Prohibitions: no multi-hull or windsurfer (hull)

Remember, when building within the restrictions of class rules, it is better to slightly error toward the smaller (permitted) size than toward the larger (prohibited) size. These rules, developed over 75 years, cover the hull and the sails. There are no rules restricting the use of single track hydrofoils on a Moth; but Darwinian principles, "survival of the fittest" apply. One Moth dinosaur is the multi-track hydrofoil which is judged to violate class rules prohibiting multi-hull boats. The winning foils are evolving toward the small elliptical shapes made of the lightest, stiffest material: carbon reinforced plastic resin (epoxy), CRP. With foil size, small is not always better. Small foils takeoff at higher speeds, so low form drag must be balanced against the high wind speed necessary to create flight. There is no advantage in having the fastest hydrofoil if the low riders sail quietly by in light winds.

Pitchpoling could be a problem with a canard array, because the smaller front foil might be overloaded on a downwind tack. To control this heavy front load, the Moth's larger foil and strut are positioned in the centerboard slot ahead of the CG. This is a conventional-airplane hydrofoil array, typical of most hydrofoil *sailboats*. The smaller aft foil is positioned at the bottom end of the rudder which is aft of the transom. The aft foil provides a small proportion of the lift, and in some points of sail, it will produce negative lift. At extreme flying height either foil can create negative lift.

Because the loads will vary with the points of sail, the front and rear foil are rigged so that each may be trimmed. Typically, Moth pilots twist the tiller to adjust the AOI of the rear foil and strut. The front foil is trimmed, at dockside, by increasing or decreasing the rate of flap deflection (gain). Shifting the crew's weight affects trim, as well. Moving the pilot's weight back increases the AOA on both wings causing the boat to fly higher. Moving forward has the opposite effect.

It is best if the foils retract for easy launching and obstacle strike damage control, but relatively slow speeds and weight restrictions will limit the possibilities for complicated retraction systems. Most Moths compromise by having removable fore and aft wings. The forward foil slides out of its place in the centerboard slot, and the aft foil has removable pins in its vertical hinges.

The hull:

> ➤ Is fabricated of a light material such as CRP or FRP.
> ➤ As an option, may have a 3/16" (5mm) foam core laminated between layers of CRP or FRP.
> ➤ Has a narrow beam with a displacement equaling at least twice the total flying weight.
> ➤ Has a narrow bow that provides for wave strikes.
> ➤ Has a broader amidships section locating the center of buoyancy near the pilot.
> ➤ Has a clean, flat bottom that creates modest lift from partial planning.
> ➤ Is fitted with a transom that has a 90° clean break from the keel to discourage upward flow (negative lift) at the turn of the stern.
> ➤ Has hiking trampolines that extend from the hull to allow the helmsman to balance against heeling moments and shift his weight to alter the pitch trim of the hull and foils.
> ➤ Uses a linear foot strap near the hull and parallel to the gunnels provide a foot-hold for the hiking pilot.

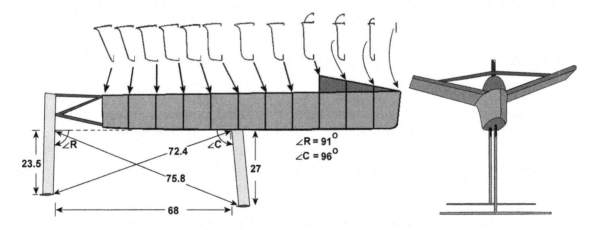

Figure 18-2. This is a typical Moth hull design suitable for adapting to hydrofoils. Dimensions, in inches, based on "The Foiling Guide" by Adam May. Hull inspired by Bill Beaver's "Hungry Beaver".

Design a Sail Powered Hydrofoil

The foils and struts:

- Each is in the form of inverted T.
- For simplicity will have a rectangular planform. Although the rectangular planform is satisfactory, the highest performing boats are now using tapered or elliptical planforms. Of course, the more complicated shape is harder to fabricate. Rectangular foils have a bonus advantage of being easily downsized by cutting off the ends of the foil to change the span, if necessary.
- Will use asymmetrical foil profiles for the main foil. The NACA 63-412 profile is popular, and there is performance data in this book. At speeds near V_{MAX} the hull will be flying at its maximum height, H_{MAX}. The main foil may be called upon to create a down force to prevent breaching. Therefore, the flap must articulate up as well as down and the height controlling wand must provide for both positive and negative flap angles.
- Under some points of sail, the rear foil may be required to provide a downward force. Therefore, a symmetrical profile may be considered, but most Moths use matching profiles, chords, and thickness for their fore and aft foils. The area is varied by tailoring the wingspan.
- The strut profile is NACA 0012. This is a symmetrical shape with 12% thickness.
- The surface is brightly polished. In tests, unpolished foils had a 25% greater drag than polished foils, according to Beaver and Zseleczky. They also made the following observation:
- Flying high is better. In their tests, reduced submergence adds about a pound of wave drag, but the form drag of the strut is reduced, and that results in a net reduction in drag. This sets the flying height at about 30-40cm, 11.8-15.8", above the water. Too much height risks breaching and/or ventilation.
- The flap hinge at the trailing edge of the foil is composed of a thin laminate of Kevlar impregnated with a rubber like epoxy resin.
- The hinge line should be as smooth as possible on the topside. A gap on the bottom-side of the hinge is acceptable.
- The hinge should not allow the passage of water from the bottom-side to the topside. This is why rubberized hinges are recommended.

The rigging:

- Will be catboat rigging (a single main sail). It is less efficient than sloop rigging, but the extra fore sail (jib) is one-sail-too-many for the busy helmsman, and 86 ft², as a practical matter, may be too small an area for two sails anyway.
- There will be no windlass. The main sheet loads are light. A pulley block with a jamb cleat will be used for mechanical advantage.
- Aluminum, CRP, or FRP, will be used to construct the mast and main boom. Consider a mainsail with a bow-shaped boom to allow quick tacks and jibes.
- The rigging is aerodynamically clean to reduce wind drag. Beaver and Zseleczky report that at 17 mph the Hungry Beaver has an aerodynamic drag of 17 lbs which is 70% of the hydrodynamic drag.

Design steps:

> ➤ Estimate weights. Gather the parts, weigh them individually, position them and calculate the CG.
> ➤ Calculate foil loads. Add a margin to compensate for sail forces. It is generally good practice to use a slightly higher wing load on the front foils for added pitch stability, however existing Moths do not seem to comply with this practice for reasons explained later in this chapter.
> ➤ Estimate maximum speed based on wind strength experienced in the region in which the boat will be sailed. Well-designed hydrofoil sailboats, on a reach, approach speeds equal to twice the wind speed.
> ➤ Because of the flaps on the main-front foil, and the trim-ability of the rear foil, our rule of thumb from chapter 4, $V_{MAX} \approx 2*V_{TO}$, will not apply to this design. Takeoff speed will be about 1/3 of V_{MAX} rather than 1/2. We will calculate foil area based on takeoff speed using full flaps. In-flight change of trim of the rear foil will be necessary to allow the maximum speed to be reached.
> ➤ Consider designing a lightweight foil retraction or removal system for trailering, storing, and obstacle strike.
> ➤ At least, provide for disassembly to allow loading on trailer and for storage.

There is a wealth of information posted by manufactures and aficionados on the web about materials, hull building, piloting techniques, etc. The goal of this chapter is to apply the math and get you pointed in the right direction. The calculations will follow approximately the same pattern established in chapter 16 where we designed Hifybe. Here are the specifics:

Determine weight and balance:

> ➤ Total weight with foils.
> ➤ Weight and lift distribution.
> ➤ Foil areas.
> ➤ Front foil gain resulting from height change.

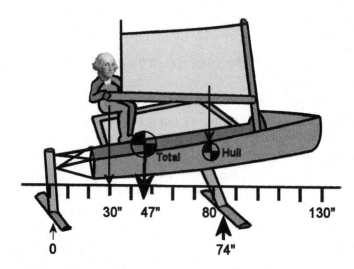

Figure 18-3.   Visualization of components and their position relative to the
reference point (stern). This and other sketches are made with Photo Shop
or Paint Shop Pro, saved as a .jpg, and printed for use in the work shop.

Front Strut length = 27 in.
V_{MAX} flying height = 12 to 16 in at AOA = 0°.
This AOA = 0°.
V_{TO}: AOA = 5°. This AOA results because the bow pitches up 5° for takeoff.
V_{TO}: Flap deflection = 0°. There is no flap deflection at takeoff because the bow is high
and the front foil is at V_{MAX} height.
V_{MAX} Flap deflection = 0° At cruise height the flap deflection = zero.
See Figure 18-6 for visualization of the front foil and height finding system.

Rudder Strut length = 23.5 in.
V_{MAX}: Flying height = 16 in. at AOA = 0°.
V_{TO}: AOA = 5°. This AOA results because the bow pitches up 5° for takeoff.
V_{MAX} & V_{TO} Flap deflection. There is no flap on the rudder foil.

Determine Torque:

Component	Weight, Lbs W		Distance from stern, In D		Torque around stern, In lbs W x D =
Pilot	170	*	30	=	5,100
Hulls, foils, sail	88	*	80	=	7,040
Totals	258	*			12,140

Dividing Torque by Weight gives the average Distance of all
Weight creating Torque. This distance is the Center of Gravity
(CG) as measured from the stern (reference point).

Determine CG:

W x D, in lbs		W, lbs		D, in
12,140	/	258	=	47

Figure 18-4. **Calculation of weight and balance.**

Measure the distance of each foil from the CG:

Distance between foils from Figure 18-2 with 6" added for strut slant and center to center measurement. 68 + 6 = 74 in.

Rear foil is 47 in. from CG. From Figure 18-3.
Front foil is 74 − 47 = 27 in. from CG.

The percentage of lever arm for each foil is:

Rear   47 / 74 = 63.5%
Front 27 / 74 = 36.5%

Disregarding the effects of sail pressure and weight shift, the percentage of weight support by each foil is:

Rear   27 / 74 = 36.5%
Front 47 / 74 = 63.5%

Determine the main foil's surface area.

The hydrofoil Moth class has undergone significant evolution since the Patterson innovations in the 1990s. Radically redesigning the Moth would be tantamount to reinventing boiling water. We can move quickly ahead by observing the established patterns represented in the following table. The data comes from Beaver, Zseleczky, Flutter and Stevo.

Main foil	Fastacraft Original	Fastacraft 2nd Generation	Bladerider	Hungry Beaver	Full force	Garda Competition (Fastacraft)	Nick Flutter	Phil Stevo
Profile	63-412	63-412	63-412	Eppler 393	63-412	63-412	63-412	63-412
Span	35.5	33.5	39.0	38.8	33.9	33.5	34.7	34.7
Chord	4.7	4.7	4.6	4.8	4.3	4.7	4.7	4.9
Ft^2	1.16	1.09	1.03	1.11	1.02	1.09	1.13	1.19
Flaps?	Trim AOI	Trim AOI	33% flap	30% flap	30% flap	30% flap	33% flap	30% flap
Planform	Rectangle	Elliptical	Elliptical	Elliptical			Elliptical	
Lift	180	180	180	180	180	180	180	180
Drag	na	9.9	na	10.3	9.7	na	na	na
L/D	na	18.2	na	17.4	18.5	na	na	na
Wing loading	155.5	164.7	na	162.3	176.5	164.7	159.1	151.3
Aspect ratio	7.5	9.5	10.2	9.4	7.8	7.1	7.4	7.1
Rudder foil								
Profile	63-412	63-412	na	Eppler 393	63-412	63-412	63-412	63-412
Span	23.6	25.6	32.7	34.6	27.6	25.6	25.6	25.6
Chord	4.7	4.7	4.0	4.5	4.3	4.7	4.7	4.9
Ft^2	0.77	0.84	0.84	0.87	0.83	0.84	0.84	0.88
Flaps?	Trim AOI	Trim AOI		Trim AOI	Trim AOI	Trim AOI	25% flap	Trim AOI
Planform	Rectangle	Elliptical	Elliptical	Tapered		Elliptical		
Lift	60	60	60	60	60	60	60	60
Drag	na	5.3	na	7.2	5.9	na	na	na
L/D	na	11.4	na	8.3	10.2	na	na	na
Wing loading	77.8	71.8	na	69.1	72.3	71.8	71.8	71.8
Aspect ratio	5.0	7.7	8.8	9.6	6.4	5.4	5.4	5.4

Figure 18-5. Comparisons of successful Moth hydrofoils.

Design a Sail Powered Hydrofoil

Based on these successful designs, we select the following foil specifications. Our selections have been biased by our goal to "tame the Moth". Therefore, our foils tend to be larger, simpler and adjustable. The dimensions best suited to our goals are:

Rudder foil:

Type: NACA 63-412 made of CRP. The trim is controlled by twisting the tiller to change the AOI. The dimensions are:
Span = 25 in
Chord = 4.75 in
Area = 119 in^2 = .82ft^2
Aspect Ratio = 25 / 4.75 = 5.3

F_{AR} = .71
R_N= 340,000@ 6mph, and 1,370,000 @ 25 mph. From Figure 4-6.

Front foil:

Chord = 4.75
Span = 35
Area = 166.25 in^2 = 1.15ft^2
Aspect Ratio = 35 / 4.75 = 7.4
F_{AR} = .80. From Figure 4-9b.
R_N = 340,000@ 6mph, and 1,370,000 @ 25 mph. From Figure 4-6.
Wand length = 42 in.
Gain = 13% / inch. From Figure 8-19.

The **height finding system** is demonstrated below:

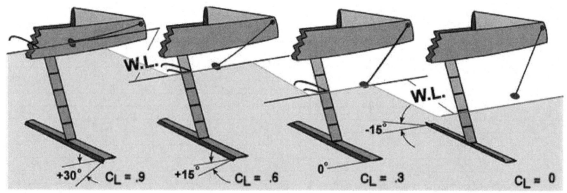

Figure 18-6. This shows the wand and flap coordination on the Moth's bow and the coefficients of lift for each flap setting. The C$_L$s were extrapolated from the chart in Figure 8-2b.

The drawing shows the flap angle is determined by the position of the wand that is hinged off the bow. The greatest flap deflection, 30°, occurs when hull-borne, prior to takeoff. Negative flap deflection, -15°, occurs at the highest level of flying. The downward force of the front flap-foil is important. It allows the V_{MAX} to exceed $2 * V_{TO}$. If it were not for the downward force created by the elevated flap at the highest flying levels, the front foil would breach the surface causing frequent high speed crashes.

Ideas: The evolution of hydrofoils on Moths is far from over. There will be many changes to be tried; some good, some not good. Here are a few ideas that could be tried (perhaps unknowingly they have been):

> ➤ Move the center board slot forward to increase the foil-base. A longer foil base increases the lever arm between the height controlling front foil and the center of rotation. This reduces the change in AOA of the rear foil for a given change in height. This may make pitch control more manageable. Presumably, it will be necessary to advance the pilot to keep 55-60% of the weight on the front foil. The mast and sail would need to move forward as well in order to keep the lateral forces of power and resistance on the same plane, and to avoid increasing the weather helm.
>
> ➤ Some anhedral may benefit one or both foils. Anhedral provides for greater heeling without the wing tips breaching the surface. The widest foil, the main, would benefit the most. Rich Miller in his hydrofoil sailboard modified his rear (main) foil to have 35 degrees of anhedral on each side and that "improbable" change lead to a startling improvement in performance.
>
> ➤ Simplify and beautify by eliminating the gantry and extending the hull.
>
> ➤ Reduce the size of the rudder foil. It is lightly loaded and possibly over-sized. This increases the minimum parasite drag. See Figure 13-5. Do not reduce the rear foil size so much that it no longer can resist pitchpoling.
>
> ➤ The Moth may be the only single-track hydrofoil with aft steering. Try using the front strut as the rudder for improved handling. Front steering uses the principle of turning under the fall for roll control.

Piloting Techniques and Troubleshooting

o Taking-off
o Cruising
o Platforming, contouring, and gain
o Turns without banking and turns that are balanced
o Single-track hydrofoils
o Avoiding wheelies and stoppies
o Jumping
o Spin takeoff
o Landing
o Weeds
o Flight safety
o Test flying and trouble shooting
o Takeoff problems
o Stability vs. maneuverability
o Yaw and roll
o Porpoising, roll instability
o Inadequate lift, excessive drag, turning, force reversal
o Making observations, ventilation, stalling, cavitation, propeller problems
o Component degradation

If you think designing and building hydrofoils is fun you'll go nuts when you first fly one. They are exciting because they truly fly. As in aircraft flying, technique is important. The technique employed depends on the conditions of flight as well as the design of the hydrofoil being flown. This is good news. Learning and employing good flying techniques are a big part of what makes flying such a pleasure. Further good news is that mistakes in flying hydrofoils are much more forgiving than mistakes with aircraft. Hopefully, the worst case involves only a swim to shore.

The conditions of flight we are going to examine are: taking-off, cruising, turning, banking, jumping, wheelies, and landing. All the types of designs previously discussed are subject to these piloting techniques.

Taking-off. There are four stages in the takeoff procedure: Hull-borne, pre-transition, transition, and foil-borne. All of these stages are usually acceptably stable, except for *transition*. Let's go through the process step by step.

When *hull-borne,* the weight of the foils and struts are deep in the water, well below the CG, and the hull itself is contributing to pitch and roll stability.

During the pre-transition stage, the bow may be high while the stern drags deep in the water. Most struts and all of the foils are submerged and the foils are at their highest angle of attack. In this condition, the ratios drag / velocity and power / velocity will be at their highest. Pitch and directional control should not be the problem. The front foil will regulate the bow's height, so the pitch-up is limited. If typically designed, the front foil will be up to flying speed during pre-transition, before the rear foil begins to lift the stern. Directional control should be adequate because all of the struts aft of the center of gravity are fully in the water. Roll should be stable because the hull is still planing on the water.

The problem starts during the transition when the hull leaves the surface and the foils, barely flying, do not have adequate authority to control roll. In powerful and delicately balanced machines, such as the Dynafoil, operator balance, wake transitions, and propeller torque will make or break a takeoff attempt.

When the transition is complete and the boat is flying at cruise or maximum velocity, the dynamics of the hydrofoil system will provide stability around all three axes.

Because of this transient instability, it is best to pass quickly through the transition. With most boats the pilot will gingerly advance the power to the maximum non-flying speed. When satisfied the boat is stable on all axes, power should be briskly increased. As soon as minimum-flying speed is achieved, there will be a rapid acceleration as the hull rises and the hull drag disappears. The speed increase will occur even though there is no additional power available. The boat has just passed through the *drag hump* (see Figure 5-4); that place on the drag curve where the hull is at its maximum speed and drag, and it is about to rise above the surface. The dramatic increase in acceleration can spook an inexperienced rider. Until confidence is acquired, it is common for a rider to throttle down and crash in response to the sudden "kick in the pants" as the boat leaps forward.

Human powered hydrofoils may take some special techniques. Because the power is limited—especially in the human powered hydrofoils I have flown—the pilot may have difficulty pushing his speed past the drag hump. The best advice is to pedal like a maniac until takeoff is achieved, then relax slightly and enjoy having the hull above the surface, the struts partially dry, and the foils lifting efficiently.

Some design help is possible. Sid Shutt uses a retractable front foil on his Hydro-ped. The foil is mounted on a frame that can pivot upwards. This provides for deployment and retraction of the foil while the surface follower continuously insures the correct angle of attack. Shutt may pedal up to maximum hull speed without the drag of a front foil or an elevated bow. When V_{TO} is achieved, he briskly pulls a lever that makes the front foil quickly and forcefully descend into the water, the newly created lift forces the bow to leap upward. The slightly elevated bow increases the angle of attack on the rear foil and the reluctant flying machine, obviously caught off-guard, is forced to leap into the air. This is a pop-up takeoff.

To achieve a pop-up takeoff, the pilot pedals forcefully while maintaining a low angle of attack of the front foil. He continues until takeoff speed is slightly exceeded, then rapidly increases the AOA allowing the boat's momentum, plus rapid pedaling, to push it through the drag hump and transition to flying before much speed is lost. As the bow rises, the AOA of the rear foil will increase and it too will rise.

The same idea could be applied to the rear (main) foil. Build up speed with a low AOI and low drag, and then rapidly increase the main foil's AOI for a pop-up takeoff. The lift of the front foil will increase with the square of the increase in speed and the bow will rise. Of course, either technique assumes the boat is designed to permit the pilot to override the AOI of the foils. Personal preparation for this vigorous feat includes strength training on bicycles, eating less and not growing older.

The technique for sail powered hydrofoils is to head across wind or slightly downwind until the maximum speed is obtained and the hull feels stable underway. A quick turn toward the wind will bring the boat to a beam reach. This is the fastest point of sail on most boats, often faster than the wind speed. Without delay the mainsail and jib should be sheeted in, weight shifted upwind and farther aft, and the tiller adjusted to obtain the maximum speed for this particular boat. If takeoff speed is not obtained, return to shore and have some iced refreshment until the wind picks up.

Your boat should be designed to takeoff in one of two ways, bow lifting first or bow and stern lifting together. If the rear foil is located at or near the transom, one way to begin flying is to increase speed until the bow rises to cruise height and the stern remains on the water. In this attitude the rear foil will have the maximum angle of attack, therefore the maximum lift for this speed. If the stern has a modest dead-rise (a rather flat bottom, laterally), the boat should be roll stable despite the high bow. Application of a little more power should nudge the boat over the drag hump. The speed will increase quickly, and the rear foil will rise in response to increased lift. The bow will remain at cruise height while the stern will rise to the point where lift = weight (at the stern). The more speed, the more the stern rotates around the front foil the more its angle of attack will decrease. This will decrease the lift generated until the rear foil finds lift equilibrium for the speed. You are flying. Again, during the transition rapid and exaggerated roll control corrections may be required of the pilot until enough speed is obtained to give adequate roll authority to the rear foil. With increased roll authority the pilot can use more subtle control adjustments.

On some designs this takeoff technique may not be possible. Hifybe and Hydro-ped, for example, have their rear foils close to amid-ship, and the stern is too narrow to support the boat by planing. Remember the WWII movies were a bomb-laden B-24 Liberator bomber would ramble forever down an interminably long runway, and John Wayne through heroic determination would will the hulking beast into the air? The B-24 does not sharply pitch up to induce takeoff. Prior to takeoff the pilot cranks in a slight up trim and when reaching takeoff speed slightly pulls back on the yoke. The plane breaks contact with the ground but never assumes a nose-high attitude.

B-24s do this because they have marginal power when fully loaded and can't offset the extra drag of a sharp pull up. With some hydrofoils the geometry will not allow the bow to rise sharply without dragging the tail. In this case, the front and the back foils must takeoff simultaneously. This may require some type of AOI override on the front foil to allow the pilot to keep the bow from rising excessively during transition.

With Hifybe's amidships main hydrofoil, exaggerated roll corrections are necessary during takeoff. This is because of its slow speed during the transition from non-flying to flying. At slow speed its main foil flippers have marginally sufficient roll authority to avoid toppling. During this wobbly transition, it is good technique to wiggle the stick a little to feel the roll control and to make small adjustments to roll excursions before they become uncontrollable.

Shutt's Hydro-ped uses a surface piercing aft main foil that creates automatic roll control. Shutt depends on a quick transition through the critical takeoff condition to avoid having the roll control overwhelmed during takeoff transition.

Without bow pitch-up at takeoff, the angle of attack of the rear foil will not be significantly augmented, so a trimming mechanism may be needed on this foil to increase the angle of incidence at takeoff. As speed increases, it may be necessary to reduce the trim while underway, because the needed AOA at cruise will be less than that required for takeoff. More speed requires less AOA.

There is actually a third way to takeoff. Hifybe was briefly tuned to takeoff stern first. During the transition, the bow would skim the water while the stern rotated upward. This takeoff attitude has no advantages, looks weird, feels funny, and risks ridicule. But you might want to try it.

Cruising an aircraft takes special technique because the pilot must be trained to trim properly to keep the nose at a certain pitch in relation to the horizon. Maintaining stable fuselage pitch is the key to consistent altitude. Failure to maintain a constant attitude will result in "chasing the altimeter." If the nose is high the altitude will increase and the speed will decrease. If the pilot reacts to excessive height and decreasing speed, he will lower the nose and descend to or through the correct altitude, but this increases the speed and makes the nose rise, etc. A cycle of correction and over-correction is started. The classic aviation solution is to react to attitude anomalies by making modest adjustments to attitude. Modest height and speed changes will follow.

In a hydrofoil the finding of height (altitude) is controlled by the properly designed front foil. If not properly designed, maintenance of a constant height will be difficult or impossible–except for very low speeds and calm conditions, as with some human powered hydrofoils on settled water. When the front foil sets the height of the bow, the attitude of the hull will not require continuous adjustment from the pilot. The hull's attitude will be determined by the trim of the rear foil as it vertically "weather vanes" behind the front foil.

Platforming and contouring. While we are on the subject of bow-pitch, let's think about how a hydrofoil should transit waves when flying. Recall that in the photo of Figure 8-13a and its text, we determined that ideally, if the struts are long enough the hull should remain level and pass over the waves smoothly, and with the hull remaining at a constant average height above the surface. This is called *platforming*.

However with short struts, relatively low speeds, and long swells; it may be advantageous to trim the boat to contour the waves, that is, have the bow rise as the wave is mounted and drop as the wave is exited. Predictably, this is called *contouring*.

Getting this right is a balancing act. Orbital currents within the wave will affect the foil's behavior. The closer the foils are to the surface the more orbital motion there is. To review orbital motion within a wave, go to the text that follows Figure 8-13.

Gain. With a submerged front foil, these orbital motions are dealt with by altering the *gain* of the surface follower. *Gain* is the percentage of change in lift divided by the inches of change in height, expressed in *percent / inch*. See the text following Figure 8-18. Too much pitch up–reduce the gain. Too little pitch up–increase the gain. It would be advantageous to be able to adjust the gain while underway.

Surface piercing foils are more difficult to tune for gain, because it is built into the geometry of the foil. Moving the center of gravity, if it is movable, is something to try. This will change the reserve (dry) area of the surface piercing foil. Moving captain and crew forward will reduce the reserve area and moving back will increase it. The more reserve area, the more reserve lift, and the greater the potential for vertical bow acceleration, or gain. Some boats do not respond well to forward shifting of the CG. For example, the Grumman hydrofoil runabout with its big surface piercing front foils becomes pitch unstable if the captain and crew move too far forward. Be prepared with any hydrofoil for unexpected results when moving the CG.

A similar effect can be had by trimming the front surface piercing foil around its lateral axis, thereby changing its angle of incidence. Increasing the AOI increases the reserve area and decreasing it has the opposite effect.

If flaps are built into the surface piercing foil, their deployment will increase gain—provided they are carefully crafted and do not cause ventilation when deflected. Incidentally, flaps on the surface piercing portion of a foil affects *gain*, flaps on the submerged portion of a foil affects *lift*.

If the CG is moved forward (or backward) and at the same time the AOI is increased (or decreased) a corresponding amount, the reserve area will not be changed. What will change is the *gain* of the front foil. See Figure 8-15, and observe that the gain in the realm of high C_{LS} is much less than the gain in the realm of low C_{LS}. The higher the gain, the stiffer the ride.

Obviously speed is a big factor in wave contouring. Like driving a Jeep over potholes; the faster it goes, the rougher the ride. At some speed wave contouring will become too uncomfortable. Then the only solution is to lengthen the struts to allow platforming, or slow the speed, to reduce the frequency of the "bumps" and allow continued contouring.

Turning and banking. For details on steering and rolling, also called turning and banking, refer back to chapters 9 and 10, but for a quick review, continue reading. The following will help the pilot in developing proper flying techniques.

Turning and banking are interrelated, but separate problems. Banking to the inside of a turn is necessary if the turn is to be balanced. All hydrofoils require the pilot to control turning, but only some hydrofoils require the pilot to control banking.

Rolling to the outside of a turn is undesirable; however, a hydrofoil can be designed to *turn without banking*. The span of the main foil usually determines whether banking is possible or not. The outside tips of wide foils will breach the surface during a relatively shallow bank. Narrow foils, especially those with anhedral, will allow sharper banking, but during a banked turn, the inboard tip of an anhedral foil will draw more depth.

A **balanced turn** is the most elegant turn. This is where the path of gravity is perceived to be passing perpendicularly through the seated pilot. In a balanced turn, the pull of gravity feels as if it is increasing, and it will not be felt as pulling to one side or the other. The "balance" is between the centrifugal forces to the outside of a turn and the gravitational forces pulling the boat down to the inside of the turn. It is achieved by the coordinated use of the available turning and roll control devices.

How roll is controlled will be dictated by the design. Some boats have ailerons or flippers near the tips of the main foil. Generally the stick or wheel is pushed or turned to the right to induce a roll to the right or to stop an unwanted roll to the left.

The rudder is an important part of roll management, regardless of whether the rudder is mounted at the bow or the stern. By applying rudder, yaw is initiated. Yaw initiates a reaction from various roll-controlling systems including: wing-tip dihedral, anhedral, swept-back wings, delta wings, and strut shadow. These are the subjects of chapters 9 and 10.

Modest dihedral near the wing tips will generate an inside rolling moment in response to pilot-induced yawing or slide slipping. To initiate a roll by using a rudder mounted on the stern, the rudder is deflected to skid the stern to the left causing a turn to the right, and the low position of the rudder creates a rolling moment to the right, the inside of the turn. The combination of rudder with the keel ahead of it, work together to create the turn, the turn generates centrifugal force to the outside (left), and the rudder is variably employed to bring these opposing roll forces into balance. Surface piercing dihedral outer wing sections are much more efficient than those that are submerged. Wide span foils generally have slower roll characteristics and they resist roll more, so the pilot can make small corrections well in advance of losing control. Narrow foils will be more maneuverable and they will roll quicker.

If the rudder is at the bow, as it usually is in canard-configured hydrofoils, it will perform differently. A rudder pulls the bow into the turn. This force to the inside of the turn applied below the roll center will cause the hull to roll to the *outside* of the turn. Look back to Figure 9-17b to visualize this effect. The pilot's input or the boat's geometry may be required to initiate an inside rolling moment to counteract the outside roll effects of the bow-mounted rudder.

Another effect of the bow rudder is its tendency to over-steer. Did the genius that invented the arrow put the feathers on the back end first or did he rely on trial and error to get it right? When a bow-mounted rudder is deflected to the right, the rudder's angle of attack increases as the bow continues to swing to the right, and the momentum of the boat propels it on course. This is a self-augmenting feedback loop. It is like an arrow with feathers mounted at the leading tip. In this case, the pilot needs to be aware of a tendency to over steer and therefore apply rudder pressure gingerly.

Still, most canard hydrofoil boats steer by the bow. This works because the major portion of the mass is near to, and supported by very large foils and struts. These large elements provide directional stability that the relatively small front foil does not overpower. If the bow strut and foil are small, the undesirable characteristics will likewise be small. In any event, the pilot must be aware that a bow-steering boat may over-steer and the rudder will contribute a rolling moment to the outside of a turn.

A small forward foil and steerable strut will be more responsive and maneuverable than an aft mounted rudder, but may require vigilance, be tricky in a turn, and require special piloting techniques. Unless properly employed, the front rudder will detract from making balanced banked turns. It may be necessary to shift the crew's weight to the inside of an anticipated turn or induce a roll moment by deflection ailerons prior to, or during, the deflection of the canard rudder. Slowly deflecting the canard rudder may allow time for the dihedral to respond to the yaw and induce the proper bank.

Single-track hydrofoils like the OU27, OU32, Hi-Foil, and the Dynafoil, have the pilot briefly steer away from then turn. Once the bank to the inside has begun, the front rudder is used to "turn under the fall" to create centrifugal force that balances the tendency to fall to the inside of the turn. For review, return to chapter 10 describing single track hydrofoils.

With these delicately balanced boats, piloting skill and technique is especially important. These boats steer and bank like a bicycle. The pilot cannot simply rotate the steering bar to the right and to initiate a right turn. Refer to Figure 10-1 and its text for an explanation of bicycle steering principles. Bicycles and single-track hydrofoils must *turn under the fall* to control their bank. To perform a turn, they must purposefully initiate the bank and then control the bank with the front steering device (rudder).

To begin a turn to the *right*, the pilot of a single-track hydrofoil must briefly and slightly steer to the *left*. The front foil will track to the left and the momentum of the hull and rider will cause them to fall to the right. The pilot immediately reacts to the right-side bank by turning to the right. He is turning under the fall. The change in direction must be powerful enough to create sufficient centrifugal force to balance gravity that will be pulling the hull down, toward the inside of the turn.

To end the turn, the pilot sharply turns the steering to the right. The increased centrifugal force will bring the hull and struts to vertical. This is literally a balancing act, and it may take some practice to master. Of course this technique will only work with while the boat is flying so it is going to take some faith for the first flight, where there must be a rapid transition from hull-borne stability to foil-borne controllability. This in-between period must be transited quickly; because during the transition, neither the hull nor the foils will have the authority to control rolling moments. A slow transition is an invitation to capsize. The experience might be compared to the line in a Paul Simon song, "You got to learn how to fall, before you learn to fly".

Note to the designer: a bike with rear wheel steering cannot be ridden (try riding your bike backwards), nor can an aft-rudder single-track hydrofoil. That is the rule; here is the exception:

The technique on aft-steering Moth-class hydrofoil sailboats would differ from that of canard steering hydrofoils. They too have a single-track configuration; however, roll control depends on balancing the sail forces against the centrifugal and gravitational forces. This is a real game of skill, as well. It goes something like this: if the boat falls windward, haul in on the mainsail sheet and increase the sail's side pressure. If falling leeward, payout the mainsail sheet. When appropriate, use the tiller to head-up or fall-off the wind to increase or decrease sail pressure. While doing that, move around on the windward trampoline to further balance the heeling forces. Also, move back on the trampoline to increase the angle of attack on both foils and move forward to decrease it. Don't forget to twist the tiller handle to trim the rear foil. The height of the bow is mercifully set by a height reading wand mechanism hinged at the bow. Now try all these moves while chewing gum. Apparently "Mothies" consider this normal behavior. A challenge would be to design a similar boat that could be flow by a rider with only one brain, two arms, and a made-for-television-viewing attention span. Look on the web for personal accounts on how to sail the tricky Moth.

Some hydrofoils, by accident of design, bank too much and need reverse roll correction to avoid falling to the inside of a turn. I have seen this in some human-powered hydrofoils. It can be associated with a stern-mounted rudder, high center of gravity, excessive tip dihedral, and very wide wingspan. One technique used to counter this outside roll is to shift the pilot's weight to the outside of the turn before initiating the turn, and then finish the turn before falling too far into the turn.

In a turn, power is an important consideration. The power consumed is in proportion to the lift created. The increase of Gs pulled in a turn will require additional power. So the pilot should increase power as the turn is entered. It is important that he never, never, reduce power while in a banked turn. The resulting slowdown will cause an instant decrease in roll control. This may result in an unnecessary and disagreeable capsize to the inside of the turn. The occasional capsize to the outside, the wrong side, is even more unpleasant.

A modified turning technique may be used in machines that can fly with slightly reduced power, like the Dynafoil. It may be helpful to enter the turn with less than P_{MAX}. When the boat falls to the inside of the turn, the reserve power can be applied to increase the centrifugal force and counteract the fall. You may recall that with the Dynafoil, and other boats with a center of propulsion far below the CG, accelerating while banking will tighten the turn. So the turn gets *tighter* and *faster*; both contribute to a rapid increase in centrifugal force.

Avoiding wheelies and stoppies

One might assume no wheels, no wheelies, but with some small motor-powered hydrofoils, like the Dynafoil, wheelies can be surprisingly easy, fun and sometimes disastrous. Because at rest the centers of gravity and pitch resistance are high while the thrust line is low, a sudden burst of power will result in a rapid pitch up. *Wheelie*, a term borrowed from stunt motorcyclists, is when the bow is pointing toward the sky and the stern toward whale poop. It can be amusing to riders and observers, but the long-term effect depends on the landing. If skill and care is taken to land straightforward everyone will be pleased. However falling backward or turning and rolling to the outside of the turn could be painful. Like with most stunts, thinking through the consequences and making little tries before gambling it all might avoid unpleasantness.

By the way, if any of you hot pilots out there can do a stoppie on a hydrofoil, let me know right away. *Stoppies*, the opposite of wheelies, are done on a motorcycle by breaking hard with the front wheel causing the rear wheel to raise high above the surface. They are considered to be an amusing success if the rear wheel drops straight down to the pavement and does not continue around the side or over the top of the stopped front wheel. Naturally these tricks would involve unnecessary danger and the author disclaims any responsibility or liability, and they are only mentioned so that the pilot will not experience them by accident. The author strongly advises any pilot against trying any such stupid stunts. Nonetheless, in a hydrofoil a stoppie would be something to see.

Stop the presses. This just in from Scott Smith, "I can do a stoppie with my jet ski. Of course it stops 3 feet under water." He says he has photos, but this is a family book–no violent images permitted.

Jumping

Most hydrofoils could be made to jump. Jumping is simply converting forward momentum to vertical momentum. A quick increase in the AOA of the front foil should to the job, especially at speed and at a depressed flying height. Crossing another boat's wake or launching off the backside of a steep wave would help get some air. The problem is landing gracefully. To recover from the jump a large increase in front foil lift will be necessary. However the front foil will be coming from above the surface and when it dives below the surface it will carry with it a bubble of air. For an instant, the foil will be fully ventilated, but this is a critical instant where maximum lift is needed. The key is to unload the front foil (rotate backward) prior to jumping. The boat should land on its rear foil. The unloaded rear foil then needs to provide very little of the lift to keep the bow from diving.

Naturally, small hydrofoils will be better suited to this trick than will large ones. The Dynafoil and the Air chair can do jumps off of a wake and flying jumps from smooth water. If you have not seen the Air chair do acrobatics, search the Internet, especially Youtube.com. The Air chair is a wide single water-ski with a hydrofoil array and strut attached to its bottom. The "chair" is attached to the top of the ski and the skier is strapped into the chair, honest. A ski boat tows the skier, ski, chair, and hydrofoils, and the jumps are so high that mid-air loops and rolls are performed.

Spin takeoff

This technique comes from the Dynafoil operation manual, and it may or may not work with another small hydrofoil boat. While the boat is resting motionless, the idea is for the pilot to throw his weight to one side, quickly leaning the boat as far as possible. At the same instant the boat leans the most, the pilot snaps on the throttle. In this posture the propeller will be near the surface and off to the side opposite the lean. The propulsion from the side will catapult the boat into a sharp turn and as it accelerates, centrifugal force will mount. About ¾ of the way through the circle the boat will reach flying speed, and at the same time centrifugal force will pull the boat to an upright position. If this works on your boat it is sure to impress the crowd, but only Dynafoil claims to have a boat that will perform the maneuver.

Landing

After taking-off, cruising, and turning there will be a landing. An unplanned landing with an aircraft often makes the evening news, but hydrofoils can land in deep water anywhere, anytime, no problem. Some designs may require slowly decreasing power to avoid a graceless splashdown, but in general one simply reduces power until the boat stops flying. Two caveats: do not attempt to land while in a turn or otherwise banked. Slowing will reduce roll authority and doing so while banking might result in capsizing.

To avoid grounding, remember that the draft will increase when the flying stops. Make sure the water at the landing site is deep enough to accommodate the foils as they descend. If the pilot finds himself inadvertently flying over shallow water the best course of action may be to continue flying and perform a quick 180 degree turn. Throttling down in shallow water is a guaranteed disaster. In the event of running aground at speed, a quick shift of weight to the aft might save the delicate front foil and also help to avoid an *endo* (forward summersault).

Weeds

During any stage of flight, weeds and debris can be a problem. To clear weeds off the foils, try yawing while underway. This is especially effective if the foils are swept-back. If necessary, stop and reverse the boat to allow the stuff to drift off the leading edge. Finally, always bring along a slender stick, perhaps with a hook on the end. When stopped, slide the stick along the leading edge to dislodge the most stubborn offenders.

High speed boats are less affected than slow ones. Human powered hydrofoils can be stopped by a gum wrapper, but the Dynafoil can power through even the notorious Florida hydrilla (coconuts as well–so I am told). At speed the effect is felt on the steerable front foil, creating a sensation similar to riding a mini bike in a ditch. Stopping in weeds ends the fun. The debris must be removed and clear water must be found before takeoff is possible.

Flight Safety

Nothing is more important than safety. Even though these flying machines have less potential for disaster than do aircraft, accidents do happen. Fortunately most accidents are preventable and there are many ways to reduce the consequences.

Follow the U. S. Coast Guard's regulations on standard boating safety. Wear–not just carry–a personal floatation device for each person. Where appropriate carry a fire extinguisher, waterproof flare, whistle, etc. Boats over 10 feet in length and all powerboats need to be registered in most states. Check in your state for safety and licensing requirements. Carry only the minimum needed fuel but always provide more than enough fuel to return to the dock. Have the fuel tank properly secured.

Never test an unproven boat without qualified observers. Observers in a chase boat are better than those on shore. If they are on shore, make certain they have some way to get to the test boat if needed. Don't forget to have a paddle on board, and don't get too far from shore unless you really have confidence in your boat. Remember that the deployed struts and foils will make paddling difficult.

Any boat, especially one that is fast, needs a clean deck. Eliminate sharp or pointed attachments. If you use a control stick, cover the pointy end with a blunt cushioned shape, and make certain that it hinges forward and is not pointing toward the pilot's soft spots.

A motorboat is safer if it has a propeller guard. Hifybe uses a circular guard surrounding the prop. It is of strong plastic, and is commercially available. Some designs, for example the Dynafoil, nests the prop below the rear anhedral foil and its strut. The motor should have an electric kill switch that triggers when the pilot leaves his seat or removes his foot from a special pedal. The boat should also have a snap throttle that shuts down when released. Some boats have spring-loaded gearshift levers and shift to neutral when the pilot takes his weight off the seat or when he removes his foot from a "dead man" pedal (Dynafoil uses this system). A bonus with the dead man pedal comes with docking. When the pilot takes his foot of the pedal, the boat stops moving.

For safety, a boat with a traditional hull, one the pilot and crew sits *in,* is preferable. Hulls you sit *on*, like Hifybe's, offer less protection against a quick rollover or sudden stop. The windsurfer board of Hifybe is exciting, but a traditional hull is recommended for safety. In addition, a boat that is straddled, may be classified as a Personal Water Craft and be subject to operating restrictions. Check whatever regulations apply locally.

In any boat, especially a hydrofoil, the pilot and crew must prepare for sudden, unexpected deceleration. What goes fast, can stop fast. Like airliners encountering clear air turbulence, all on board are at ease because routine flying can be disarmingly smooth and uneventful. If the flying stops, the hydrofoil becomes hull-borne and the slow-down will be dramatic. In preparation, everyone on board must be sitting properly, facing forward, and holding on to something. Obviously, safety belts offer effective protection when crashing, but no one wants to be strapped into a sinking boat–should the worst occur.

Wear protective clothing. Weather permitting, a wet suit will help protect against abrasions and bruises, and a buoyant bicycle helmet will help protect against head injuries. While on the water a minor head bump can cause a big headache.

Be safety conscious. This list of precautions may have inadvertently overlooked something. Ultimately, it is the responsibility of the builder and the pilot to build and fly safely. Be careful.

So far in this book we have explored the important aspects of hydrofoils: history, flight characteristics, design parameters, and actual designs. We have followed the title: *Hydrofoils: Design, Build, Fly.* What if after careful studying and constructing a hydrofoil, it won't fly?

The final subject is *troubleshooting*, what to do if things don't go as planned. In effect, this is a synopsis of the entire book, and all the subjects mentioned here will have been explained in detail in previous parts. To keep it brief and easy to navigate, I have usually not referenced the source chapters or figures, but the reader is encouraged to search the Index and Table of Contents to find and review those subjects as needed.

Test flying and troubleshooting:

Takeoff problems:

> In a displacement-type hull with the foils and struts deployed for takeoff, there may be inadequate power if the maximum hull speed cannot be reached.
> In a planing hull with the foils and struts deployed for takeoff, there may be inadequate power if the minimum planing speed cannot be reached.
> There may be excessive drag from hull, struts, or foils. All must be clean, streamlined, and not oversized.
> One component may be interfering with another causing proximity drag. Except for intersections, keep foils, struts and hull at least two chords away from each other. *Chord* in this case is the largest of the foil's or the strut's chord. One foil should not be in another's wake, unless carefully planned to take advantage of the first foil's up-wake.
> Check for strut and foil ventilation. The vacant space inside a hollow foil may contain enough air to create a lift-destroying bubble. Even submerged foils must be airtight. This condition corrects itself once the air is displaced with water, but because it is intermittent, it may be a difficult problem to diagnose. Air may be coming down the outside of any strut or the inside of a hollow strut. Surface-piercing foils provide a path for air at the point where they penetrate the water.
> Propeller ventilation could be the result of air or exhaust gas coming down a prop shaft or a strut.
> Propeller ventilation can result from surface proximity. If the propeller has too large a radius relative to its depth, or is too close to the surface, it will draw in air.
> Incorrect propeller. Too big, too small, too much pitch, too little pitch. The propeller must allow the engine to operate at an rpm to generate sufficient power to overcome the takeoff drag hump. Either too high or too low of an rpm at takeoff may result in insufficient power.
> Original manufacturer's propellers are compromised designs where efficiency is one of several design criteria. Weed shedding, safety, and economy are a few of the competing criteria. Aftermarket racing propellers are typically more efficient.
> Excessive friction in the drive train is a problem that especially plagues human powered hydrofoils.
> Unplanned wing warp may occur when lift is created. This can kill lift.
> A foil's angle of attack is too low resulting in insufficient C_L.
> The foil's angle of attack is too high resulting in a stall and/or excessive drag. If the foil is too small, the induced drag may be excessive.
> The foil is too big causing excessive parasite drag.
> Banana shaped hull, or banana dihedral. The inverted curve is like a wing upside down. The faster it goes the more downward lift is created sucking the hull or foil deeper below the surface.
> A bow-high takeoff attitude caused by either excessive bow foil lift or insufficient aft foil lift. A deep running propeller will contribute to pitch up.

➤ Tail squat is a similar condition. This may occur when the CG and the main foil are amidships, like Hifybe's. Even a modest elevation of the bow will force the stern to deeply penetrate the surface causing excessive drag. This type of design requires the foil forces, fore and aft, to be carefully balanced to allow takeoff without pitching up.

➤ With outboard motors or inboard/outboard motors the engine trim is critical. The propeller shaft should run in line with the slipstream.

Stability vs. maneuverability and the steps to balance them:

Things that detract from stability and/or maneuverability:

➤ Loose or flexible structure or wings.
➤ Loose or flexible control linkage.
➤ Uncontrolled ventilation.
➤ Uncontrolled cavitation.
➤ Operating at angles of attack approaching or exceeding the stalling angle.
➤ Operating foils in depths less than one chord.
➤ Foil fouling: seaweed, debris, surface damage, paint flaking, etc.
➤ If the motor is used to induce yaw, be careful not to allow the prop wash to flow over the lifting surfaces. The prop wash flowing over a foil will affect lift, and redirecting the prop will cause lift imbalances.
➤ Some outboard motors eject their exhaust gasses through the hub of the propeller. Like air, these gases can cause a serious ventilation problem if allowed to flow in the vicinity of a hydrofoil wing. The gas will attach itself to the upper, vacuum, side foil and significantly destroy lift. The gas bubble will be difficult to shed and it will be replenished by new gas after the old has departed.

Things that increase yaw (Directional) stability:

➤ Position rudder well aft of the CG and provide sufficient separation from the keel.
➤ The keel must be adequate. The *keel* in a hydrofoil is the largest wetted component as seen from the side of the craft. It is typically the strut(s) of the main foil, and the main foil.

Decrease yaw stability:

➤ Positioning the rudder forward of the CG will promote over steering. Forward steering is not self-correcting in the sense that an arrow has self-correcting steering.
➤ Flaws in foils and struts will reduce the generation of side forces.
➤ An inadequate keel will reduce yaw stability.
➤ When foil-borne, too much of the rudder or keel may become un-wetted.

Increase yaw maneuverability:

➤ Position the rudder forward of the CG and keel.
➤ A deep running rudder is more effective than a shallow running one.
➤ Increase the rudder size to increase its effectiveness.
➤ Increase the aspect ratio to increase efficiency.

Things that decrease yaw maneuverability:

➤ Positioning the rudder aft of CG will discourage over steering.
➤ If the rudder emerges from the water as the craft becomes foil-borne it will then be ineffective.
➤ Decreasing rudder or keel size will decrease its effectiveness.

Roll (lateral moment) to the *inside*. The design characteristics that cause roll moments to the inside of a turn or yaw:

➤ Small angles of dihedral in the wing sections near the tips will cause a roll to the inside of a turn in response to yawing.
➤ Anhedral generally decreases roll *stability*, but increases roll *control*.
➤ Swept wings, in single-track hydrofoils, add slightly to positive roll response to yawing.
➤ The shadow effect from a centerline strut in a single-track hydrofoil contributes a small amount of inside rolling moment when yawing.
➤ Wing tips operating near the surface may benefit from the surface effect to augment roll control.
➤ A rudder aft of the keel that applies its force significantly below the center of gravity will generate an inside rolling moment.

Roll (lateral moment) to the *outside*. The design characteristics that cause roll moments to the outside of a turn or yaw:

➤ Excessive dihedral reduces or reverses the lever arm acting on the roll center.
➤ Anhedral (except special designs like the Hi-Foil type of front foil).
➤ Narrow wingspan.
➤ A rudder that is located forward of the keel and/or CG.

Characteristics that increase roll maneuverability:

➤ Anhedral that is coupled with lift altering devices—ailerons, flippers, spoilers, etc.
➤ Pilot controlled ailerons.
➤ Pilot controlled wing-warp.
➤ A deep running large rudder.
➤ Having a solid structure, struts, and foils.
➤ When the rudder has its pivot point at or behind its center of pressure it will self-deflect. This would usually be undesirable, except when extreme maneuverability or amplified pilot input is the goal.

Piloting Techniques and Troubleshooting

Characteristics that decrease roll maneuverability:

> ➢ Dihedral in the outboard wing sections increases roll stability.
> ➢ Rudder placement forward of center of gravity will contribute to adverse roll.
> ➢ Loose or flexible struts and wings limit the control force that can be applied.
> ➢ An undersized rudder may be ineffective in contributing to roll.

Exceptions:

In the previous text on roll management, it is considered to be a good thing if corrective forces cause the boat to roll to the inside of the turn. Single-track hydrofoils that steer by the bow are different. They use their front foil and strut combination as a rudder and the rolling force created during a turn is to the *outside* of the turn. They turn *under the fall*, and use centrifugal force to cause the boat to roll to the outside to counteract the natural tendency to fall in the direction of the lean. For this to work special piloting technique is necessary. To commence a turn to the right, the pilot briefly and slightly turns the bow rudder to the left to initiate a bank to the inside, right side, of the planned turn and then stops the boat from tumbling inward by turning sharply right, into the turn.

The types of boats that require this technique have very little roll stability, but they have strong roll control. Because this is a balancing act, the pilot must be provided the tools that provide enough, but not too much, roll corrective force coupled to the steering. If the boat tends to fall to the outside of a turn, its corrective roll force is too much, it must be reduced by altering the design. If rolling is coupled to the pilot's efforts to steer, the relationship between rolling and turning must be correctly proportioned.

Design features that reduce the rolling moment to the outside of the turn are (the canard configuration is assumed):

> ➢ Move the CG aft to bring it directly above the lateral center of resistance, review Figures 10-7a and b and their text.
> ➢ Move the main foil forward to increase its load. This has the same effect as moving the CG. In either case, the foil sizes may need to be altered to maintain appropriate the wing loading.
> ➢ Link the motor strut or aft rudder to turn in the opposite rotation of the front rudder. In the OU32 the ratio of rotation of fore and aft rudders is 3 to 1.

Porpoising of the front foil:

> The gain is too low between the surface follower and the front foil's variable lift system.

> The front strut is not streamlined, or it is excessively yawed, allowing air to travel down to the foil.

> Some part of the variable lift mechanism is sticking.

> With a variable AOI foil the pivot should be forward of the aquadynamic center, which is usually about 25% of the chord length aft of the leading edge. Usually the pivot is best placed at or ahead of the aquadynamic center. Placing the pivot aft will cause a "reverse arrow effect" and the foil will be directionally unstable.

> Excessive flow pressure against the vertical control rods causing jamming. Control rods should be shielded from free stream forces. The best place to shield a control rod is inside a hollow strut.

> Especially with surface piercing front foils, too much up-trim of the rear foil may lead to porpoising. To up-trim, the rear foil's AOI is reduced, thereby reducing its lift, causing the boat to pitch up. The up-pitch causes a upward directing of the propeller thrust vector at the same time the increased AOA of the front foil is causing increased lift. The combined forces will cause the front foil to rapidly rise, followed by a collapse in lift.

> With his usual eloquence, Scott Smith describes the experience with his Grumman hydrofoil runabout, when the rear foil's AOI is trimmed too high: "From a planing position in the water, the thrust of the prop combines with the lift from the front foils to cause a bow-up condition. As the bow rises and speed increases, the over-trimmed rear foil 'catches up' (remember, lift increases with the square of the velocity) and raises higher than the front, causing the front foil's AOA to decrease, and the bow to drop. When the hull contacts the water the rear foil settles back down, and the process begins repeating. The front foil never breeches in this circumstance".

Roll instability:

> Too little dihedral minimizes the dihedral effect.

> Too much dihedral directs the lift vectors to pass through or under the center of rotation. This diminishes or reverses the roll lever arm.

> The foil span can be too narrow causing too short a roll lever-arm, and too quick a roll period.

> Breaching and ventilating of the foil tips through the surface when banked will cause a collapse of the lift on the high side.

> When front steering is implemented, it will create a rolling moment to the outside, and may contribute to roll instability if not specifically planned for.

> Anhedral detracts from roll stability. Ironically, anhedral contributes to effective roll *control* where ailerons, flippers, spoilers, etc. are employed.

Inadequate lift or excessive drag created by the wing.

> ➢ The foil's surface–especially the upper surface–must be smooth. Smoothness is especially important from the leading edge to 1/3 the chord aft. The foil should be smooth like the painted fender of a new automobile, except where special boundary layer agitation is being implemented as with some form of turbulator.
> ➢ There is waviness, especially on upper surface of the foils.
> ➢ The foils or struts have sharp leading edges contributing to flow separation at modest angles of attack.
> ➢ Air leakage inside a hollow strut is causing ventilation.
> ➢ Depending on design and conditions, high speed may trigger cavitation. The speed of inception varies but 40 mph is an approximate minimum.
> ➢ Excessive angles of attack cause stalling. This is virtually independent of speed, ventilation, or cavitation.
> ➢ The foil profile being used might be inappropriate. Usually duplication of tested and popular aerodynamic profiles will bring good results. Don't invent a foil section unless you really know a lot about doing so.

Turning is difficult:

> ➢ The rudder may be too small or too much of it is unwetted at flying height. It must be large enough to initiate a turn by forcing the boat to yaw.
> ➢ The keel or stationary strut may be too small. In this case, the rudder initiates a yaw but boat skids straight ahead.
> ➢ The keel is too long, causing excessive lateral stability. More than one keel acts like a long keel.
> ➢ Multiple foils and struts along the length of the boat will act as a long keel.
> ➢ The rudder or keel ventilates or stalls because it is being turned too sharply, has too sharp a leading edge, or has a rough or pitted surface.
> ➢ The rudder is too close to the keel so the turning lever arm is insufficient. Applying a rudder rigged like this will result in side slipping but little turning.
> ➢ Be certain that the rudder has a full range of rotation in both directions.

Force reversal (unanticipated consequences) Surprises are experienced with rudders, keels, or foils. Force is expected in one direction but occurs in the opposite direction. Here are some possible reasons:

> ➢ When a sharp turn to the right results in a sudden turn to the left, ventilation is first suspected. The unanticipated collapse of lift (or side force) may allow forces in the opposite direction to overwhelm.
> ➢ Wing warp can result when a foil has its support offset too far fore or aft of the aquadynamic center, or when the materials used in its construction are inadequate. High aspect ratios and low thickness ratios contribute to stiffness problems. If the structure is inadequate, any twisting force created by lift may change the angle of incidence.

Making observations, hints on how to make them:

> - Use a mirror on a horizontal pole to observe under the hull.
> - Mount a disposable or waterproof camera on a pole to record what's happening under the hull.
> - A chase boat with observers, still cameras, or video cameras can gather useful information.
> - A fly-by of a dock or boat will allow others to make observations, or take videos or photographs for review.

Ventilation suspected? Here's what to look for:

> - White water will be visible on the lifting side of the foil. The whiteness indicates the mixing of air and water. It differs from cavitation whiteness in that it does not collapse and disappear downstream. The bubbles will come to the surface. The white water will trail back from the point where air enters the vacuum of the foil. At flying speeds the white water cannot move forward of its source.
> - Bubble ventilation is different. Once air has entered the low pressure topside of a foil, it may attach itself and be difficult to shed. The bubble does not lose air and it does not require additional air to sustain itself. The source could be a hollow strut or foil with a pinhole where air exits until the air in the void is replaced with water.
> - When a foil breaches, it may acquire an air bubble, and after re-submerging momentarily resist shedding it. Until the bubble is shed, normal lift will suffer.

Stalling suspected? Check out these confirming characteristics:

> - This is a condition of turbulent flow on the lifting side of a wing. It is the result of high angles of attack that exceed the fluid's ability to continue orderly flow over the curved upper surface. Turbulent water, without air vapor, will be clear and will not have the white water appearance of ventilation or cavitation.

Cavitation considered? Look for these indications:

> - Cavitation is a product of speed. Below 40 or 50 mph there is insufficient dynamic force at low angles of attack to create a vacuum high enough to cause water to vaporize on the lifting side of the wing. Of course, a fast spinning propeller may reach cavitation speeds independent of the speed of the hull. Cavitation cavities collapse without leaving a trail of bubbles.

Component degradation:

> - Don't run aground or beach a hydrofoil unless the foils are retracted. Even little chips and scratches degrade the performance of a foil.
> - Avoid flutter of a foil, strut, rudder, etc. Rapid flexing will destroy an otherwise strong part.

> Electrolysis, galvanic corrosion, is caused by immersing components made of dissimilar metals. To avoid this problem, connect all exposed metals to a less noble wetted part such as a sacrificial zinc. Also avoid contact between dissimilar metals, such as using brass bolts in an aluminum strut, unless separated by an electrical insulator, such as a plastic liner.

> Avoid loose parts. For example, a bolt left to range-free in the bilge of an aluminum boat can quickly hammer a hole in the bottom.

> Pitting of cavitating parts is eliminated by ending the cavitation.

> Rust is avoided by avoiding ferrous metals. All steel should be stainless. Any part that is suspected of being rust-able is checked by touching it with a magnet. Most stainless steels will only slightly attract a magnet (there are some exceptions).

Propeller problems: ventilation, stalling, cavitation, low rpm, or high rpm.

> *Ventilation* creates a trail of bubbles and the engine rpm increase dramatically. However, some engines vent their exhaust gasses through an enlarged hub on the propeller, and this too will leave a trail of bubbles. Don't confuse this exhaust gas with ventilation air. The engine is designed to release its exhaust like this, so it should not cause propeller ventilation. Operating the prop too close to the surface can cause propeller ventilation. The solution is to increase immersion by lengthening the outboard motor's shaft, cutting down the transom, or flying lower. The problem can also be caused by air passing down the motor shaft, especially in the shaft's wake. Improve the streamlining of the shaft, fashion a ventilation fence on the motor shaft, or try attaching a commercial delta-shaped hydrofoil to the ventilation plate to block air entry. To reduce unnecessary induced drag, any added ventilation fence should be kept to a neutral or low angle of attack, and it should be limited to the smallest effective size.

> Propeller *stalling* causes the engine to over speed, because it is not getting a "bite" in the water. In stalling there should be no trail of ventilation bubbles. Usually this is the result of too great a propeller pitch, poorly formed blades, rough blades, or damaged blades. The prop should be highly polished or smoothly painted. Nicks and dings are not acceptable.

> *Cavitation* is the result of excessive propeller speed. The solution is to slow down or change to a propeller designed to cavitate. These types are standard on racing motorboats. Also, surface irregularities disturb the local flow patterns and may promote early cavitation. Check propellers for nicks, pitting, and bent blades.

> When the engine will not reach sufficient rpms to produce high power, it is often the result of too great a propeller pitch, too much diameter, or too many surface irregularities.

> When the engine over-speeds, it can be the result of an undersized propeller, insufficient pitch, ventilation, cavitation, stalling, or too many surface irregularities.

Bibliography

Books:

Abbott, Allan V. and David Gordon Wilson; *Human-Powered Vehicles*, Human Kinetics Publishers, Champaign, Illinois 1995.

Abbott, Ira H. and A. E. von Doenhoff; *Theory of Wing Sections*: *Including a Summary of Airfoil Data* (Dover Books on Physics) (Paperback), Dover Publications, New York 1959.

Anderson, David F.; Scott Eberhardt; *Understanding Flight*, McGraw-Hill International, New York 2001.

Anderson, John D. Jr.; *Introduction to Flight*, fifth edition, McGraw-Hill International, New York 2005.

Barlow, Jewel B.; William H. Rae Jr., and Alan Pope; *Low-Speed Wind Tunnel Testing*, third edition, John Wiley & Sons, Inc., New York, 1999

Boileau, John; *Fastest in the World: The Saga of Canada's Revolutionary Hydrofoils*, Formac Publishing Company Limited, Halifax, Nova Scotia 2004.

Bornhoft, Simon; *High-Speed Boats*: Lerner Publications, Minneapolis 1999.

Bruce, Robert V.; *Bell: Alexander Graham Bell and the Conquest of Solitude*, Cornell University Press, Ithaca, 1973.

Dalton, Stephen; *The Miracle of Flight*, Firefly Books Ltd., Buffalo 1999.

Eppler, Richard; *Airfoil design and data*, Springer-Verlag, Inc., New York, 1992.

Hoerner, Sighard F.; *Aerodynamic Drag*, revised edition, privately published, Midland Park, New Jersey, 1965.

Hook, Christopher and A. C. Kermode; *Hydrofoils*, Pitman, London WC2.

Horiuchi, Kotaro; *Locus of a Boat Designer 2*, published in Japan by The Boat Association of Japan, 2006, 1-2-17, Hamamatucho Minato-ku, Tokyo (105-0013).

Hurt, H.H. Jr.; *Aerodynamics for Naval Aviators*, NAVWEPS 00-80T-80, 1965.

Jones, Robert T.; *Wing Theory*, Princeton University Press, Princeton, New Jersey, 1990.

Bibliography

Keiper, David A.; *Hydrofoil Voyager: Williwaw, from Dream to Reality and Toward the Sailing Yacht of the Future.* Hinsdale Press, USA.

Kershner, William K.; *The Advanced Pilot's Flight Manual*, Iowa State University Press, Ames, Iowa.

Larrabee, E. Eugene; Propellers for Human Powered Vehicles, *Human-Powered Vehicles*, Human Kinetics Publishers, Champign, Illinois, July 1995.

Lien, Neil C.; *Monitor Hydrofoil Sailboat*: Design in Review, Published by author.

McLeavy, Roy; *Hovercraft and Hydrofoils*, Arco Publishing Co, Inc, New York.

McLeavy, Roy; *Jane's Surface Skimmer Systems*, McGraw Hill International, New York.

Morwood, John; *Sailing Hydrofoils*, AYRS Publication No. 74, Published for the Amateur Yacht Research Society in Hythe, England, 1970.

Munson, B. R., D. F. Young and T. H. Okiishi; *Fundamentals of Fluid Mechanics* 2006.

Prandtl, L. and O.G. Tiejens; *Applied Hydro-and Aeromechanics*, Dover Publications, Inc, New York, 1934.

Selig, Michael S. et. al.; *Airfoils at Low Speeds*, H. A. Stokely, Virginia Beach, Virginia, 1989.

Shutt, Sidney G.; *Human-Powered Vehicles*, Human Kinetics Publishers, 1995.

Skene, Norman L.; *Elements of Yacht Design*, Sheridan House, New York, 2001.

Smith, Hubert C.; *The Illustrated Guide to Aerodynamics*, 2nd edition, TAB Books, a Division of McGraw Hill International, New York, 1992.

Simons, Martin; *Model Aircraft Aerodynamics*, fourth edition, Special Interest Model Books Ltd., Poole, Dorset, UK, 2002.

Von Mises, Richard; *Theory of Flight*, Dover Publications, Inc., New York, 1959.

Wegener, Peter P.; *What Makes Airplanes Fly?* Second edition, Springer-Verlag, New York, 1998.

Young, Warren C. and R.G. Budynas; *Roark's Formulas for Stress and Strain*, McGraw Hill International, New York, 2002.

Magazine articles and academic papers:

"An 11.5 ft. one-person hydrofoil developed by Italian designer Rentato Castellani of Verbania can hit 35 mph with an 18-hp outboard engine", *Popular Mechanics,* September 1967. Print.

Advanced Marine Vehicle, numbers CD-ROM 1, 2 ,3, and 4 in the series of reference and historical AMV document releases. International Hydrofoil Society. Print.

Barr, Roderick; "Ventilation Inception of Surface Piercing and Submerged Foils and Struts", Advanced Hydronautics, Inc.

Brooks, Alec N., Allan V. Abbott, and David Gordon Wilson; "Human-Powered Watercraft", *Scientific American*, December 1986.

Dawson, Dudley; *Yachting,* Volume 205, Number 4, Publisher Ed Baker, New York, Print.

Eames, M. C. and E. A. Jones; "HMCS Bras d'Or–An Open Ocean Hydrofoil Ship", *Advanced Marine Vehicles,* International Hydrofoil Society compact disk #3. Print.

"Free Blueprint Sheet one & Sheet two: Flying Platform Boat." *Popular Science* May 1960. Print.

Gallager, Sheldon M.; "Now You Can 'Fly' Your Own Outboard." *Popular Science* June 1959: 178+. Print.

Jackson, William D.; "Build Your Own Hydrofoil Speedboat", *Science and Mechanics,* February 1960. 176-179. Print.

Jenkins, George, Cdr U.S. Navy, (Ret); "Patrol Combatant Missile (Hydrofoil) PHM History 1973 – 1993", *International* Hydrofoil Society compact disk. Print.

Muncie, Robert C.; *Development and Testing of Fully Submerged Hydrofoils with Drag Vane Control Installed on 15 Foot Runabouts,* Grumman Aircraft Engineering Corporation, International Hydrofoils Society AMV CD #2.

Parken, Blaine R.; "Experiments on Circular Arc and Flat Plate Hydrofoils in Noncavitating and Full Cavity Flows, Department of the Navy, Bureau of Ships", 1956, International Hydrofoils Society AMV CD #4.

Pfister, Herbert R.; "How I Fitted Oak Hydrofoils To My 14-Foot Runabout", *Popular Science,* June 1960.

Bibliography

Speer, Thomas, E.; "The Basiliscus Project - Return of the Cruising hydrofoil Sailboat", The 15th Chesapeake Sailing Yacht Symposium, Annapolis, Maryland.

Silverman, Abe; "Scale effect on Clark Y airfoil characteristics from NACA full-scale wind-tunnel tests"; NACA-report-502, 1935.

Schmidt, Theodore; "Propeller Design", *Human-Powered Vehicles,* Human Kinetics Publishers July 1995.

USA. NASA. "Entry Aerodynamics at Lunar Return Conditions Obtained from the Flight of Apollo 4". by Ernest R. Hillje; Vol. TN D-5399. NASA, 1969. Print.

USA. NASA. "Tests of N.A.C.A Airfoils in the Variable Density Wind Tunnel". By Eastman N. Jacobs and Robert M. Pinkerton; NACA Technical Note No. 391. Print.

Wade, R. B.; *Water Tunnel Observations on the Flow Past a Plano-Convex Hydrofoil,* Division of Engineering and Applied Science, California Institute of Technology, Report No. E-79-6, Pasadena, California 1964.

Wenzinger, Carl J.; *Wind-Tunnel Tests of a Clark Y Wing Having Split Flaps with Gaps,* NACA Technical Note No. 650, 1938.

Patents:

Cline, David J.; Dynafoil patent: #3,804,048, April 16, 1974.

Hubbard, M. Robert, et al.; Boeing hydrofoil forward strut patent: #3,742,890, July 3, 1973.

Meacham, W. M. and L. E.; Hydrofoil Patents: #857,951, June 25, 1907; #955,343, April 19, 1910; #1,186,816, June 3, 1913.

Nott, P. T. M.; Hi-Foil patent: #3,456,609, July 22, 1969.

Shutt, Sidney G.; Hydro-ped Patents: # 4,711,195, Dec. 8, 1987; # 3,762,353, Oct 2, 1973; 3,747,549, July 24, 1973.

Web Sites:

Airfoil coordinates, etc.: Selig, Michael, Department of Aerospace Engineering, University of Illinois at Urbana-Champaign: http://www.ae.uiuc.edu/m-selig/ads.html

"Characteristics of 78 Related Airfoil Sections from Tests in the Variable-Density Wind Tunnel": Report No. 460: http://www.aeronautics.nasa.gov/docs/rpt460/airfoils.htm

"Control Systems for International Moth on Hydrofoils", Miller, Chris; Glasgow University: http://culnane.navidat.com/dc/moth/papers/ConSys.pdf?nocache=813679636

Decavitator: http://lancet.mit.edu/decavitator/

Engineering resources: http://www.engineersedge.com/calculators.htm

"Full Scale Measurements on a Hydrofoil International Moth", Beaver, Bill, and John Zseleczky; The 19th Chesapeake Sailing Yacht Symposium, Annapolis, Maryland, March 2009: http://www.moth-sailing.org/download/CSYSPaperFeb09.pdf

Horsepower formulas, iProcesSmart: www.iprocessmart.com/

Hydroptère: http://www.hydroptere.com/_en/

Human powered boats, photos: http://www.humanpoweredboats.com/Photos/HydrofoilHPBs/HydrofoilHPBs.htm

International Hydrofoil Society: http://www.foils.org/

Bibliography

L/D: http://www.absoluteastronomy.com/topics/Lift-to-drag_ratio

L/D: http://ntrs.nasa.gov/archive/nasa/casi.ntrs.nasa.gov/19930091575_1993091575.pdf

Mason, W. H. "Experiment 7 – Aero/Hydrodynamic" Clark Y airfoil testing: http://www.aoe.vt.edu/~devenpor/aoe3054/manual/expt7/text.html

Moth Bladerider: http://www.bladerider.com.au/

Moth, Fastacraft: http://www.fastacraft.com/moulded_foils.html

Moth, Adam May, The Foiling Guide: http://www.int-moth.org.uk/worddocs/Foiler%20Sailing%20Guide1_Intro.pdf

Miller, Rich; San Francisco Bay Boardsailing Association (SFBA), Newsletter May, 1997. His 28 page technical paper is available through the International Hydrofoil Society, http://www.foils.org/miller.htm.

NACA airfoil series, explanation of: http://people.clarkson.edu/~pmarzocc/AE429/The%20NACA%20airfoil%20series.pdf

Publisher of this book: http://peacockhillpublishing.com/

Talaria IV: http://mysite.verizon.net/res6pe7p/

Videos of hydrofoils by the author, viewed over 1,100,000 times: http://www.youtube.com/results?search_query=ray+vellinga&search_type=

Wing sections analysis software, Dreese, John; http://www.dreesecode.com/index.html

Index

Index

Cover Images

Front cover:

The author on Hifybe (High Flying Banana).

Back cover, Clockwise, starting at upper left:

Hobie's Trifoiler, with permission from Hobie Cat Company.

Quest, Hybrid Hydrofoil Small Waterplane Area Ship (HYSWAS), with permission from Maritime Physics Corporation.

Todd Miller doing a wheelie on his Dynafoil, photo provided by Todd Miller.

The author on Hifybe, by Pat Vellinga.

Dwight Filley in his Mach .03.

USS High Point, PCH 1 of the US Coast Guard, US Government photo.

Harry Larsen flying his Talaria IV.

Steve Ball on Dragonfly and Dwight Filley on Foilplay.

The author on Steve Ball's Flying Kayak, photo by Steve Ball.

Terry Hendricks with his hydrofoil knee-board.

Unless otherwise noted, all photos are by the author with permission from the subjects.

CPSIA information can be obtained at www.ICGtesting.com
Printed in the USA
BVOW09s1514010716

453909BV00001B/10/P